Engineering the Future:
Science, Technology, and the Design Process

Teacher Guide

**National Center for
Technological Literacy**®

Museum of Science, Boston

Published by

Mount Kisco, NY

Published by It's About Time.

Cover Photo Credit: PhotoDisc "Popular Objects" by Ryan McVay, PhotoDisc "Portfolio," PhotoDisc Volume 95 "Youth Culture," PhotoDisc Volume 4 "Science, Technology and Medicine" Version 2

It's About Time
333 N. Bedford Road
Mount Kisco, NY 10549
www.its-about-time.com

Printed in the United States of America
1 2 3 4 5 6 CK 16 15 14 13 12
ISBN: 978-1-60720-515-9

Project Team
Museum of Science, Boston
Project Director: Cary I. Sneider
Program Manager: Julie Brenninkmeyer
Curriculum Developers: Johanna Bunn, Lee C. Pulis, Joel Rosenberg, Dan Tyman
Editor: Rebecca Pollard Pierik
Contributing Writers: Benjamin T. Erwin, Donald Foster, Chris Mrowka, John Ost
Content Reviewers: Kate Bielaczyc, Beth Miaoulis, Nancy Schalch, George Taliadouros,
    Laurette Viteritti, Camille Wainwright
Researchers: Kate Bielaczyc, Carol Symmons, Shih-Ying Yao
Assistants: Katy Capo, Heather Hathaway
Artist and Designer: Braden Chang
Interns: Bohn Barrayuga, Michael Habib, Christian Irwin, Jane Ko, Doug Kraus, Nancy
    Levoy, Richard Phannenstill, Ben Simms, and Shirley Theodore
Production Services: Publishing Solutions Group, Inc.
President of the Museum of Science and Director of the NCTL: Ioannis (Yannis) M. Miaoulis
Associate Director of the NCTL for Formal Education: Yvonne Spicer
Vice President of Publishing: Rich Blumenthal

**National Center for
Technological Literacy**®

Museum of Science, Boston

Engineering education for all

The goal of the NCTL is to foster appreciation and understanding of the human-made world by infusing technology and engineering into K–12 schools and museums nationwide. By applying science and mathematics as well as engineering processes, children and adults will solve real world problems and learn about the creation and implications of technologies.

For more information, visit www.nctl.org.

Acknowledgments

The Project Team at the Museum of Science, Boston would like to thank the original group of teachers and their students who field-tested the early drafts, as well as the teachers and students who tested the second and third drafts of the curriculum. The quality of the materials is largely due to their critical comments and wonderful ideas for improving the projects and text.

We also want to express our heartfelt thanks to these individuals who contributed significant time and creative ideas to bring the essential qualities of engineering to all high school students: Louise Allain, Grafton; Stephen Bannasch, Concord Consortium; Michael Baron; Jeff Bindon; Richard Boohan; David Bouvier, Framingham High School; Diane Brancazio, Belmont High School; John Burns, Agawam High School; Peter Cheng; Per Christiansen; Joseph Clement, Beverly High School; Jeff Coda; Charley Corley, Winchester Middle School; Marilyn Decker, Boston Public Schools; Angel Dos Santos, Tech Boston; Pat Dube, Beverly High School; Robert Damus; Ari Epstein; Hans Fuchs; Tom Gilbert, Northeastern University; Brian Gravel, Tufts University; Steve Gundrum, Pinkerton Academy; Chris Harper, Pinkerton Academy; Slater Harrison; Friedrich Herrmann; Mark Holthouse, Westwood High School; Fred Hopps, Beverly High School; Eduard Job; Georg Job; Ted Kahn, Design Worlds for Learning; Ken Klayman, Wachusett Regional School District; Eric Klopfer; Allen Kubicki, Doherty Memorial High School; Sarah Low, Pinkerton Academy; Pat Maroni; Beth Miaoulis; Robert Moeser; Juan Paniagua, Northeastern University; David Perron, Pinkerton Academy; Beth Powers; John Scalese, Pinkerton Academy; Kristin Sharpe, Pinkerton Academy; Christine Shaw; David Shipstone; Steven Smith, Newburyport High School; Katy Snider, Pinkerton Academy; Mel Steinberg; Howard Stone; and Haruna Tada, Tufts University.

Special thanks are due to the teachers and their students who invited us to film the videos that accompany the Teacher Guide: Nancy Schalch, Fred Hopps, and Joe Clement, Beverly High School; Dan Moriarty, Whitman-Hanson Regional High School; Chris Connors, Duxbury High School; and Joy Bautista, Boston Arts Academy.

We also thank our colleagues at the Museum of Science for their collaborative spirit and hard work: David Murray, Lydia Beall, Becki Hosier, John Pickle, Henry Robinson, Lesley Kennedy, Jeff Mehigan, and Isabel Lopes.

This program was made possible through grants from the U.S. Small Business Administration, Massachusetts Technology Collaborative Renewable Energy Trust, Lockheed Martin, Cisco Systems, Inc., National Institute of Standards and Technology, and the Highland Street Foundation.

Field Test Teachers

Original Draft Version

Massachusetts
Spencer Bernstein, East Bridgewater
John Chiffer, Gloucester High School
Ramiro Gonzalez, Boston Arts Academy
Fred Hopps, Beverly High School
Kurt Lichetenwald, Gloucester High School
Rick Murillo, Ipswich High School
Thomas Rosa, Milford High School
Nancy Schalch, Beverly High School
Marc Seiden, Boston Arts Academy
John Skorupski, Belchertown High School

Second and Third Draft Versions

Florida
Odalys Sanchez-Reye, G. Holmes Braddock Senior
High School

Maine
Loren Arford, Mid-Coast School of Technology
Gary Miers, Mid Coast School of Technology
Bill Thomas, Mid-Coast School of Technology
William Thompson, Piscataquis Community High
School

Maryland
Michael Ames, Northwest High School
Amy Gensemer, Clarksburg High School
Raquel Marshall, James E. Blake High School

Massachusetts
Charles Acquista, Monument Mountain Regional
High School
Robert Ayers, Advanced Math and Science Charter
School
Kurt Barkalow, Career Development Center School
Michael Bastoni, Plymouth North High School
Rachel Bauer, Boston Collegiate Leadership
Academy
Joy Bautista, Boston Arts Academy
Chris Beaton, Ashland High School
Spencer Bernstein, East Bridgewater High School
James Besarkarski, Lunenburg High School
Burton Bjorn, Sutton High School
John Blackington, Wareham High School
Kevin Blute, Mashpee High School
Donna Brewster, Beverly High School
John Burns, Agawam High School
Donna Burrill, Brockton High School

Sharon Campsey, Taconic High School
Leo Carey, Charlestown High School
Rachel Chagnon, Boston Community Leadership
Academy
Lawrence Cheever, Canton High School
John Chiffer, Gloucester High School
Mike Clark, The Engineering School
Ken Cody, Newburyport High School
Pasquale Compagnone, South Shore Charter Public
School
James Connolly, Holliston High School
Chris Connors, Duxbury High School
Eileen Correia, Bishop Feehan High School
Ken Cray, Greater Egleston Community High School
Margarita Crowell, East Bridgewater High School
Steven Cushing, Advanced Math and Science
Academy Charter School
Keith Davis, Drury High School
Jim Dellot, Dedham High School
Beth Dichter, Northampton High School
Keith Donaldson, Smith Leadership Academy
Charter Public School
John Donohue, Worcester Vocational High School
Martin Drexhage, Tantasqua Regional High School
Shaune Ducharme, Shepherd Hill Regional High
School
Mary Durkin, Tyngsborough High School
Karen Elofson, Mansfield High School
Brenda Erickson, Murdock Middle High School
Nicole Finnie, Quaboag Regional Middle High
School
Ted Fiust, Arlington High School
Mike Fontaine, Murdock Middle High School
John Fusco, Winchester High School
Mark Gaddis, Northbridge High School
Bill Gallant, Amesbury Middle School
Franklin Garcia-Mansilla, West Roxbury High
School
Mike Gargan, Danvers High School
Michelle Getherall, Woburn Memorial High School
Blake Gilson, Beverly High School
Ramiro Gonzalez, Boston Arts Academy
James Gorman, Northbridge High School
Tom Gralinski, Amherst-Pelham Regional High
School
Patrick Greatorex, Charlestown High School
Mark Greene, East Longmeadow High School
Tom Gusek, Worcester Vocational High School
Dave Haluska, Dedham High School
Lisa Henderson, TechBoston Academy
Mark Herman, Norwell High School

Fred Hopps, Beverly High School
Norm Immerman, Drury High School
Gary Janulewicz, Mashpee High School
Charles Kacamburas, Winchester High School
Anne Kirkman, Franklin High School
Ross Kowalski, Norwell High School
Thomas Kress, Northampton High School
Erica Lamica, Westfield Vocational Technical High School
Kevin Lauritsen, Worcester Vocational High School
Donald Lavin, Shrewsbury High School
Andrew Leblanc, Nashoba Regional High School
Todd Les, East Longmeadow High School
Kurt Lichtenwald, Gloucester High School
Michael Looney, Mashpee High School
Rebecca Lothrop, Clearway School
James Louis, TechBoston Academy
Robert MacMillan, Shrewsbury High School
Teresa Marx, Excel High School
Mike McClaughlin, Lunenburg High School
Sean McGowan, Bedford High School
Robert Melnik, Minnechaug Regional High School
Bob Meltz, Manchester-Essex Regional High School
Rick Merullo, Ipswich High School
Karla Montano, Tyngsborough High School
Dan Moriarty, Whitman-Hanson Regional High School
Paul Muller, English High School
Peter Nassiff, Burlington High School
Dan Nelson, Milford High School
Winston Nicholls, Boston Community Leadership Academy
Alexander Njoku, Boston Arts Academy
Sal Nocella, Mashpee High School
Martin Nugent, East Bridgewater High School
Rich Nycz, Norwell High School
Mark O'Malley, Lunenburg High School
Matt Ostrander, Wahconah Regional High School
Victor Pereira, Excel High School
Ann Perry, Bishop Feehan High School
David Potts, Nauset Regional High School
Joseph Ramos, Somerset High School
Bruce Rawley, Millbury Memorial Junior-Senior High School
Bob Richard, Pembroke High School
David Roberts, Westfield Vocational High School
Elizabeth Roberts, Monument Mountain Regional High School

Mike Rontaine, Murdock Middle High School
Thomas Rosa, Milford High School
Peter Rosen, Clearway School
Don Ross, Dedham High School
Deborah Rossman, Pathfinder Regional Vocational Technical High School
Niki Russell, Frontier Regional School
Stephen Saxenian, South Amheart Campus
Nancy Schalch, Beverly High School
Luke Simpson, Chatham High School
John Skorupski, Belchertown High School
Richard Skrocki, Shepherd Hill Regional High School
Stephen Smith, Newburyport High School
Helen Sullivan, Tyngsborough High School
Karen Tatro, Gateway Regional High School
Allyn Taylor, Burncoat High School
Joye Thaller, The Engineering School
Jim Thomas, Amhearst Regional High School
Bill Travers, Danvers High School
Stephen Tulli, Ayer High School
Marsha Turin, TechBoston Academy
David Utz, Wahconah Regional High School
Phil Vachon, Burlington High School
Ray Vallee, Murdock Middle High School
John Vdovjak, Ludlow High School
Laurette Viteritti, Swampscott High School
Dave Vose, Canton High School
Anja Wade, Quaboag Regional Middle/High School
Peter Wahlstrom, Quoba Regional High School
Mietian Wang, Boston Community Leadership Academy
Erica Wilson, The Engineering School
David Young, Hopedale High School
Joseh Zahka, Bedford High School

Michigan
Joe Grigas, Lake Fenton High School
Gerti Schrattenthaler, Detroit Community High School
Jennifer Tews, Lake Fenton High School

New Hampshire
Scott Edwards, Woodsville High School
Karen Fabianski, Conval High School
Ken Martin, Laconia High School - Huot Technical Center
Gil Morris, Conval High School

New Jersey

Anat Firnberg, Tenafly High School
John Grater, Burlington County Institute of
Technology
Frances Kenny, North Arlington High School
James Lincoln, Marylawn of the Oranges Academy
Peter Murdoch, Marine Academy of Science and
Technology
Michael Polashenski, Mountain Lakes High School
Curt Rodney Taylor, Delran High School
Dario Sforza, Secaucus High School
Dennis Villavicencio, Plainfield High School
Gerald Votta, Williamstown High School
Robert Weldon, Burlington City High School
Kenneth White, Mountain Lakes High School

New York

Rayhan Ahmed, Metropolitan Corporate Academy
Ayodeji Awolusi, Freedom Academy High School
Susana Hernandez, Automotive High School
Aaron Nolan, Charter School for Applied
Technologies
Sharon Percival-Calder, Freedom Academy High
School

Pennsylvania

Charlene Berti, Wyoming Area Secondary Center
Josh Elliott, Carl Sandburg Middle School
Kevin Hardy, Gettysburg Area High School

Vermont

Carl DeCesare, Southwest Vermont Career
Development Center
Ken Fritjofsen, Spaulding High School
Daniel Lejeunesse, Spaulding High School
Tom McSweeney, Spaulding High School
Adrian Sebborn, Southwest Vermont Career
Development Center
Miranda Voegeli, Spaulding High School

Welcome!

Welcome to *Engineering the Future: Science, Technology, and the Design Process*

Engineering the Future is a full-year course designed to introduce students to the world of technology and engineering, as a first step in becoming technologically literate citizens. Additionally, the course will help beginning high school students answer the question, "Why should I study math, science, and engineering if I don't plan on a technical career?" Through this course's practical real-world connections, students have an opportunity to see how science, mathematics, and engineering are part of their everyday world, and why it is important for *every* citizen to be technologically and scientifically literate.

Engineering the Future maps directly to the *Standards for Technological Literacy* (ITEA 2000), *Benchmarks for Science Literacy* (AAAS 1993), and *National Science Education Standards* (NRC, 1996), as well as many state science frameworks. Major goals of the course, which reflect these standards, are as follows:

Goal 1. Students will develop a deep and rich understanding of the term "technology." Students learn that the technologies we take for granted—TVs and DVDs, refrigerators and furnaces, the food on our dinner plates, cars and power plants—were created by people through "the engineering design process."

Goal 2. Students develop their abilities to use the engineering design process. Students take on the role of engineers and apply the engineering design process to define and solve problems by inventing and improving products, processes, and systems.

Goal 3. Students will understand the complementary relationships between science, mathematics, technology, and engineering. By learning about the work of practicing engineers, students get an "insider's view" of how engineers apply mathematical skills and scientific knowledge to solve problems and meet human needs and desires.

Goal 4. Students will understand how advances in technology affect human society, and how human society determines which new technologies will be developed. Students learn through a variety of examples how everyone is affected by changes in technology and how people influence future technological development by the choices they make as workers, consumers, and citizens.

Goal 5. Students will be able to apply fundamental concepts about energy to a wide variety of problems. The concept of energy is fundamental to all of the sciences, but it is also challenging to learn. So, as to build a useful mental model of energy, students will learn to apply the same energy principles to thermal, fluid, and electrical systems.

In brief, the course is intended to help today's high school students understand the ways in which they will engineer the world of the future—whether or not they choose to pursue technical careers.

Instructional materials for *Engineering the Future* include an *Engineer's Notebook* and textbook for each student, and this Teacher Guide.

The *Engineer's Notebook* guides students in their day-to-day activities. It provides detailed instructions and datasheets for design challenges and supporting activities, as well as rubrics so that students will understand how their work will be evaluated. The *Notebook* is divided into four booklets for the four major projects of the course. Each booklet is hole-punched so it can be inserted into a 3-ring binder, and pages are perforated so that a task can be torn out neatly, stapled, and given to the teacher for assessment.

The textbook is written from the viewpoints of practicing engineers. Men and women from various ethnic and cultural backgrounds tell what it's like to practice their profession, and how they came to do what they do. Through these first-person stories, students learn important concepts that relate to their own design projects.

Assessment Tools for this course include:
1) **In-class assessments.** The task guidelines suggest ways to lead discussion and observe student work, which will help you determine how well students are learning and make appropriate course corrections.

2) **Project rubrics.** Rubrics for assessing individual and team performance on creative engineering design tasks are included in the *Engineer's Notebook* so that students can see how their work will be evaluated.

3) **End-of-unit tests.** This Teacher Guide includes four project tests, which you can administer to your students after each quarter of the course. These are included in the last section of this Teacher Guide, under the heading "Assessment Tools." Also included in that section are self-evaluation forms for teamwork and ideas for using concept maps to assess student learning.

In addition to this Teacher Guide, the staff of ETF is continuing to develop new activities and resources. For the latest information, check www.keypress.com/etf, as well as the Museum of Science Forum for ETF teachers at http://etf.mos.org.

The most important element of the course is you, the teacher.
Your understanding of the content, your enthusiasm for the subject, and your ability to engage your students in creative and analytic thinking are by far the most important resources at your command.

Table of Contents

Introduction

The idea that all students should learn about technology and engineering is relatively new on the educational landscape. The high school curriculum we take for granted today was largely shaped by the Committee of Ten, chaired by Harvard President Charles W. Eliot. More than a century ago, the Committee published a definitive report about what all students should learn (Eliot, 1893).

The Committee's report called for high school students to study English and mathematics, modern languages, history and geography, and the sciences—physics, astronomy, chemistry, and natural history, which we now call biology. Except for dropping the requirement that all students should study ancient Latin and Greek, the Committee of Ten's report still describes the high school curriculum of today.

Now, after more than a century, an educational revolution is gaining momentum. National leaders in government, industry, and education have realized that in order to maintain our strength among industrialized nations, we must build a technologically literate citizenry. A major step in accomplishing this goal was taken in 2000 by the International Technology Education Association with the publication of standards that describe what everyone should know and be able to do in the areas of technology and engineering (ITEA, 2000). In 2001, the Commonwealth of Massachusetts followed suit with the first state-level curriculum framework that mandates technology and engineering be taught to *all students at all levels K–12* (Massachusetts, 2001). A recent state-by-state analysis (Koehler et. al, 2007) found that nearly all state frameworks call for some technology and engineering education with an emphasis on technology and society issues, while a number of states—New York, Pennsylvania, Vermont, and Delaware—call for the kind of in-depth learning about the engineering design process found in the Massachusetts framework.

In 2002, the National Academy of Engineering published an influential report that presents a compelling case for making technology an integral part of everyone's education. According to the report, entitled *Technically Speaking: Why All Americans Need to Learn More About Technology:*

> As far into the future as our imaginations can take us, we will face challenges that depend on the development and application of technology. Better health, more abundant food, more humane living and working conditions, cleaner air and water, more effective education, and scores of other improvements in the human condition are within our grasp. But none of these improvements is guaranteed, and many problems will arise that we cannot predict. To take full advantage of the benefits

and to recognize, address, or even avoid the pitfalls of technology, Americans must become better stewards of technological change. Present circumstances suggest that we are ill prepared to meet that goal. This report represents a mandate—an urgent call—for technological literacy in the United States (Pearson, 2001).

Nonetheless, there is still widespread misunderstanding about the curriculum needed to support technological literacy. National leaders speak of the need for education in science, technology, engineering, and mathematics (STEM), but they often emphasize only science and mathematics to the exclusion of technology and engineering. *Engineering the Future* is aimed at bridging the gap between the abstract knowledge of science and mathematics and the critical problems we face today, and that our students will encounter in the world of tomorrow.

Why engineering?

Engineering and technology are two sides of the same coin. *Technologies* are the processes and products that people have developed to solve problems or meet human needs and desires. *Engineering* is the practice of modifying or creating new technologies. The term "engineering" has been selected for the title of this course, rather than "technology," for the following reasons (Wicklein, 2003):

- A focus on engineering helps to clarify that this course is about technology education (the designed world) rather than educational technology (use of computers in teaching).

- The term "engineering" is better understood and valued than "technology" by the general public, although misconceptions about both terms are common.

- The fundamental principles of engineering (especially the design process and using systems) provide a solid framework to design and organize a curriculum.

- Engineering provides an ideal platform for integrating mathematics, science, and technology.

Just as science education is associated with professional scientists, engineering education is associated with professional engineers. Both engineers and scientists are well-compensated and highly respected career pathways, and it's important that all students learn about these professions before they make choices in their school careers that would rule either of them out.

Where does this course fit in the high school curriculum?

Engineering the Future **is not** intended to provide training in specific vocations. It **is** meant to help all students—whether they eventually choose to attend a university, another tertiary education institution, or enter the world of work—better understand the designed world and the wide variety of career paths a person might take in designing, manufacturing, maintaining, or using technologies.

For some students, the course will open career interests that would otherwise have lain dormant, until it is too late for them to enroll in elective science and math courses, and gain entry to technical studies at a college or university. Consequently, the intended placement of this course is in the first year of a high school student's career.

Alternatively, *Engineering the Future* can serve as a capstone course for high school juniors or seniors, so that students can apply to practical situations all that they learned in high school, ranging from science and math to history, social studies, communication— even art and music. You may also use this course to provide an excellent introduction to the field of engineering for students who are considering technical careers.

Who should teach this course?

The most important qualification for teaching *Engineering the Future* is a desire to foster students' creative talents and analytical skills. Other valuable qualifications include the ability to lead discussions that encourage students to question their assumptions and consider new ideas as well as to help students work effectively in teams to brainstorm ideas, make decisions, and to build and test prototypes.

Regarding educational background and professional licensure, teachers who have a state license to teach technology/engineering in grades 6–12 are already fully qualified (under No Child Left Behind legislation) to teach this course. However, we envision that licensed physics and mathematics teachers will not find it difficult to learn the additional skills they will need to teach this course. The Museum of Science has created and is testing an online program to enable teachers to gain the additional knowledge and skills they need to teach this course, and to receive graduate credit toward further certification and licensure. For more information on how to enroll in this course, check out our web site at www.mos.org/etf.

Which department should be responsible for this course?

Engineering the Future is designed for *all* students, not just those in an accelerated program to become engineers, or for students in vocational tracks. Because it has a strong science laboratory component, most schools include it in their science department, along with chemistry, physics, and biology. However, it could also be included in the technology department. Some schools have even changed the name of their science departments to "Science and Technology" to recognize the value of integrating these two fields. While any of these solutions is feasible, it will be important to choose the solution that best supports acceptance of the new course by students, parents, and guidance counselors and that best demonstrates the integration of math, science, technology, and engineering.

Whatever home department is chosen for *Engineering the Future,* the course should not stand alone but be one step in a sequence of courses that students take as they progress through high school. When students complete this course, they will have a broader understanding of the wide variety of technical careers that are open to them. Some students may wish to take more courses in science or math, or more specialized courses in technical fields. However, not all students will wish to become involved in science and technology as careers. By providing alternative sequences, students will have opportunities to choose pathways that are consistent with their current interests and desires while keeping their options for the future open.

What are the goals of this course?

Engineering the Future was designed with a "backward design process," as described in the book *Understanding by Design* (Wiggins and McTigh, 1998). When using this approach, you should be explicit about the evidence that we would expect students have attained in the goals of the course. We have operationally defined the five course goals as follows:

Goal 1. Students will develop a deep and rich understanding of the term "technology." As evidence of this understanding, students will:

- Describe at least ten different technologies—objects and processes that have been modified to suit human needs and wants.

- Explain that technologies are modified or invented through the engineering design process, which consists of several steps: defining the problem, conducting research, generating possible solutions, selecting and refining one solution, constructing a prototype, testing and evaluating the prototype, communicating the solution, and redesigning.

- Give examples of how three different kinds of professional engineers bring creative ideas to life.

Goal 2. Students will develop their abilities to use the engineering design process. As evidence of this understanding, students will:

- Demonstrate the ability to use the engineering design process to solve a problem or meet a challenge.

- Give an example showing that the steps of the engineering design process can be immensely fruitful, but need not be followed slavishly.

- Describe two different contexts—such as a city, the human body, or an automobile—in which systems analysis can help to solve problems.

- Function effectively as a member of a team.

Goal 3. Students will understand the complementary relationships among science, technology and engineering. As evidence of this understanding, students will:

- Demonstrate the ability to apply energy concepts to solving engineering design problems.

- Explain how advances in technology have made new discoveries in science possible.

- Give examples of how mathematics can help engineers solve problems.

- Describe the relationship between science and engineering.

Amy Smith, featured in Chapter 1 of the ETF textbook, is a mechanical engineering instructor from MIT who developed a screen-less hammer mill, pictured here, in response to a need in developing countries. (Photo by Kristin Joyce.)

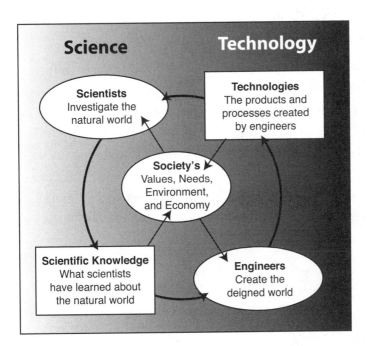

This diagram illustrates the relationship between science and technology, and how these fields are related to human society:

- A scientist's goal is to investigate the natural world. An arrow leads to the results of inquiry—scientific knowledge. The ever-changing body of scientific knowledge informs engineers as they create and improve upon the designed world.

- Continuing the circle, engineers produce various technologies, including products and processes designed to solve problems and meet human needs.

- The final arrow, completing the circle, represents the idea that a variety of technologies help scientists conduct their investigations of the natural world.

Goal 4. Students will understand how advances in technology affect human society, and how human society determines which new technologies will be developed. As evidence of this understanding, students will:

- Describe at least six differences in prevailing technologies that make the lives of today's teens different from the teens of 100 years ago.

- Explain how society determines which new technologies are brought to market. Illustrate at least two examples.

- Give at least two examples of new technologies that have unintended effects, and tell why these effects are positive, negative, or both.

- Give at least two examples in which the negative environmental impacts of past technologies are being reduced by the development of new technologies.

- Summarize two different scenarios of a future world—one in which citizens thoughtfully choose which technologies should be developed, and one in which there is no careful planning for technological change.

Goal 5. Students will be able to apply fundamental concepts about energy to a wide variety of problems. As evidence of this understanding, students will:

- Describe situations in which a difference in temperature, pressure, or electrical potential drives the flow of energy through a system.

- Explain why energy input is required to produce and maintain a difference in temperature, pressure, or electrical potential.

- Describe the sources of resistance to energy flow in thermal, fluid, and electrical systems.

- Give examples to illustrate that the rate of energy flow is directly proportional to a difference in temperature, pressure, or electrical potential, and inversely proportional to the resistance in these systems.

Why focus on safety?

A safety briefing is an important part of any class in which students are constructing projects. There are several areas where safety needs to be highlighted: using power tools; large machine tools; smaller tools such as utility knives or hot glue guns; and preventing skin contact and inhalation of adhesives, paints, and fine particles. Students should also be aware of the emergency equipment around the room such as fire extinguishers, exits and evacuation maps, eyewashes, and communication procedures in the event of an emergency. Some teachers have students and their parents sign a safety contract that lists the tools the students will be using, the safety rules, and why it's important for students to act responsibly.

What do students need to know about energy?

Energy concepts are difficult to learn; yet understanding energy is essential for virtually all fields of science and engineering. In biology it's important to understand how organisms obtain and transform energy for life processes, and how energy flows through ecosystems and food webs. In earth and space science, students learn that energy from the sun drives wind and ocean currents, and that thermal energy inside the earth moves continents and causes volcanic eruptions and earthquakes. In physics, the law of energy conservation is one of the most important ideas that students are expected to learn and apply in solving problems. And our daily use of electricity and fuel keeps hundreds of thousands of engineers employed designing more efficient ways to generate energy and reduce our impact on the environment.

In this course, we have decided to focus on energy for several reasons:

- Energy offers a useful set of ideas for understanding the world around us.
- Energy is a foundation concept in all fields of science and engineering.
- Energy concepts are difficult for students to learn, and misconceptions about it are widespread.

There are many reasons why students so often have misconceptions about energy. In everyday life we use the term "energy" loosely to describe how we feel, or how hard we work. In science the term is more precisely defined, but sometimes the definitions are confusing. In physics, for example, energy is usually defined as "the capacity to do work." However, students also learn that in energy transformations some energy is always lost to the environment in the form of heat that *cannot* do work. In chemistry and biology, students learn about energy in different contexts and only rarely see the similarity of energy concepts across disciplines. In this course, we avoid these problems by focusing instead on the following energy principles:

1) Energy is like a substance in that it can flow from one place to another—but it is not a substance.

2) The rate at which energy flows is directly proportional to a difference in temperature, pressure, or electrical potential. In other words, "difference drives change."

3) Energy input is required to maintain a difference in temperature, pressure, or electrical potential. This idea is summarized as "It takes a difference to make a difference."

4) The rate at which energy flows is inversely proportional to resistance.

If students are to benefit from learning about energy early in their high school experience, they need to learn it in such a way that they can apply it readily in new situations. This is the idea of *transfer* of learning. Educational research strongly indicates that transfer will occur more readily if the concept to be taught is presented in different contexts, and if students are guided in recognizing how the abstract concept can be applied in those different contexts (Bransford, Brown, and Cocking, 1999). Those abstract concepts are the energy principles listed above, which students apply in three different contexts.

Temperature differences drive change. In Project 2.0 students are asked to design an energy-efficient building. An important consideration in doing so is to minimize the loss of thermal (heat) energy through walls by increasing the resistance using insulation. However, no matter how well it is insulated, maintaining a difference between indoor and outdoor temperatures requires the input of energy using a furnace or air conditioner.

Pressure differences drive change. In Project 3.0 students use inquiry to figure out how an engine transfers energy, and how energy is transferred through pneumatic and hydraulic systems. They also explore how pipes of various sizes and shapes resist the flow of energy through pipes.

Electric potential differences drive change. In Project 4.0 students are guided in designing circuits, and measuring current, voltage, and resistance. Through activities they see that the flow of electrical energy increases if there is a greater electrical potential difference (measured in volts) and decreases if there is a greater resistance (measured in ohms).

By emphasizing the use of energy concepts in these three different contexts, you can help your students develop a more flexible, useful, and transferable concept of energy that will serve them well in later years, both in school and in life.

Why is teamwork important?

Our extensive interviews with engineers have confirmed that good engineering requires a team effort. Therefore, students must learn how to work effectively in teams. There is some tension between the encouragement of teamwork and independent work, given the need for teachers to assign individual grades for students. The tension is considerably reduced if expectations are clearly presented to the students for each activity. Suggestions for how to do this will be offered at various points in the Teacher Guide and built into the *Engineer's Notebook*.

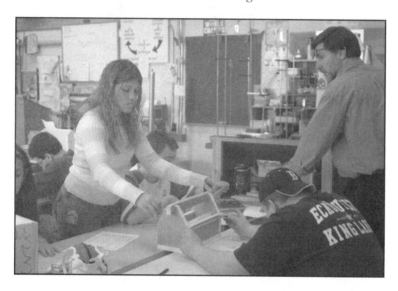

What math and science will students learn?

In this course, the students do more than read about engineering. They also take on the role of engineers themselves. Like engineers, they are asked to undertake projects to meet certain human needs. Unlike much of schoolwork that has right and wrong answers, the projects can be completed successfully in a variety of ways.

The course is divided into four sections, called projects, each of which takes about eight weeks to complete. The primary purpose of Project 1.0 is to engage students in using the engineering design process to meet human needs. The students are encouraged to be creative while meeting the criteria and constraints of the problem.

Engineering is characterized by the application of math and science to ensure that designs are not only pleasing to the eye, but they also function as intended. Students practice fundamental mathematical skills and the engineering design process in all four projects, and apply science concepts and processes in Projects 2.0, 3.0, and 4.0.

On the following pages is a brief summary of the four projects, including the design work guided by the *Engineer's Notebook*, the related chapters in the text, and learning objectives.

Project 1.0: Design the Best Organizer in the World

Project 1.0 begins with a video of an industrial design team at work. Then students undertake their first project—to design a better cell phone holder. They also learn how to make engineering drawings, a skill that they will use throughout the course. During the next design challenge, which is the major project of the first unit, the students work in teams to conduct marketing surveys to find out what kinds of organizers people would like to purchase. The concept of an "organizer" also helps students recognize the vast array of technologies that exist in the world around them. Student teams design, draw, and construct models of their organizer concepts, then redesign their organizers for manufacturing. Finally, they build a prototype for testing with the intended audience.

Readings—Manufacturing and Design

As students work through the activities in the *Engineer's Notebook,* they come across assignments in the textbook that relate to their class activities. The chapters in Unit 1 of the text, which correspond to Project 1.0 of the *Engineer's Notebook,* are as follows.

Chapter 1: Amy Smith, an engineering instructor at MIT, explains how she works with her students to design tools that improve lives half a world away.

Chapter 2: Inventor **Shawn Frayne** shares the design process—an approach to solving engineering problems—and explains why it's more of a guideline than a rule.

Chapter 3: Jamy Drouillard (pictured at right) is an aeronautical engineering student with high-tech dreams. In this chapter he describes his own design process, which includes analyzing toy technology and developing computer simulations.

Chapter 4: Lam Loc, a Computer-Aided Design (CAD) technician, explores engineering drawing techniques and explains why a picture is worth more than a thousand words to engineers.

Chapter 5: Robert Hartmann, an electrical engineer at an industrial design firm, explores how companies use the design process to develop products for the market.

Chapter 6: Araceli Ortiz, a former manufacturing engineer at Ford, tells the story of the automobile's rise to fame and explores how companies decide what to mass-produce.

Chapter 7: Dudley Green, a process engineer at Teradyne Corporation, shows that every product and every technology is a part of an interconnected system that is, itself, designed.

Chapter 8: Christine Epplett, a developer at New Balance Athletic Shoe, takes students through the process of designing and mass-producing popular footwear.

Chapter 9: Inventor **Saul Griffith** illustrates why nature knows best when it comes to building better manufacturing systems.

Science and Mathematics Content

Skills and Concepts from the Notebook	Concepts from the Text
Engineering Skills and Concepts • Engineering design process (define the problem, research the problem, develop possible solutions, choose the best solution, create a prototype, test and evaluate the prototype, communicate the solution in drawings and words, redesign) • Criteria and constraints • Trade-offs • The importance of teamwork • Optimization • Markets (niche markets, mass markets) • Cost-benefit analysis • Life cycle analysis **Mathematics Skills and Concepts** • Length measurements • Area and volume calculations • Mass measurements and density calculations • Engineering drawing techniques: orthographic, isometric, oblique, and perspective **Manufacturing Concepts** • Manufacturing technologies (molding, casting, separating, forming, assembling, finishing)	**Engineering Concepts** • Engineering design process (define the problem, research the problem, develop possible solutions, choose the best solution, create a prototype, test and evaluate the prototype, communicate the solution in drawings and words, redesign) • Criteria and constraints • Trade-offs • The importance of teamwork • Engineers and engineering • Appropriate technologies • Microenterprise • Markets (niche and mass markets) • Manufacturing technologies (molding, casting, separating, forming, assembling, finishing) • Assembly line vs. batch production • Systems • Universal systems design • Optimization • Inventory • Life cycle analysis **Mathematics Concepts** • Scale drawings • Computer-Aided Design (CAD)

Engineering the Future Teacher Guide
©2008 Museum of Science, Boston

Project 2.0: Design a Building of the Future

Project 2.0 introduces students to the problems of urban sprawl. To address these problems, the students learn about the "new urbanism" movement in which city planners, architects, and engineers work together to design structures that serve a variety of functions. Students are challenged to work in teams to design a structure for housing and at least one other function, such as office space, retail shops, or manufacturing facilities. But first they need to determine how to design structures that will bear heavy loads, how to test materials that have the properties needed in different parts of the structure, and how to design a building that minimizes the amount of energy needed to maintain a comfortable temperature. Finally, they apply the concepts and tools of science to design a building that is structurally sound, thermally efficient, and promises to help solve the problems of urban sprawl.

Readings—Sustainable Cities

By reading the text, students learn how designers draw on mathematics and science to design structures and systems that will stand the test of time, promote the health and well-being of residents, and preserve more of the natural world.

Chapter 10: Peter Park, an urban planner in Denver, describes the key elements of the world's greatest cities as well as a new and improved design for his own.

Chapter 11: Field engineer **Kirk Elwell** explores the various forces and loads that a structure must be designed to withstand as he describes the design and construction of a major Boston bridge.

Chapter 12: Structural engineer **Bill Baker** explains how he's engineering the world's tallest structure to withstand sky-high forces.

Chapter 13: Prity Rungta, a construction manager in Toronto, Canada, describes the complexity of building a house on time and on budget.

Chapter 14: Geotechnical engineer **Cathy Bazán-Arias** explains why engineers need to understand the land they are building on.

Chapter 15: "Green" architect **Chris Benedict** explains why conventional heating systems can be bad for the environment, and how to design a building that conserves energy while keeping its inhabitants warm.

Chapter 16: Lauren Stencel (pictured at left), a college student, describes how she's helping to build a home that uses the sun for its energy needs.

Science and Mathematics Content

Skills and Concepts from the Notebook	Concepts from the Text
Mathematics Skills and Concepts • Measurement of population density • Scale, ratio, proportions • Algebraic reasoning • Creating, reading, and interpreting graphs **Mechanics and Construction Skills** • Failure mechanisms: compression, tension, bending, torsion, and shear • Measure tensile and compressive strength; graph results • Interpret stress and strain • Measurement of mechanical properties: elasticity, plasticity, elongation • Calculation of live loads and dead loads • Calculation of mechanical advantage • Analysis of beams and trusses • Green building design **Energy Concepts** • Conductors and insulators • Difference drives change • Heat and temperature • Flow of thermal energy $Q = (A \times \Delta T)/R$, where A = area, ΔT = temperature difference, R = R-Value" • R-values used to rate thermal conductors • Convection, conduction, radiation	**Mechanics and Construction Concepts** • Geotechnical engineering • Construction engineering • Cities and towns are designed systems • Properties of different materials • Materials testing methods • Interpreting stress and strain curves • Dead loads and live loads • Trusses and load distribution • Compression, tension, and shear forces • Failure mechanisms: compression, tension, bending, torsion, and shear • Foundations • Properties of construction materials • Project management • Green architecture • Urban Sprawl • Multi-use buildings **Energy Concepts** • Difference drives change • Energy transfer and storage • Heat and temperature • Insulators and conductors • Thermal resistance

Engineering the Future Teacher Guide
©2008 Museum of Science, Boston

Project 3.0: Improve a Patented Boat Design

Project 3.0 invites students to build a "putt-putt boat" that is powered by a thermal/fluid engine. The challenge is to apply fundamental concepts of energy to understand how the boat works, and then redesign it. Lab teams work together in a series of activities to learn how energy is transferred through the boat system, from a candle that provides energy input, to the jets of water that propel the boat forward. These experiments involve the behavior of compressible gases and noncompressible fluids, conduction of thermal energy, and the concept of resistance to fluid flow in pipes. As students build knowledge of the science behind the putt-putt boat, they take on the role of working engineers and produce a patent to communicate their ideas.

Readings—Going with the Flow

What do a rocket engine and a sewer system have in common? Some of the concepts that explain how liquids flow through pipes can also be used to understand how moving fluids make engines run—including those that power cars, boats, and planes.

Chapter 17: Bob Brown, design engineer at Woods Hole Oceanographic Institute, describes how he's overhauling the deepest-diving manned submersible in the country.

Chapter 18: Astronautical engineer **Aprille Ericsson** shares how she's designing a spacecraft that will bring Martian material back to Earth.

Chapter 19: Activist **Josh Tickell** tells the story of how he reworked his diesel van to run on leftover cooking fuel.

Chapter 20: Chris Langenfeld, design engineer at DEKA Research, explains why it's sometimes better to look to history when designing low-emission engines.

Chapter 21: Professor of thermodynamics **Ron DiPippo** describes how geothermal wells might provide a solution to some of the problems associated with burning fossil fuels for energy.

Chapter 22: Rebecca Steinman (shown left), a nuclear engineer, explains how a nuclear reactor is designed to provide electric power safely without creating air pollution.

Chapter 23: Environmental engineer **Lisa Bina** leads a tour of a major city's sewage system and explains how it has been redesigned to protect residents and wildlife.

Science and Mathematics Content

Skills and Concepts from the Notebook	Concepts from the Text
Hydraulics & Pneumatics • Compressibility of gases • Incompressibility of liquids • Open and closed pneumatic systems • Open and closed hydraulic systems • Pneumatic pump • Hydraulic press • Fluid resistance **Thermodynamics Concepts** • Boyle's Law: $P/V = $ Constant • Charles' Law: $V/T = $ Constant • Gay-Lussac's Law: $P/T = $ Constant • Pascal's Law • Carnot engine • Engine efficiency • Convection, conduction, radiation **Manufacturing** • Contents and purpose of patents • Die and mold design and manufacturing • Brake-forming manufacturing process • Die-press manufacturing process • Quality control • Prototype testing • Patent process	**Hydraulics & Pneumatics** • Properties of fluids • Compressible and noncompressible fluids • Pressure • Pressure at depth • Open and closed systems • Working fluid **Thermodynamics Concepts** • Relationship between temperature, pressure, and volume • Thermal expansion • Work as a form of energy • Engine (internal and external combustion) • Efficiency • Stirling engine • Fluid resistance **Fluid-Thermal Systems for Electrical Power** • Geothermal energy • Nuclear energy • Power plant design • Steam turbine design • Renewable and nonrenewable resources • Pollution and nuclear waste

Engineering the Future Teacher Guide
©2008 Museum of Science, Boston

Project 4.0: Electricity and Communication Systems

To spark students' interest, Project 4.0 begins with a communications activity in which the students build a circuit to control a scoreboard numeral and create a binary code for each numeral. They then conduct a variety of activities to learn about the basics of circuit electricity using fun Snap Circuits™. With a strong foundation in electricity, students then explore various communications systems using microphones, speakers, laser diodes, and fiber optics. Students also learn about electrical power systems and why some systems work better than others for different applications. Throughout the unit the students design and test circuits to solve specific problems, from detecting rodents in the basement to controlling two fans so they run at variable speeds.

Readings—Power to Communicate

In this unit, students find out how electricity is generated and distributed to millions of people daily. They also explore how electrical systems are integral to communication technologies such as telephones, internet, cell phones, and satellite systems.

Chapter 24: Computer scientist **Dave Clark** describes the digital world of computers and explains his role in designing the Internet.

Chapter 25: Sol Lerner, a computer programmer, develops systems that can "understand" human speech.

Chapter 26: Nanette Halliburton, a test engineer at Cisco Systems, Inc., explains how information can travel encoded as light through fiber-optic cables.

Chapter 27: Carnegie Mellon professor and communications engineer **Alex Hills** describes how he developed satellite communication systems in rural Alaska.

Chapter 28: Museum of Science curriculum developer **Joel Rosenberg** shares a model for electricity that he found while designing this course.

Chapter 29: Chemical engineer **Soung-Sik Kim** (pictured at left) explores how electricity can be generated more efficiently with less environmental impact.

Chapter 30: Electrician **Ken McAuliffe** explains the complex process of wiring a large building for electricity.

Chapter 31: Christine Bordonaro, a materials engineer at Evergreen Solar, explains how engineers have harnessed the energy of the sun to generate electricity.

Chapter 32: Entrepreneur **Jim Gordon** describes how developing a wind farm off Cape Cod illustrates the controversy that surrounds energy technologies.

Science and Mathematics Content

Skills and Concepts from Notebook	Concepts from the Text
Electricity and Electrical Systems • Electrical components: batteries, bulbs, wires, sockets, resistors, variable resistors, LEDs, photoresistors, switches, capacitors, etc. • Parallel and series circuits • Schematic diagrams • Electrical conductors and insulators • Function and use of ammeters • Function and use of voltmeters • Ohm's Law $\Delta V = I \times R$ • Control systems • Multimeter functions (zero adjust, ranges) • Calculating energy and power in circuits • Photovoltaic circuits • Relation between motors and generators **Electronics Concepts** • Building an amplifier and numeric display • Digital and analog signals • Storage and retrieval of data • Speakers and microphones **Optics & Communications Concepts** • Exploring infrared remote-control devices • Total internal reflection • Electromagnetic spectrum • Encoding and decoding messages • AM and FM signals • Fiber optics	**Electricity and Electrical Systems** • Charge • Circuit • Current and voltage • Alternating Current (AC)/Direct Current (DC) • Electrical conductors and insulators • Electrical load • Electrical resistance • Electrical power • Electrical distribution grid • Ohm's Law • Generators and motors **Electronics Concepts** • Encoding and decoding signals • Transmitters and receivers • Cell phones and satellites • Wireless networks • Binary code • Digital and analog signals • Internet **Optics & Communications Concepts** • Reflection and refraction • Total internal reflection • Fiber optics • Electromagnetic radiation • Electromagnetic spectrum • Waves and frequencies

Engineering the Future Teacher Guide
©2008 Museum of Science, Boston

What facilities and equipment are required?

Engineering the Future is a laboratory course in which students will be expected to design, build, and test prototypes. While students will learn a great deal from their textbooks and discussion sessions, they will not be able to understand what engineering is all about unless they have opportunities to actually do it themselves. The list of laboratory facilities, equipment, and consumable materials you will need to teach the course is included in this guide. These materials have been kept to a minimum to keep costs as low as possible.

Projects 1.0 and 2.0, which comprise the first semester, require materials such as cardboard, tape, glue, graph paper, and tools such as scissors, utility knives, and so on. These materials are widely available and best purchased locally. Projects 3.0 and 4.0, the second semester of the course, involve more specialized materials: syringes and tubes for hydraulic and pneumatic activities, Snap Circuit™ electricity kits, and so on, which must be purchased from a limited number of suppliers. Details for purchasing kits for these materials are included in the "Materials" section of this Teacher Guide.

Regarding facilities, some sort of shop or laboratory where students can fabricate their inventions with cardboard, glue, wood, and nails, and conduct experiments involving water and electricity would be ideal. However, a wood shop is not absolutely essential for teaching the course. Teachers can modify the requirements for constructing scale models and prototypes based on the facilities available and their own expertise in teaching students how to use various tools. Also, you will need space to store student projects between classes.

Moveable tables and chairs will enable students to interact in small teams as they work on their projects, and still allow them to assemble for large-group discussions.

What teaching methods are used in this course?

A variety of teaching methods are used in this course, including textbook reading, small-group and large-class discussions, and both individual and team design challenges. These different methods are suggested with the understanding that not all students learn the same way. Some have a greater need to explore and invent on their own, while others need more structure. There is a guiding philosophy to this course.

First, we recognize the importance of the ideas and skills that students bring to the learning situation. Students are therefore encouraged to share their initial ideas and approaches to problems and to consider these initial ideas in light of new information and insights provided by the teacher, the course material, and other students. That is why small- and large-group discussions are essential.

Second, we recognize that conceptual change is not always easy or immediate. Sometimes students need to struggle with conflicting ideas so that they may construct a more meaningful and consistent understanding of the content. For example, students often struggle to understand that engineers do not consider the "failure" of a model design to be a bad thing. Failures help engineers find weaknesses, so that their next design will provide a better solution to the problem.

Third, it is simply not possible for students to learn the engineering design process from the textbook alone. The activities are absolutely essential. In many cases, high school students have no previous experience solving problems that require them to think "outside the box," while at the same time subjecting their designs to specific criteria and constraints. Finding an elegant solution to a problem can be immensely satisfying to your students, but it can also be very frustrating. That is why they are called "design challenges."

Fourth, the engineering design process is at the heart of what engineers do. Even though most engineers do not follow this cyclical process step-by-step, it nonetheless provides a pathway for thinking, just as the inquiry method does for scientists.

Finally, there is no substitute for a teacher who is sensitive to the various learning styles of his or her students and capable of modifying a lesson on the spot or taking advantage of a "teachable moment" to help students raise their understanding to a higher level.

The following chart illustrates that scientific inquiry and engineering design are parallel processes with many similarities:

Scientific Inquiry	Engineering Design
Formulate a question.	Define a problem.
Research how others have answered it.	Research how others have solved it.
Brainstorm hypotheses and choose one.	Brainstorm solutions and select one.
Conduct an experiment to test the hypothesis.	Create and test a prototype.
Modify hypothesis based on results.	Redesign solution based on test results.
Draw conclusions and write paper.	Finalize design and make drawings.
Communicate findings orally and in writing.	Communicate design in words and drawings.
Investigate new questions.	Define new problems.

Although engineering design is emphasized in most of the projects, there is a very strong emphasis on scientific inquiry in Project 3.0, in which students need to figure out how their putt-putt boat works in order to improve on the design. Engaging in this process is very important for the students to learn how energy flows in thermal and fluid systems, which leads to an understanding of the physical principles that underlie the operation of engines.

There is one more notable difference between teaching the mathematics of science versus the mathematics of engineering. Science is a global enterprise, so the metric system is uniformly used in scientific laboratories and classrooms worldwide. Engineers, however, must work with the materials and equipment provided by their culture, and for students in the U.S. that is the English system of units. It's not possible to go to a lumberyard in the U.S. and order wood by the meter, or to inspect a bill from the electric utility to find the cost of electricity in joules rather than kilowatt-hours. So, in this course we use the system of units that will be easiest for students to apply in the world around them.

How do the tasks incorporate the "Five Es"?

Each task of a project in ETF addresses at least one of the "Five Es": Engage, Explore, Explain, Elaborate, or Evaluate (Bybee, 1966). Demonstrations, quick-builds, or focus questions motivate engagement. Students do hands-on explorations that lead to discovery. Once students have explored the concepts, questions naturally arise, so they are ready for the teacher's (or another student's) explanation. Activities that involve the students in applying what they just learned give them opportunities to elaborate and extend their understanding. Finally, benchmark questions and rubrics help the students evaluate their own work with input from the teacher. When teaching, you may want to modify the balance of the Five Es to provide purposeful reinforcement or emphasis to meet your own students' needs.

Why are readings and discussions important?

The textbook chapters provide information and encourage thinking that would not be possible with hands-on projects alone. Citizens are rarely asked to vote on whether or not they would like to see a new technology developed and introduced. Nonetheless, as workers and consumers in modern society, we collectively make those decisions every day. All new technologies that enter the mainstream—such as automobiles, telephones, and, more recently, cell phones—result from the collective actions of millions of individuals. These technologies, in turn, have a profound effect on human societies. The readings and questions encourage students to think about the effects of technological revolutions of the past and recognize how their own actions will affect the world of the future. Class discussions about the readings are a very important means of helping your students fully grasp these important ideas.

Why is the course organized around projects?

Student learning is often measured by "on demand" tests. However, a person's performance in the world of work is rarely measured in that way. Instead, employees at all levels are evaluated based on their productivity and their ability to work well with others. Projects are an excellent way to encourage teamwork and individual contributions to the efforts of a group. Projects are also an engaging vehicle for communicating key concepts and providing opportunities for students to develop skills related to technology and engineering. Consequently, instead of using the term "unit" to name the major divisions of the activities in the course, we refer to these as "projects." While in common language the term "project" means any planned undertaking, engineers use the term to mean a major piece of work with a clear goal, process, and endpoint. Engineering projects almost always involve teams of people with complementary skills who apply their knowledge and creativity to reach the overall goal.

What are the tasks?

Each project is further broken down into "tasks." Each task is an essential learning experience, which ranges in length from one to ten class sessions. Tasks begin with focus questions to orient students to the central ideas, and a set of objectives to guide the teacher in ensuring that the students are moving toward specific understandings and skills. Breaking large projects into small tasks can be very helpful to students who may at first be overwhelmed by a major project.

Why should you collaborate with other teachers?

As a teaching method, collaboration with other teachers at the school site can make it possible for students to see the connections among various school subjects. Connections with science and math are obvious, but there are often good connections with art and graphic design teachers, as well as English and social studies teachers. For example, if you are aware that your students are studying American history, you might want to add a reading on Benjamin Franklin's role in understanding the nature of electricity while they learn about his role as a diplomat and statesman in their history class.

How can you best communicate with your school community?

Parent's Night or Open House is an obvious way to get feedback from parents. You might also want to send a note home on occasion asking parents to share what they have heard from their students about the class and to offer any suggestions they might have. Parents and others in the school community often have great connections to local industries that are willing to contribute materials to schools. As well, identifying engineers and technicians that are in contact with the students, such as friends and relatives, and inviting them to come speak to the class is a great motivator for learning. Finally, to build interest and enthusiasm for engineering in your school, you may want to communicate with the rest of the faculty and student body about what your students are doing. Arranging for displays of student projects is an excellent way to share your students' work with the school, and the video about *Engineering the Future* we provide on the DVD in this Teacher Guide is another way of communicating what this course is all about.

How can you learn more about teaching ETF?

Teaching this course for the first time may be challenging for many teachers. Science teachers might be unused to supervising students in the safe use of tools, or the logistics involved in building projects, especially if there is no shop space available. Technology teachers may be unfamiliar with the energy concepts, or techniques for engaging students in the inquiry process. To help teachers meet these challenges, the developers of *Engineering the Future* have also created professional development programs and materials.

Professional development materials include a DVD with an overview of the course, and Teacher Tips, which are short video clips about key concepts in the unit. Other programs include presentations at teachers' conferences; multi-day teacher institutes; an online professional development course, which can be taken for graduate credit; as well as an online discussion forum. To learn about programs currently available, check the web site at the Museum of Science in Boston www.mos.org/etf or Key Curriculum Press www.keypress.com/etf.

We invite your feedback

The remainder of this Teacher Guide provides detailed suggestions for presenting the four projects and each task of the course. In order to improve these materials, your input is absolutely essential. As you complete each project, please take notes, and then write to tell us what you and your students have done, what worked, what didn't work, and what we can do to improve the course. Send your suggestions to editorial@keypress.com.

Thank you, and welcome to the community of people who teach *Engineering the Future*.

References

American Association for the Advancement of Science (AAAS, 1993). *Benchmarks for Science Literacy.* New York, London: Oxford University Press.

Bransford, John D., Brown, Ann L., and Cocking, Rodney R. Editors (1999). *How People Learn: Brain, Mind, Experience, and School.* National Research Council. Washington, D.C.: National Academy Press.

Bybee, R. W. (Ed.). *National Standards and the Science Curriculum: Challenges, Opportunities, and Recommendations.* Dubuque, Iowa: Kendall-Hunt Publishers, 1966.

Eliot, Charles W. Chair (1893). "Report of the Committee of Ten," to the National Education Association. As reported in *The Graves of Academe,* by Richard Mitchell.

International Technology Education Association (ITEA, 2000). *Standards for Technological Literacy (STL): Content for the Study of Technology.*

Faraclas, Elias W., Giblin, David, Kazerounian, Kazem, Koehler, Chaterine M., and Moss, David M. (2007). "The Nexus Between Science Literacy and Technical Literacy: A State by State Analysis of Engineering Content in State Science Frameworks." *Association for Science Teacher Education (ASTE) 2007 Conference Proceedings.* Also available online at http://aste.chem.pitt.edu/proceedings/2007proceedings/index.htm/.

Dugger, William and Meade, Shelli. (2004). "State of Technology Education in the US." *Technology Teacher.* October, 2004.

Massachusetts Department of Education (2006). *Massachusetts Science and Technology/Engineering Curriculum Framework.* May 2001. Also available online at http://www.doe.mass.edu/frameworks/scitech/2001/0501.pdf/.

National Research Council (NRC, 1996). *National Science Education Standards.* Washington, D.C.: National Academy Press.

Pearson, Greg and Young, A. Thomas, Editors (2002). *Technically Speaking: Why All Americans Need to Know More About Technology.* Washington, D.C.: National Academy Press.

Wicklein, Robert C. (2006). "5 Good Reasons for Engineering as THE Focus for Technology Education." *The Technology Teacher.* 65(7), 25–29. Also available online at http://www.uga.edu/teched/conf/wick_engr.pdf/.

McTighe, J. and Wiggin, G. (1998). *Understanding by Design.* Alexandria, VA: ASCD.

Materials List

Printed materials. Textbooks, *Engineer's Notebooks* and Teacher Guides for this course are available from Key Curriculum Press. We recommend that you purchase one textbook and one set of all four *Engineer's Notebooks* for each student. Students are expected to write in their *Engineer's Notebooks*, so new ones need to be purchased yearly. Textbooks may be used again in subsequent years. However, in any given year each student should have a textbook so that he or she can take their textbooks home. In subsequent years only the *Engineer's Notebooks* will need to be replaced. You can find current prices and ordering information at www.keypress.com/etf.

Supplies and equipment. The cost of supplies and equipment—which need to be purchased in addition to the books—is a little more difficult to calculate; it depends on what is already available and the cost of local materials. Initially you will need to purchase one set of durable equipment, which can be used for any number of classes, provided they are not taught at the same time. Additional consumable materials will need to be purchased for additional classes. In subsequent years, only consumable materials need to be replaced, as well as any durable items that may have been lost or damaged.

Kits. Information on where kits can be purchased will also be available via the web at www.keypress.com/etf.

If you are assembling your own kits, you'll find that suggested items and vendors are listed, but many of the items may be in your storage room, or found at lower costs from other sources. The only case in which there is a single source is the electricity Snap Circuits™ kits from Elenco Electronics Inc.

Many items come in bulk or may be purchased at a lower price in bulk. Be sure to ask vendors if they give educational discounts. For some projects, the students may want to bring in their own materials as part of their design research. Optional items are indicated in the "Amount" column. If the item is not marked "optional," the student needs to do the activities in the *Engineer's Notebook*.

The lists are organized by project. When a piece of equipment is used in several tasks, it appears just once, for the first instance in which it is needed. A sufficient quantity will be listed so that there will be enough for later tasks.

This list is still in development, so items may be changed/improved/removed. All suggestions are welcome! Send suggestions to editorial@keypress.com.

Check the following web site for updates: www.keypress.com/etf.

Tools and General Supplies

In some schools students have access to a prototype lab or wood shop with a variety of hand tools and power tools, along with safety instruction and supervision provided by an experienced teacher. However, if facilities and expertise are not available, students can still have an excellent experience building scale models and prototypes using the materials listed below.

Most of the work in this course will be done in groups of four students. A convenient method is to assemble a tool box for each group, and place 1/4" plywood on the tables for cutting and gluing. The plywood sheets are especially important in science labs or other classrooms that are not normally used for construction projects. Following is a set of recommended tools and supplies.

Toolbox for Every Group of 3–5 Students—Durable Equipment

Amount	Durable Equipment	Source
1	plastic tool box	hardware store
1	hammer	hardware store
1	set of screwdrivers	hardware store
1	pair of pliers	hardware store
1	pair of leather gloves	hardware store
2	squeeze clamps	hardware store
4	retractable utility knives	office supply
1	stapler	office supply
1	glue gun	office supply
4	rulers	office supply
2	pairs of scissors	office supply
optional: 1	steel measuring tape	office supply
optional: 1	spring scale that measures in ounces and grams	office supply
optional: 1	T-square, right triangle	office supply
Amount	**Consumable Supplies**	**Source**
1	package assorted sandpaper	hardware store
1	package assorted nails	hardware store
1	package assorted screws	hardware store
1	package glue sticks (glue gun)	office supply
1	roll transparent tape	office supply
1	roll masking tape	office supply
4	pencils	office supply
1	package assorted elastic bands	office supply

General Supplies for the Classroom

Amount	Durable Equipment	Source
32	safety goggles or glasses	science supply
8	meter sticks or yard sticks	hardware store
16	sheets of 1/4" × 2' × 2' plywood or wallboard as cutting surface for each student station	hardware store
1	electric hand drill, variable speed, and set of drill bits	hardware store
1	saw for straight cuts	hardware store
1	coping saw or jig saw	hardware store
2	vise grips	hardware store
16	simple calculators	office supply
Amount	**Consumable Supplies**	**Source**
1	large newsprint pad or roll of butcher paper	office supply
8	sets of colored felt markers	office supply
32	sets of colored pencils	office supply
	paper towels or rags	grocery store
	extra materials to occasionally stock the tool boxes	office supply

Project 1.0: Design the Best Organizer in the World

In Task 1.2 all students will make a cell phone holder from manila folders and masking tape. In Task 1.3 they will learn to make drawings using both quad-ruled and isometric graph paper. In Task 1.8 your students will make scale models of their organizers. These can be made from corrugated cardboard using recycled boxes or purchased from an art supply store. Alternatively, the students can use foam core. While foam core is a little more expensive than cardboard, it can be cleanly cut, bent, and assembled into a very attractive scale model.

You will need to plan ahead for Task 1.9, in which your students will build prototypes of their organizers. Most teachers have students make these from wood, using inexpensive pine boards and plywood. However, a few teachers have encouraged their students to use a wide variety of materials, such as fabric or plastic. Choose materials that can be cut and assembled in your workspace with the available tools. Be prepared to tell your students what materials they will have to work with by the time they start designing, in Task 1.4.

Durable Equipment for Several Classes

Amount	Equipment and Supplies	Source
50	simple blocks for drawing	toy store
optional: 1 set	density cubes	Science Kit**
optional: 1 set	equal mass cube set	Science Kit**

Consumable Supplies for a Class of 32 Students

Amount	Equipment and Supplies	Source
32	manila file folders	office supply store
100 sheets	isometric graph paper	art supply or online*
100 sheets	quad-ruled graph paper	art supply or online*
20 – 16" × 20" sheets	foam core or recycled cardboard	art supply store
optional	other building materials as needed: 8 – 1" × 6" × 8' pine or fir, clear, for building organizers 8 – 1/4" × 2' × 2' plywood for building organizers	lumber yard

* Graph paper can be purchased from some art supply stores or graphic supply stores. However, you may be able to download a template from a number of web sites and then copy the template for your students.

** Science Kit and Boreal Laboratories—www.sciencekit.com.

Project 2.0: Design a Building of the Future

Durable Equipment for Several Classes

Amount	Equipment and Supplies	Source
1	analog bathroom scale	department store
8	set of weights or 2-liter soda bottle	Science Kit or grocery
1 – 5" × 7" sheet	aluminum for crusher	hardware store
3 – 2" × 4" × 8'	pine or clear fir board for crusher	lumber yard
2 – 9" long	steel angle for crusher	hardware store
as needed	nuts, bolts, and washers for crusher	hardware store
8	light bulbs and sockets	hardware store
1 sheet	temperature-sensitive, liquid crystal, sheet (cut into 8 pieces)	Science Kit

Consumable Supplies for a Class of 32 Students

Amount	Equipment and Supplies	Source
4 boxes of 250	straight drinking straws	grocery store
20 – 16" × 20" sheets	foam core or corrugated cardboard	art supply store
5 boxes of 100	paper clips	office supply store
500 sheets (1 ream)	notebook paper or copy paper	office supply store
1 roll	kite string	sports store
16	cardboard rolls from paper towels	home
8	sheets of construction paper	art supply store
8	plastic produce bags	grocery store
1	8 lbs. of Portland cement	hardware store
1	8 lbs. of fine to medium sand	hardware store
1	8 lbs. of aggregate (gravel)	hardware store
2 – 6 ft. tubes	1/2" diam. pipe insulation (cut to 3")	hardware store
32	plastic cups for mixing cement	grocery store
32	plastic spoons for stirring concrete	grocery store
8	cardboard boxes	grocery store
16	overhead transparencies (windows)	office supply store
8	variety of insulating materials	hardware store
optional: 1–8	measuring cups or 500 ml graduated cylinders	chem. supply

For the final project, Task 2.9, in which students build a scale model of a building of the future, use materials left over from the previous projects: cardboard or foam core, overhead transparencies for windows, etc.

Project 3.0: Improve a Patented Boat Design

Durable Equipment for Several Classes

Amount	Equipment and Supplies	Source
1 – 4	commercial putt-putt boats	Buzzboats*
4	boat test channels (wallpaper tray or circular planter saucer)	hardware store
16	10cc syringes (small syringe with labeled measurements)	McMaster**
16	50cc syringes (large syringe with labeled measurements)	McMaster**
32	female quick-turn (luer) syringe caps	McMaster**
32	female quick-turn (luer) × 1/8" twist lock fittings	McMaster**
12 ft.	1/4" I.D. tubing	McMaster**
16	1/8" × 1/8" × 1/8" Barbed Tees, clear polycarbonate	Ark-Plas***
32	1/8" × 1/8" barbed checks (one-way) valve, silicone/polycarbonate	Ark-Plas***
1	1" × 6" × 8' pine wood for hull press	hardware store
1 bottle	nail polish remover (acetone)	drug store
2	500 ml Pyrex™ beakers or other glass containers	chem. supply
1	clothes pin or squeeze clamp	grocery store
1	immersion heating coil or hot plate	chem. supply
4	drinking birds	Science Kit****
1	water rocket	toy store

* Buzzboats—www.buzzboats.com/poppop.htm.

** McMaster-Carr—http://www.mcmaster.com.

*** Ark-Plas—http://www.ark-plas.com.

**** Science Kit and Boreal Laboratories—http://www.sciencekit.com.

Engineering the Future Teacher Guide
©2008 Museum of Science, Boston

Consumable Supplies for a Class of 32 Students

Amount	Equipment and Supplies	Source
4 packages	matches/lighters	grocery store
4 packages	birthday candles	grocery store
12 – 48	tea lights	grocery store
32	empty soda cans cut into 2" × 8" strips (or 1 coil 0.005" thick aluminum shim stock 6" × 100" [cut into 50 strips 2" × 6"])	recycling or McMaster**
32	empty 1/2 gallon juice cartons (or 1 box of 24 poly file folders [makes 48 boat hulls])	recycling or office supply
8 packages	5-minute epoxy—Loctite	hardware store
8 tubes	GE 100% Silicone II Adhesive/Sealant	hardware store
2 pkg. of 100	clear flexible straws (~1/4" dia.)	grocery store
1 box	disposable polyvinyl (or nitrile) gloves (not latex)	hardware store
1 box	toothpicks	grocery store
1 package	thumbtacks	office supply
1 pkg. 24	9" balloons (1 bag)	grocery store
	aluminum sheets (pie pans) for hull (or qty 1 0.010" formable aluminum sheet 6" × 24" [makes 4 hulls per sheet])	grocery store or McMaster**
1 16 oz. bottle	liquid soap with visible particles in suspension	drug store
1 pkg. of 100	stirrer straws (~1/8" dia.)	grocery store
	Leftover materials from previous activities	

Project 4.0: Electricity and Communication Systems

In Project 4.0 students use a customized kit of Snap Circuits™ available from Science Kit and Boreal Laboratories, http://www.sciencekit.com organized as follows:

1) **Student Kits** include all of the materials needed for every four students.

2) **A Teacher Kit** includes the materials in a Student Kit, plus extra parts to replace lost or damaged components, as well as additional durable materials.

Student Kits (for every four students)

Each student kit will be broken down into three smaller boxes. Two of the boxes will be for teams of two students each. For Task 4.1 and many of the other activities the students will be using just these materials. The third box includes a number of other parts for tasks that involve groups of four students. Following is a list of parts included in each of the three boxes.

Boxes 1 and 2 will each contain the following parts for pairs of students:

Durable Kit Parts for Groups of Two Students

Durable Components	Elenco #	Number in Student Kit
battery holder	6SCB1	2
slide switch S1	6SCS1	2
single snap conductor	6SC01	7
conductor with 2 snaps	6SC02	6
conductor with 3 snaps	6SC03	6
conductor with 4 snaps	6SC04	1
conductor with 5 snaps	6SC05	1
conductor with 7 snaps	6SC07	1
light bulb 2.5V/0.3A	6SCL1B	3
2.5V lamp socket	6SCL1	3
jumper red	6SCJ2	1
jumper black	6SCJ1	1
resistor 10 ohms		1
resistor 100ohms	6SCR1	2
photosensitive resistor	6SCRP	1
7-segment LED display	6SCD7	1
adjustable resistor	6SCRV	2
capacitor 470uF	6SCC5	1
red LED	6SCD1	1
green LED	6SCD2	1
analog meter	6SCM2	1

motor	6SCM1	1
fan blade	6SCM1F	1
power amplifier IC	6SCU4	1
base grid	6SCBG	1
alligator clip, red		1
alligator clip, red		1

Box 3 in the Student Kit will contain the following parts for groups of four students:

Durable Components	Elenco #	Number in Student Kit
FM module	6SCFM	1
speaker	6SCSP	1
microphone	6SCX1	1
solar cell B2	6SCB2	1
two-spring socket	6SC?1	1
electromagnet	6SCM3	1
magnet		1
hand-crank generator		1
multimeter	9M105	1

Teacher Kit

The Teacher Kit will include one four-student kit, plus the following durable equipment and supplies.

Amount	Durable Equipment and Supplies	Source
1	Hula Hoop	toy store
16	copper nails	hardware store
16	galvanized (zinc coated) nails	hardware store
8	magnifier (10x or greater)	school supply
1	TV remote-control device	home
2 – 5	various designs of flashlights	home or hardware store
optional: 1– 16	ping pong balls	toy store
optional: 1– 16 of each	blue LEDs, red LEDS and green LEDs	hardware store

Consumable Supplies for a Class of 32 Students

Amount	Consumable Equipment and Supplies	Source
40	batteries AA (4 for each student kit + extra)	hardware store
8	lemons	grocery store
1	ball of steel wool	hardware store
8 oz.	salt	grocery store

Engineering the Future Teacher Guide
©2008 Museum of Science, Boston

Project Guides

Orientation to the Project Guides

The project guides in this section serve as a teaching guide to the four projects that make up the *Engineer's Notebook*. Each project is divided into several tasks. The Gantt charts at the beginning of each major section list all of the tasks and the approximate time each task is expected to take. Most tasks require more than one class session. Some extra class sessions are allowed at the end of each project for groups that require a little more time. Groups that finish early can develop more elaborate final reports, or may engage in optional activities.

Organizing projects into smaller tasks is meant to reflect the ways that engineers organize their projects. Also, breaking large projects into small tasks represents an effective strategy in cases where students may at first be overwhelmed by a major project.

Although lesson plans are presented in some detail with numbered steps, they are meant as guidelines only. Feel free to modify the lessons as needed to address your students' needs.

Project 1.0:   Design the Best Organizer in the World:
Manufacturing and Design

Project Guide

Project 1.0: Design the Best Organizer in the World introduces your students to the world of engineering. The first three tasks provide foundation skills. In Task 1.1 students watch a video of an industrial design team at work. They immediately apply what they learn to design a better cell phone holder in a quick and engaging activity. They learn more about what engineers do by reading the stories of working engineers in their textbooks, and they learn how to make engineering drawings—a skill they will need throughout the course.

Tasks 1.4–1.11 lead students through the steps of the engineering design process to accomplish the major project—designing the world's best organizer. Students define the problem and conduct market research to find out what kinds of organizers people need and are willing to pay for. They redefine the problem in terms of criteria and constraints, generate several possible solutions, choose the best one, develop that idea further, and build a mock-up and prototype. They test the prototype with the intended audience, modifying it if necessary, and propose a sequence of manufacturing processes to produce large quantities of the organizer. They also determine how the weight of the product would change if made from different materials. The students then calculate what it would cost to produce, ship, and market their product. Finally, they present their designs to the class and receive feedback; this helps them to consider how they might redesign their organizer so that the final product is the best one.

This is an example of a **Gantt chart**, which is used by engineers to break a large project down into smaller tasks with time estimates. Each column represents five classes; each bar is the *estimated* number of classes needed per task. Schools with double lab periods will require approximately half this number of class periods. This chart also lists the text chapters assigned in each task.

Project 1.0: 45-Minute Class Periods	5	10	15	20	25	30	35	40	Text Chapter
Task 1.1: What Is Engineering? Students express ideas, view, and discuss a video about design and innovation.	▇								1
Task 1.2: Design a Cell Phone Holder. Examine needs, sketch possible ideas, create mock-ups, and estimate costs.	▇								2, 3
Task 1.3: Engineering Drawing. Learn how to make oblique, perspective, orthographic, and isometric drawings.		▇	▇						4
Task 1.4: Define the Problem. Define the major problem to be solved, including criteria and constraints. Form a team.			▇						5
Task 1.5: Research the Problem. Identify competition and possible customers. Conduct a survey to determine needs.				▇					6
Task 1.6: Develop Possible Solutions. Brainstorm and sketch possible solutions to the problem. Share ideas with other members of the team.				▇					
Task 1.7: Choose the Best Solution. Analyze solutions with respect to criteria and constraints, and select the best solution.					▇				7
Task 1.8: Create a Prototype. Learn safety rules; make orthographic drawings of the selected design, then construct a scale model and prototype.					▇	▇			
Task 1.9: Test and Evaluate. Evaluate against the criteria and constraints, consider materials, and suggest a manufacturing process.						▇			8
Task 1.10: Communicate the Solution. Teams prepare and present their design solutions.							▇		9
Task 1.11: Redesign. Students suggest improvements and turn in all work.							▇		

Engineering the Future Teacher Guide
©2008 Museum of Science, Boston

Preparing to Teach Project 1.0

Introduction

A *scale model* is a three-dimensional model of the design that is constructed with a set scale factor. For example, if the scale factor is 1:4 ("one to four"), then all measurements on the model are one-fourth the length they will be in the final design. A *prototype* is the first of its kind, usually constructed at full scale (scale factor 1:1) from the materials that will be used to manufacture the final product.

Fabricating scale models and prototypes is a very important part of this course. It may be the only opportunity your students will have in high school to build something of their own design. Students not only learn construction skills from this task—they also learn how ideas can evolve as an actual object takes visible and tangible form.

Some schools already have prototype labs, equipped with hand and power tools for fabricating designs out of wood, plastic, fabric, metal, or other materials. Other schools are located near technical schools where teachers can work together, sharing tools and expertise in teaching students how to work safely with various tools and materials. However, even if facilities for fabricating prototypes are not available at your school, students can make fairly sophisticated scale models. For students building scale models in a regular classroom, you'll need to plan ahead for how to protect table and desktops, and to store your students' projects as they develop.

Timing will vary depending on both the teachers' and students' interests. Certain tasks may take more time than indicated in the Gantt chart if you add the teaching of CAD, or woodworking techniques, or if you have the students make video presentations. However, in general, while the first two weeks of activities involve only simple materials, by the third week (Task 1.4) you will need to decide what materials the student teams will use to make scale models and prototypes of their organizers, so they can design with the allowable materials in mind. *All students should construct scale models from cardboard or foam core, whether or not they can go on to fabricate prototypes.*

Choosing Materials for Scale Models and Prototypes

Most of the materials for Project 1.0 are inexpensive and easy to obtain. The most difficult challenge for some teachers will be determining what materials their students can use to fabricate scale models and prototypes.

Scale models can be made from manila folders, corrugated cardboard, or foam core, which are thick and stiff enough to represent more durable materials. Corrugated cardboard can be cut from discarded boxes, but the process is time-consuming. Foam core is a "sandwich" made with two sheets of heavy paper enclosing a polystyrene foam core. Foam core is easy to cut and shape with a utility knife, and can be purchased in various thicknesses from art or craft supply stores. Both cardboard and foam core can be fastened with masking or scotch tape, or glued with paper glue or a glue gun.

Prototypes are most commonly made from wood, but other materials are possible as well. When doing Task 1.4, your students will ask about what materials will be available. You should be specific about the type of material and the dimensions and amount of material that each team can use. (For example, one teacher limited each team to a 1 × 6 pine board, 8 feet long, with the option of using 1/4 plywood and various pieces of scrap molding.)

Safety

There are safety rules for using both hand and power tools. Whenever students are allowed to use tools of any sort, the lesson should be preceded by a demonstration on how to use the tools safely.

Task 1.1:	**What Is Engineering?**
Overview	Task 1.1 introduces students to the technological world and the people who create it. The class starts with students reflecting upon engineering, technology, and design. Students' answers will allow you to gauge their current level of understanding. To further **engage** the students, you can play the "The Deep Dive" video that shows how a team from the industrial design firm IDEO created a better grocery cart in just five days. The students are introduced to the design process that lies at the heart of engineering. They can discuss the video and start to observe the vast array of technologies in their everyday world. (See also "Background and Further Suggestions" at the end of Task 1.1.)
Five Es	**Engage** students in the engineering design process and learn about their initial concepts of technology and engineering.
Time Frame	2 class periods
Focus Questions	• How and why do industrial designers work in diverse teams? • How do industrial designers improve current technologies?
Objectives	Students are able to: • Identify some processes engineers and designers use to meet people's needs • Explain why teamwork is valuable in solving problems • Define "technology" broadly as all of the ways that people have modified the natural world to meet human needs or desires

Materials	For the class:
	    1 video or DVD "Nightline: The Deep Dive" (recommended)
	    1 video "PBS Kids: Design Squad" (additional option)
	
	For each student:
	    1 *Engineer's Notebook*
	    1 *ETF* textbook
	
	Students are asked to bring to class:
	    1 loose-leaf binder with 1-1/2 rings

Preparation	**Video:** Prior to the class, watch the video and review the suggested list of questions for class discussion, below. The suggested video is from the television show *Nightline*; the episode is called "The Deep Dive." The video can be purchased through the ABC News (product code N990713 01) at www.abcnewsstore.com. *Engineer's Notebooks* are organized in four "projects," each lasting about eight weeks. It is best to hand out only one notebook at a time.

The notebooks should be kept in loose-leaf binders, so students can insert completed homework. Pages for each task can be removed and handed in for you to check homework, then returned to the binders.

Engineering the Future **textbooks** are intended to be taken home for reading and writing assignments.

1st Class

1. **Welcome students.** Discuss the purpose of the class, which is to help them understand the world of technology and the engineers who create and improve technologies.

2. **Hand out Project 1.0** of the *Engineer's Notebook* and have the students write their names on the top of each page. Explain that as they work through each page of the notebook they should write their name at the top and, when finished, initial and date it at the bottom. Professional engineers do this to protect their ideas from rival companies, in case there is a patent dispute. You may also tell the students that this is the first of four projects in this course.

3. **Ask students to read the introduction to Project 1.0 on page 5.** Ask them if they have any questions about the course.

4. **Point out the timeline (Gantt chart) on page 6.** Explain that this course is organized like an engineering project. Like real engineers, the students will be asked to complete the tasks on schedule so that the entire project will be finished on time.

5. **Ask students to complete the task and answer the questions on pages 7 and 8.** Tell them that these pages are intended to see what they already know about engineering. They should not worry if they don't know the answers yet; they'll have the opportunity to learn more during the term (or quarter).

6. **Ask students to tear out pages 7–8 and collect their papers** to look at later, to gauge their current level of understanding, and to provide a baseline for what they will learn in the course. The questions will also alert the students to what they should pay attention to in the course. (See Assessment under 2nd Class.)

7. **Introduce the 22-minute video "Nightline: The Deep Dive,"** a TV news story about a company called IDEO. This is part of the introduction because it shows students what they will be doing for the rest of the course.

8. **Lead a large group discussion about the video.** Guide the discussion with questions such as the following (possible answers in parentheses):
   • What were the different team member roles in the video? (Human factors experts, designers, artists, etc.)

- Did everyone in the team have an engineering background? (No.)
- What steps did the team follow? (Define the problem, observe how people actually use grocery carts, generate lots of ideas, sketch, vote for the best ideas, combine ideas, build prototype.)
- How did they make sure that everyone's idea was considered? (Have a leader, mutual respect, posting ideas on the wall.)
- Is this what you thought engineers did? (Answers will vary.)

During the discussion, encourage the students to share their ideas; try to avoid criticizing or correcting them. Ideas to highlight are that engineers work in teams with a variety of expertise in order to come up with different solutions. All suggestions are respected and evaluated fairly in order to develop a good solution. The video also shows students the kind of work they will be doing in this course.

9. **Assign homework.** Ask the students to make a list of at least 25 different technologies that they see in a day. To help them in this assignment, give the technical definition of "technology"—all of the ways that people modify nature to suit human needs or wants. Explain that technology refers both to **products**, like clothing, buildings, and most of our foods, and **processes**, such as the methods of weaving cloth, cooking food, or constructing buildings. *Tell the students not to include any particular object* on their list, such as a particular car or piece of clothing, but rather to list *kinds* of objects or processes. For example, Chevrolets, Cadillacs, and Jeeps are not three different technologies; they are all cars with internal combustion engines. An electric car (or a hybrid that combines electric and gasoline engines) is a different technology because it works on different principles.

2nd Class

1. **Discuss homework: Technologies.** Ask the students to name some of the technologies they listed. The main purpose of the exercise is to help students expand their understanding of "technology" and not to be too critical of cases in which they list a particular object. Point out that an individual object is an *example* of a technology.

2. **Conclude Task 1.1** with a discussion of the focus questions. For example:
   - How and why do industrial designers work in diverse teams?
   - How do industrial designers improve current technologies?

3. **Hand out *ETF* textbook.** Explain that this textbook is different from others in that every chapter is written from the viewpoint of an actual practicing engineer or someone who works closely with engineers. There are two major purposes for the textbook: 1) to communicate important ideas about engineering and 2) to communicate the variety of things that engineers do. Both of these purposes will help the students with their projects.

4. **Assign homework.** Ask students to read Chapter 1 in the textbook and to answer the questions at the end of the chapter. They should write their answers on separate sheets of paper so they can insert them into their notebooks later.

Assessment

The objectives of Task 1.1 are for students to identify *some* of the processes that a team of designers uses to solve problems, and to *expand* their understanding of "technology." Do not expect them to have a full grasp of these ideas yet. You can gather evidence about what they have learned so far by listening to their ideas during the discussion and looking over their answers for pages 7–8.

1. **Survey on pages 7–8.** Refer to the "Answer Key" below.

2. **Answers to the textbook questions** at the end of chapters are in the "Teacher Guide to the Textbook" section later in this Teacher's Guide.

Answer Key

EN Page 7: Getting Started
This is a pre-test to diagnose your students' current understanding of technology and engineering design. Reading their answers will help you understand what they think about technology and engineering. These questions (along with others) will be on the unit test at the end of the quarter so you can see what they learned along the way.

1) Examine this open-ended question to see what kind of technology your students select.
   1. Do they have a narrow view of technology as computers, cell phones, or other high-tech devices? Or do they have a broader understanding of technology as any product or process that meets a human need or want?
   2. When asked to improve a technology, do they first investigate what may be needed by talking to people and observing how they use it?
   3. Do they define the problem in terms of criteria and constraints?
   4. Do they generate several ideas and make a prototype to test, or do they just build the first thing that comes to mind?

Page 8: What Do You Think?
1) All of the following are clear examples of technology: A, B, C, E, F, J, K, L, M, N, and O. Many people consider G, "Language," to be a technology, so that could be a correct answer. Students could also make a case that D, "Trees," are examples of technology because most of today's trees have been planted purposely, or may be hybrids. I, "Water," might be considered a technology if you take into account filtration and fluoridation of certain systems. Also, H, "Rocks," and P, "Sand," could conceivably be technologies if they are created artificially.

2) A mock-up is a "C. Rough 3-D model."

3) The IDEO video makes the following points: B, "People bring different points of view to the task"; D, "Different people have different skills"; and E, "The product is usually better than if only one person did the work." A and C are not necessarily true.

4) This question is challenging because scientists, designers, engineers, and inventors have jobs that overlap. Following are the "best" answers to this question:

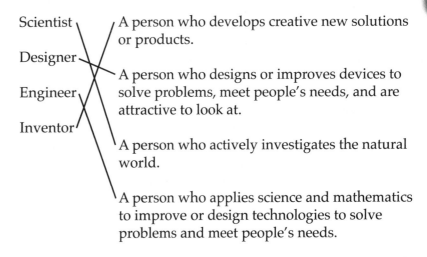

Scientist — A person who develops creative new solutions or products.

Designer — A person who designs or improves devices to solve problems, meet people's needs, and are attractive to look at.

Engineer — A person who actively investigates the natural world.

Inventor — A person who applies science and mathematics to improve or design technologies to solve problems and meet people's needs.

Reminder: Answers to the questions at the end of the chapters in the textbook are found in a later section of this guide, "Teacher Guide to the Textbook."

Background and Further Suggestions

Most people have a limited understanding of technology, thinking of it only as computers or electronics. In fact, the term "technology" refers to all ways that people modify nature to suit human needs or wants. The primary purpose of this first task is to broaden your students' understanding of technology so that it includes the wide variety of human-made products and processes in the world around them. Help your students expand their vision, rather than emphasizing the correct definition.

The secondary purpose of Task 1.1 is for students to recognize that all of the technologies around us—simple things like pencils and paper as well as complicated technologies like computers and airplanes—were designed by engineers. Later, in Task 1.2, they will learn a more precise definition of "engineer" versus "industrial designer" and "scientist"; for now, they need to realize that teams of people spend a lot of time and effort learning how people use technologies, so they can design improvements and create new technologies.

Task 1.2:	Design a Cell Phone Holder

Overview

In Task 1.2 the students are challenged to redesign an everyday object—in this case, a cell phone holder. The purpose of this task is to engage each student in a short version of the engineering design process. They also build a mock-up; use mathematics to determine cost; and learn about the work of industrial designers, engineers, and scientists.

Five Es

Engage in the cell phone task; **Explore** the need; **Explain** what engineers, industrial designers, and scientists do.

Time Frame

3 class periods

Focus Questions

• How do people use a given technology?
• How are technologies redesigned to meet people's needs?
• What is a mock-up and how does it help the design process?
• How is mathematics used to determine costs and feasibility?
• What do industrial designers, engineers, and scientists do?

Objectives

Students are able to:
• Explain how everyday products are designed
• Summarize the engineering design process
• Construct a mock-up (model)
• Estimate the wholesale and retail costs of an item
• Describe similarities and differences in the work of industrial designers, engineers, and scientists

Materials

For the class:
    6–8 rolls of tape (transparent or masking)
    6–8 pairs of scissors (for cutting manila folders)

For each student:
    1 manila folder
    1 ruler
    1 calculator

Preparation

Have materials available to make **mock-ups** for the class. Calculators will be helpful during the second and third class periods.

Be prepared to help students with the math problems. Many high school science and technology teachers find that some students come to high school without the ability to measure, find area and volume, or make simple calculations. This is an opportunity to help your students build a firm foundation of math skills that they can use for all of their science, technology, and math classes throughout high school. Provide whatever assistance they need to understand these calculations because they will do similar math on their own later, when they design an organizer.

1st Class

1. **Discuss the homework: Chapter 1.** Spend about 15 minutes discussing the students' answers to the questions at the end of Chapter 1 of the textbook. Ask students for their answers to some of the questions. (You'll find answers to these questions in "Teacher Guide to the Textbook.") You may also want to ask the students some of the following: "How is the work done by the IDEO team in the video and by Amy Smith and her students similar? How is it different?" (Both the IDEO team and the MIT team are problem solvers. The major difference between these groups is the clients they serve. Amy Smith and her students serve people in developing countries, while the IDEO group serves corporations, mostly in the U.S.)

2. **Introduce Task 1.2.** Have the students read page 9 to learn about the challenge.

3. **Introduce the engineering design process.** Students should look at pages 10 and 11, and notice all headings. Explain that these are steps in the engineering design process. They will see these steps many times in this course.

4. **Define the problem.** Call attention to the box on page 10, "Define the Problem." Ask what should be added so that the students will know when they've succeeded. (Possible answers: it will protect the cell phone, be easy to get to, inexpensive, etc.) Have the students write additional ideas in the box.

5. **Research the problem.** Have students work in pairs to write their answers to the questions in this section. Remind them about the part of the *Nightline* video in which the team members observed how people actually used a shopping cart. Observing how people use the technology is one method; interviewing people is another.

6. **Develop possible solutions.** Ask each student to sketch some ideas in the box at the bottom of page 10 that would meet some of the needs identified during the research phase.

7. **Choose the best solution.** Call students' attention to the top of page 11, where they are asked to choose one solution to build. Urge them to look back at their definition of the problem before they decide.

8. **Students construct "mock-ups."** Explain that a *mock-up* is a rough model showing what a design will look like in three dimensions. Ask the students to construct a mock-up of their best design using scissors, rulers, manila file folders, and tape.

9. **Provide assistance as needed. While students are working on their models, circulate around the room and:**
   - Ask students to describe the purpose of their design.
   - Provide tips to help students with cutting (separating), joining, and drawing.
   - Have students clean up when they are finished or, if there is time, go on to the second class period.

10. **Homework: Chapter 2.** Ask the students to read Chapter 2 and write the answers to the questions. They should insert these into their *Notebooks*.

2nd Class

1. **Allow time** for students to finish making their mock-ups and then sketch them in their *Notebooks*. (Students do not need to use any particular technique in making these drawings. They will learn about various types of engineering drawings later.)

2. **Communicate.** Have each student stand and show off his or her cell phone holder, explaining what it does, and how it's different.

3. **Point out the engineering design process wheel** at the bottom of page 11 that summarizes all of the steps in the design process. Tell them that the last step—Redesign—usually takes place when the product has been used for a while and people come up with ways to improve it.

4. **Have students turn to "The Cost of Manufacturing" on page 12.** If your students are good at math, they can work on their own; if you think they'll need help, form teams of 2–3 students. Before they begin, explain that engineers often use mathematics to figure out whether or not a particular idea is feasible by considering the associated costs of manufacturing and distribution. So they should be sure to record their efforts.

   1) **Cost of Materials on pages 12–13.** Students should practice estimation by figuring out how much material they'll need for their cell phone holders. The material should be large enough to cover the front, back, and sides of a cell phone. A little extra will be needed around the edges to sew or glue the fabric together. Units should be in square inches (in.^{2}) because the material is measured in yards. Emphasize the meaning of these calculations by having a student sketch how a square yard (or meter) of the material would be cut up. Two halves of a piece of material will not make one whole cell phone holder. These scraps must be thrown away.

   2) **Cost of Labor.** These estimates are based on the "piece work" method of manufacturing where labor is calculated per item. Although most factories today are automated, there is still a "labor cost per unit" that must be calculated. See the Answer Key, below, for more information.

3) **Overhead Cost.** You may need to explain the idea of "overhead" to your students. Again, this is a very simple estimate of business maintenance costs.

4) **Total Cost of Production.** Students add up the costs to see how much it will cost them to produce one cell phone holder.

5) **Manufacturer's Mark-up.** Ask students why they would not want to mark-up the product too much (people would choose a cheaper product from a competitor) or too little (there would be no profit).

6) **Packing for Shipment.** This problem can be solved by dividing the total volume of the box by the volume of one cell phone holder, or by sketching the box and marking off a layer of cell phone holders, then seeing how many layers can be placed in the box. In most cases, the second method is more meaningful, as only whole cell phone holders can be packed. Discuss these ideas with your students so that they visualize inside the volume of the box packed with cell phone holders, and that they do not simply manipulate the numbers. **Answers should be given in in.³**

7) **Retail Pricing.** Help students with this section as needed. Be sure they write down on the bottom of the page whether or not they think people would pay that price. Encourage the students to check out the cost of cell phone holders in stores to see if they will be competitive.

8) **What Are the Trade-Offs?** "Trade-off" is a very important concept in engineering. After the students have finished, lead a discussion about trade-offs. For example, the cell phone holder would be cheaper if made from a cheaper material, but then it wouldn't hold up as well. What other trade-offs might make the cell phone holder more saleable? Have your students write their ideas about trade-offs on page 17.

Note: If necessary, allow time the next day for students to finish this section.

5. **Assign homework: Chapter 3.** Ask students to read Chapter 3 in their textbooks, and to answer the questions at the end of the chapter. Tell them to bring in their homework from Chapters 2 and 3 the next day.

3rd Class

1. **Allow time** for the students to finish their calculations, and discuss trade-offs if they did not have time to do so during the second class.

2. **Discuss the homework.** Discuss students' answers to Chapters 2 and 3. Emphasize the work of engineers and designers.

3. **Benchmarks on page 18.** Ask the students to read about "The Work of Engineers" in their *Engineer's Notebook*, and to answer questions 1–3. These questions are intended to help students recognize that they acted as *designers* when designing their cell phone holders, and they started acting as *engineers* when they applied mathematics to the question of feasibility.

4. **Explain** that engineers apply many different ideas and skills in science and mathematics to improve or develop new technologies. You may also want to explain that many people confuse *science* and *engineering*. For example the term "rocket science" can be misleading. Engineers design rockets—not scientists! Invite questions about these distinctions.

5. **Conclude Task 1.2** with a discussion about the focus questions.
   - How do people use a technology? (Pick an example.)
   - How are technologies redesigned to meet people's needs?
   - What is a mock-up and how does it help the design process?
   - How is mathematics used to determine costs and feasibility?
   - What do industrial designers, engineers, and scientists do?

Answer Key

EN Page 14: Cost of Labor
1) $120
2) $600
3) $31,200
4) 48
5) $2.50

Some calculations depend on the costs of material, which will vary depending on the size of the students' cell phone holders.

EN Page 14: Overhead
$2.00

Assessment

Collect pages from the students' *Engineer's Notebooks*, including their homework, to see whether or not they are achieving the objectives of Task 1.2. That is, are students able to:
   - Explain how everyday products are designed?
   - Construct a mock-up?
   - Calculate the wholesale and retail cost of an item?
   - Describe similarities and differences in the work of industrial designers, engineers, and scientists?

You may want to have students staple together Task 1.2 pages and their answers from Chapters 2 and 3 before handing them in.

Since students will revisit the engineering design process in Task 1.3, they do not need to summarize all of the steps at this point. However, they should understand the distinctions between the roles of designer, engineer, and scientist. If their homework indicates that some confusion exists, plan on a class discussion the next day to clarify misunderstandings before starting Task 1.3.

Background and Further Suggestions

Although teamwork will be important starting in Task 1.3, this first hands-on activity enables each student to engage in his or her own creative design activity from the start. The idea for this activity evolved from early discussions with technology/engineering teachers who explained that students should start with a hands-on experience as soon as possible. This way, they first see the design process in action (video) and then have an opportunity to do it themselves.

The research portion, which in this task is a class discussion, is intended to focus students' attention on meeting other people's needs. That is what makes this an industrial design activity, as opposed to an art activity in which the students only need to be concerned with their personal sense of what is attractive and helpful.

Students must do the mathematics calculations in this task. Doing so communicates that engineering is more than creating artistic designs. Mathematics is almost always involved in one way or another—applied to practical ends. In this case the students do some "back-of-the-envelope" calculations to see how much a cell phone holder will cost to make, how many will fit into a box for shipment, and what its retail price is likely to be. Furthermore, the skills they practice—especially measuring, calculating area, and volume—provide a foundation for the concept of density, which they will encounter later in this project when they decide what materials should be used to manufacture their organizers.

Extensions

You might want to encourage students who are especially excited by the cell phone holder design activity to actually make one as an extra credit project. They should use a piece of vinyl, canvas, or some other material that is durable yet easily cut and sewn with needle and thread. A flap of Velcro can be used as a fastener. The project should include a testing period in which the student uses it for a while to see how well it functions, and then writes a report on ease of use, durability, points of failure, suggested improvements, and so on.

Task 1.3:	Engineering Drawing

Overview

The goal of Task 1.3 is for students to learn how to create engineering drawings and to understand why they are important. The activity begins with a game to illustrate why precise drawings are important in communicating how to construct something. Then, students learn to make the four types of drawings and to identify two—orthographic and isometric—as the most important drawing methods for engineering. Students who have access to CAD systems may learn how to make isometric and orthographic drawings using computers instead of hand-drawing methods.

Five Es

Engage the students by illustrating the need for drawing; **Explore** the four types of drawings; **Explain** how to make these drawings; and **Elaborate** by making several drawings.

Time Frame

Approximately 7 class periods

Focus Questions

• Why are engineering drawings important?
• What kinds of drawings are most useful to engineers and why?

Objectives

Students are able to:
- Explain why engineers use precise drawing methods
- Recognize the difference between isometric and orthographic drawings
- Make orthographic and isometric drawings of simple objects

Materials

For the class:
1 example of a scale model, such as a miniature car or plane
1 cardboard box (recommended)
1 utility knife (recommended)
1 pair of leather gloves for cutting (recommended)

For each pair of students:
1 manila folder
2 sets of 2–4 blocks (e.g., wooden blocks, dominoes, or Lego® blocks)

For each student:
1 ruler
1 pencil
3–4 sheets of quad-ruled drafting paper
2–3 sheets of isometric drafting paper

Preparation

Practice making isometric and orthographic drawings so that you can demonstrate these techniques and help students as needed.

Adjust the difficulty of the introductory game by choosing simple rectangular blocks or dominoes, or more complex shapes like Lego® pieces.

Suggested Teaching Tool: Prepare a cardboard box to demonstrate orthographic views by cutting off the top and making a fairly large "window" in all four sides. Tape a simple scale model to the bottom middle inside the box. Students will be able to look through the windows and top to view front, side, top, and back views. This model can be used in conjunction with the student explanation on page 22 in the *Engineer's Notebook*.

View the MOS interactive module on technical drawing at www.mos.org/etf under "Teacher Support" on the ETF course web site. A "Technical Drawing" link can be found at the bottom of the page.

1st Class

1. **Introduce the game.** Ask your students to turn to the first page of Task 1.3, where it describes a game. Explain that the purpose of the game is to learn about basic concepts behind engineering drawings in a way that is fun and challenging. (Wait to hand out blocks until you've demonstrated how to play the game.)

2. **Demonstrate the setup.** Explain that this game is played by two people who sit facing each other. Each pair will receive the same set of blocks and a manila folder. They stand up a manila folder between them as a visual barrier. (Demonstrate how to do this.) The blocks are divided between the two players, and each person arranges their blocks however they want, *so that their opponent cannot see.*

3. **Explain how to play.** Students have two minutes to sketch the arrangement of blocks so that the other team member can arrange them in the same way, without seeing the actual blocks. After two minutes, one team member gives the other his or her drawing. The other team member has just two minutes to rearrange his or her blocks as shown in the drawing. The student who made the drawing can watch what the partner is doing, but must do so silently, and without moving any blocks.

   After the partner has rearranged his or her blocks, the barrier can be removed. The team should observe how accurately the arrangement of blocks was copied, and what about the drawing helped or hindered the task. The students then replace the manila folder barrier and switch roles. The student whose drawing is about to be used will need to rearrange his or her own blocks and give the drawing to the other student. Again, the student who made the drawing can watch the other student, but may not give hints.

4. **The students start playing the game.** Entertain questions until everyone understands how to play the game. Act as the timer, so that all of the students start and finish their drawings at the same time. After the first student rearranges his or her blocks to match his or her partner's drawing, call the students' attention, and ask, "How accurate were you? What about the drawings was helpful? What was confusing?"

5. **The students switch roles.** When the second student has finished arranging the blocks according to the drawing, again ask, "How accurate were you? What about the drawings was helpful? What was confusing?"

6. **If there is time,** and you have additional blocks, have the students play the game again with more blocks, or more complex shapes. Make sure there is time for the students to discuss what they learned from the more complex problem.

7. **Wrap up** the activity by asking students what they learned from the game. Ask, "How easy or difficult would this task be if they were restricted to describing only in writing how to arrange the blocks, rather than using drawings? How difficult would it be to create something really complicated, like an entire house or a skyscraper or an airplane?" (Emphasize that drawings are a helpful way to show how to make something, but only if they are drawn in a way that is very clear, *and* if the person looking at the drawing knows how to interpret it.)

2nd–3rd Classes

1. **Introduce scale.** Scale is a challenging concept for many students because it involves ratios. Ratios are used in many other situations in this course—to calculate density, pressure, and other engineering and physics concepts—so it is worth the time it takes to help your students understand scale in this activity. Ask them to read page 20 and answer the questions at the bottom of the page. Help students who need extra help, and tell the other students to go on and answer the questions on page 21.

Answer Key

EN Page 20: Understanding Scale

1) $1\frac{1}{2}$ inches, which can also be written as $1\frac{1}{2}$ or 1.5

2) 3/1 or 3:1

EN Page 21: Practice with Scale

1) 1:8
2) 1:12
3) 6 inches
4) 18 inches
5) 160 inches
6) It should be 200 inches. You would need to increase the wall length by 40 inches.

Engineering the Future Teacher Guide
©2008 Museum of Science, Boston

2nd–3rd Classes
Continued

1. **Introduce different types of drawings.** Pages 22–23 provide a brief overview of four types of drawings. It is best to describe these drawings to the class as described below, before you have them read the two pages. If you wish, you can draw these before class and cover them with sheets of paper rather than drawing them in front of the students.

   A. **Isometric Drawings.** Draw (or uncover) an isometric drawing on the board of the L-shaped object. Explain that "iso" means "same" and "metric" means "measure." So all sides of the object are drawn to the same scale. You can measure all of the sides of an isometric drawing, and if you know the scale you can figure out how big the object is. Edges are drawn at 30° to the horizontal.

   B. **Orthographic Drawings.** Orthographic drawings are the familiar front, back, side, top, and bottom drawings that most students have seen. Sketch these views of the L-shaped block on the board. Show all six views and point out that in most cases only three views (front, side, and top) are needed to fully describe an object.

   C. **Oblique Drawings.** This is the way most people show that an object is three-dimensional, by drawing lines at about a 45° angle from the front. Demonstrate how to make an oblique drawing of the L-shaped block, and explain that it is not very useful to engineers because it's impossible to determine how big the actual object is from the drawing.

   D. **Perspective Drawings.** Draw a front view of the L-shaped block, and a distant horizon. Draw lines from all corners of the block to a point on the horizon. Draw additional lines to show where the drawing of the block ends. You can also shade side faces to give the drawing more depth. Explain that artists use this method to show a 3-D object.

2. **Invite questions,** then have the students read pages 22 and 23.

3. **Demonstrate how to make orthographic drawings.** Have students turn to pages 24–25 and explain how to create orthographic drawings.

   If you have made a cardboard box as recommended in the "Preparation" section, show the class the view box, and explain that orthographic views of an object are like looking through "windows" of a box. Turn the box so that all of the students can see through all the windows.

   On the board, quickly sketch a 3-D view of the object and write in the most important dimensions.

   Draw a front and side view of the object in the box. Label these "front" and "side."

Ask the students, "What other views should I draw to show the complete object?" (Back, the other side, top, and bottom.)

Six Views. Explain that complete orthographic drawings show all six views of an object: front, back, left and right sides, top, and bottom. However, in some cases only three or four views are shown if that is enough to show all the important details.

4. **Explain construction lines,** and have students read pages 24–25. Invite questions.

5. **Dimensions.** Have students read page 26 of their *Engineer's Notebook* to see how dimensions are indicated. Illustrate this on the board with the orthographic drawings you have already made. Have students turn back to the bottom of page 25 and draw in dimensions of the L-shaped block.

6. **Title blocks.** Call students' attention to the title block at the bottom of page 26. The scale is identified in the title block, which is also where the designer's name and the identification of the part is located. **Explain that in the future you will want them to draw in title blocks at the bottom-right corner of all engineering drawings.**

7. **Practice.** Ask the students to read page 27 and complete the orthographic drawings of the objects shown as 3-D isometric drawings. Suggest that they start by drawing construction lines from the top and right-side drawings to see where they converge. It will then be easy to draw in and label the drawing correctly. It should look like the following:

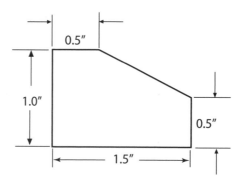

8. **Dotted lines.** Ask students to notice the dotted lines in the drawing on the bottom of page 27. What do those lines mean? (Dotted or dashed lines show hidden features of the object, as though you could look "through" it with X-ray eyes.) Ask the students to draw the missing (right-side) view of this object. It should look like the following:

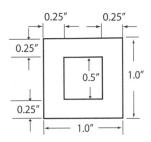

9. **Holes and circles.** Ask students to turn to page 28 to see how holes and circles are drawn. The students are asked to make a sketch of what the original object looks like. The answer should be a sketch of a 1 cube with a ¼-diameter hole drilled through the middle, such as the following:

Orthographic Drawing Practice

10. **Make an orthographic drawing.** Hand out one of the blocks used in the game, or another simple shape, to each student, and a sheet of quad-ruled graph paper. Ask them to make an orthographic drawing of the block. Tell them to make the drawing full scale. In other words, an inch on the block equals an inch on the paper. So they must measure the block with a ruler before they start drawing.

11. **Practice Drawing II: Convert from isometric to orthographic.** Have the students make an orthographic drawing of the object shown on page 29. Before the students begin, lead a brief discussion of how many drawings will be needed (3), the dimensions of the object, and how they would go about it. Then give the students time to work, helping as needed. Their final drawings should be similar to the following:

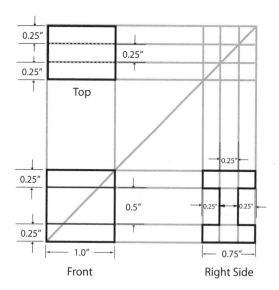

Front   Right Side

12. **Further practice in converting isometric to orthographic drawings.** Have your students turn to page 30 and make three orthographic views of a house, following the bulleted hints next to the isometric drawing of the house. Their final drawings should be similar to the following:

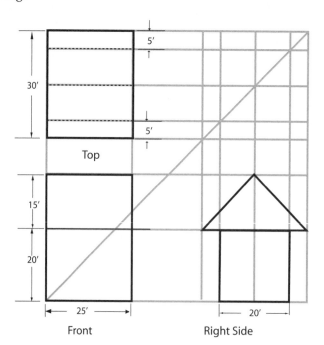

Front   Right Side

13. **Homework.** Ask the students to select a more complex object at home and to make an orthographic drawing of it. They can make a full-scale drawing if they wish, or a scale drawing. Remind them to measure and to indicate the dimensions in their drawings.

**4th–5th Classes
Isometric Drawing
Practice**

1. **Pick up homework.** Ask the students if they had any difficulties with the assignment. Discuss any problems the students may have encountered. (Look over the drawings after school to see if there are any common problems you may need to correct.)

2. **Introduce isometric drawings** as shown on page 31. These are more difficult to draw, but most students enjoy creating a 3-D effect. Illustrate this method on the board by following the instructions on page 31. Notice that it is like sculpting in that you begin by drawing a solid that completely encloses the object. Then draw lines to define the edges and, finally, remove the "excess material."

3. **Have students practice isometric drawing** on pages 32–34. You will notice that some students have better visualization skills than others; this may be the first time that they are asked to draw something that challenges them. Assure them that perfecting this type of drawing takes years of practice—but using a pencil is *always* key. It is common for students to make oblique rather than isometric drawings. Look for this error or other problems that the students encounter, and provide help and encouragement. Drawings on pages 32 and 33 should look like the following:

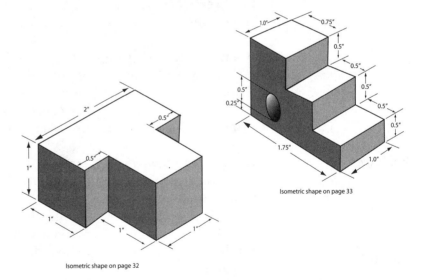

Isometric shape on page 33

Isometric shape on page 32

4. **Help students with their isometric drawings.** Some students may grapple with orthographic and isometric drawings. They may need an extra day to complete the assignment or some extra homework to help them along. These are the two most important kinds of drawings for engineers.

5. **Demonstrate oblique and perspective drawings on the board.** Then ask the students to read pages 35 and 36. Do not spend too much time on these! What is important is that the student can identify the differences in these two types of drawings, and distinguish them from isometric drawings. When the students have finished reading, ask them some questions such as:

- **How does oblique differ from orthographic?** The illustration below the orthographic drawing on page 35 shows an oblique drawing of the same object. At first glance, how does the drawing look different? (It seems to be solid, or it is in 3-D.)
- **How does perspective differ from oblique?** (In a perspective drawing, side and top lines converge at a point in the distance. In an oblique drawing, they are parallel to each other.)
- **How does isometric differ from oblique?** (In an oblique drawing, the front face is shown just as it would appear in an orthographic drawing. Have the students compare the orthographic and oblique view so they can observe this. In an isometric drawing, the object appears to be turned, so you see it as though you are looking from the upper-right corner of the object.)
- **How does isometric differ from perspective?** (Perspective drawings are meant to fool the eye. While it is the most convincing way to draw an object so it looks three-dimensional, the dimensions are not drawn to scale. Isometric drawings look a little distorted, but all dimensions are accurate and to scale. That's why they are so useful to engineers.)

5. **Practice.** If there is time, have the students practice drawing oblique and perspective drawings on page 37.

6. **Assign homework: Chapter 4.** Ask students to read Chapter 4 in their textbooks, and to answer the questions at the end of the chapter. Tell the students that they can try the drawing assignments if they wish, or wait until they come to the next class. Their answers to the questions can be inserted right after Task 1.3.

6th–7th Classes

1. **Discuss the homework: Chapter 4.** This chapter describes what it's like to make engineering drawings as a profession. Start with open-ended questions such as:
- Why do you think Lam Loc likes his job so much?
- What do you think it would be like to draw as a career?
- What did you learn about the different types of drawings from this chapter?
- Why does Lam Loc say that in engineering a drawing is worth more than a thousand words?

2. **Discuss the pros and cons of different methods.** On page 38 of their *Engineer's Notebooks*, have each student write in their answers to the pros and cons of the four different types of drawings.

3. **Students share ideas.** After they've finished, invite the students to share ideas with one other student. Tell them that this is not a test, and they can add ideas that they had not thought of before.

4. **Which drawings are best for engineers?** Hold a large group discussion about which kinds of drawings are best for different purposes.

5. **Draw cell phone holder designs.** As a culminating activity, have students make isometric and orthographic drawings of the cell phone holders they designed in Task 1.2.

6. **Extra practice.** Depending on the schedule you have and the students' skill level, you may want to reserve a few extra days for drawing practice. Or have students who are working ahead revisit the block-drawing game and see how their communication skills have improved.

7. **Drawing by computer.** Learning how to use Computer-Aided Design (CAD) software is an engaging experience for many students. If at all possible, introduce students to one of the CAD programs currently available for students.

8. **Conclude Task 1.3** by discussing the focus questions.
   - Why are engineering drawings important?
   - What kinds of drawings are most useful to engineers and why?

Assessment

Evidence of student performance consists of their drawings, including those they do at home and those they do in class. Do not be too critical of their first drawings, as it takes some time to develop engineering drawing skills. However, as they develop skills, spot check their drawings for qualities such as the following:

Types of Drawing: Check to be sure they do not confuse isometric with oblique or perspective.

Hidden Lines: Note if they have shown hidden edges using dotted or dashed lines.

Accuracy: Check to see whether they have measured the object accurately and then drawn the object accurately, especially with orthographic and isometric drawings.

If the students have several problems, focus on one at a time.

Background and Further Suggestions

There are several reasons why engineering drawing is prominent in educational standards, and why it is included in this course. First, the ability to produce or interpret engineering drawing is an essential skill for a wide variety of professions, as well as a potentially useful capability in any situation that requires pictorial thinking or communication, such as planning a home carpentry project or describing the scene of an accident. Second, the process of learning engineering drawing methods introduces students to a new way of looking at the intersection of art and technology, which they can see around them every day. Finally, engineering drawing offers a way for students with strong visual skills to excel in the highly verbal environment of most schools.

Orthographic drawing is presented first in Task 1.3 in part because it is a familiar form to most students. Maps and floor plans are common examples of the "top view," and illustrations of the front or sides of objects and buildings are commonly shown in books and advertisements. A second reason is that isometric drawing is far more engaging, and once students have the opportunity to make isometric drawings, it's hard to get them to spend time on the more detailed and tedious orthographic drawing exercises.

Computer-Aided Design, or CAD, is the method of choice among professional engineers. Some technical high schools have CAD software linked with software and hardware for Computer Aided-Manufacturing (CAM). With CAD/CAM systems, students can design an object then have computer-driven machine tools, or 3-D printers, actually create the object they designed. Most of the instructions for this task are broad enough to be useful whether your students will be learning to draw by hand or using CAD.

Some teachers who have CAD systems for their students like to have them spend two or three days doing hand-drawing first, to learn basic principles and get a "feel" for what the computer is doing. Others start students using CAD right away. Whatever method you use, students need to learn how to produce and interpret orthographic and isometric drawings, and to distinguish these two methods from oblique and perspective drawings.

While CAD is a very helpful tool, it is not essential for students to learn engineering drawing as a useful skill.

References and Resources
Check out the ETF online tutorial about Engineering Drawing at http://www.mos.org/etf/support.html.

Click on the "Technical Drawing" button at the bottom of the page.

Define the Problem

Overview

Starting with Task 1.4, your students will apply the engineering design process systematically to prepare for the major design challenge of the unit: to create a new product that will save a company that produces and sells organizers. Task 1.4 focuses on the first step of the engineering design process: to define the problem in terms of criteria and constraints. Another purpose of this task is to establish cohesive teams, in which every member can make important and unique contributions.

Five Es

Engage students in the new task—to design an organizer.

Time Frame

2 class periods

Focus Questions

• What is the problem you're trying to solve?
• How will you know when you've solved it?
• How do changes in technologies affect people's lives?
• Why are design teams more effective than lone inventors?

Objectives

Students are able to:
  • Name many of the technologies that surround them and describe how they are organized
  • Learn how the engineering design process applies to a specific challenge
  • Develop preliminary ideas for a marketing study

Materials

No special materials are required for Task 1.4 except for the students' *Engineer's Notebook* and pens or pencils.

Preparation

Materials for prototypes. Decide what materials are feasible given your budget and facilities. Show sample materials so students will see what they will have to construct their organizer prototypes. Be specific in terms of the dimensions and amount of materials that will be allowed for each team. For example, one teacher limits each team to a 1" × 6 × 8 pine board, plus as much 1/4 plywood and scrap molding as they need.

Materials for scale models. Corrugated cardboard or foam core can be used to represent wood or other durable materials.

Important: All students should construct scale models, whether or not they can go on to fabricate prototypes.

Before starting this series of class sessions, you will need to:
  1) Decide what materials to use for scale models (e.g., manila file folders, cardboard) and prototypes (e.g., foam core, wood).
  2) Determine where the students will work.

3) Locate storage shelves or boxes for all teams to use.
4) List all equipment and supplies the students will need.
5) Work with other teachers as needed to schedule facilities.
6) Purchase all materials and tools.

Teams. Prepare to assign the students to teams of three to five students with a wide range of skills. Some teachers prefer all-girl and all-boy teams so that no gender dominates when it comes to building things.

Read the scenario on page 40. The purpose of this scenario is to illustrate how technological change impacts people's lives, and the importance of engineering to solve serious problems and meet people's needs. It also provides a context for the main challenge of this unit. If you know of businesses in your local region that have had setbacks due to technological change, you may want to call these to your students' attention.

Organizers were selected as the first major challenge because they are gender neutral, and because thinking about organizers is a way to highlight the vast number of technologies that surround you every day.

To further contextualize the challenge, you may want to suggest some local needs for organizers. For example, your school's theater troupe may need program stands, or the art teacher may need a closet organizer. This might require full shop access and/or collaboration with another teacher. On the other hand, if your students tend to take initiative, it may be best not to be too directive so they can define their own project.

1st Class

1. **Discuss the Engineering Design Process.** On page 39 the students will see the steps of the engineering design process that was introduced in the first three chapters of their textbook. Ask the students how many of these steps they followed in designing their cell phone holder. (They should recognize that they did not go through the entire engineering design process…yet.) Engage the students in a discussion about how producing a cell phone holder could have been improved by following all of these steps (bigger market research effort, more time to develop different ideas and materials, further testing, etc.).

2. **Introduce the scenario.** Have the students read page 40, which describes the main challenge for the rest of Project 1.0. When they are finished, ask volunteers to paraphrase the scenario.

3. **What's an organizer?** Call students' attention to page 41, which defines an organizer as "anything designed to keep smaller things so they stay together and are easy to find and retrieve when needed." Ask the students to fill in the table by listing at least five organizers that they see around the room, along with the things organized by each one.

Engineering the Future Teacher Guide
©2008 Museum of Science, Boston

4. **Explore the concept of an organizer.** When the students are finished, ask them to name some of the things on their lists. At first students are likely to think of just the things they normally call "organizers," such as desk organizers or file drawers. If necessary, encourage them to think more broadly. If there are doubts, apply the definition to see if it fits. For example:

   - Book cases organize books so it's easy to find the book you want.
   - Wallets organize money, cards, and photos so they are easy to access.
   - Pockets organize change or other things you want to carry with you.
   - Computers organize information so it's easy to access when you want it.

5. **Why are organizers important?** Ask the students to answer the questions at the bottom of the page:

   "What would this room look like if the organizers disappeared but the things in them remained?" (A mess!)

   "How is a house like an organizer?" (It organizes people and the things they need for living. Different functions occur in different rooms.)

6. **What's the problem?** On page 42 the students are asked to define the problem presented in the scenario, and to list the criteria and constraints that are part of the problem definition. Ask the students to recall the following definitions of "criteria" and "constraints" from their reading:

   Criteria are the desired elements of the final product.

   Constraints are the limitations to the design or design process.

   Give the students time to fill in the blank spaces on the page, first by defining the problem in their own words, and then by listing criteria and constraints. Let them think about it on their own for a while, before holding a discussion about it.

7. **Discuss criteria and constraints.** Students may have difficulty coming up with criteria and constraints; the scenario does not directly provide these. Invite them to share their ideas about what the criteria might be and elaborate what is meant by criteria and constraints. See if you can get them to generate more of their own ideas by asking more questions. For example:

   To generate ideas about criteria: In order to "save the company," what qualities will you look for in a new product? (It needs to be attractive, to fulfill a need, to be better than competing products, cheaper than the competitors, colorful, and so on.)

To generate ideas about constraints: What limitations do you think you should place on yourselves when you design this product, so it will have a chance for economic success? (It should not be too costly, or too big and heavy, or require a lot of care and maintenance.)

8. **Conclude the class** by having the students share what they've written about criteria and constraints of the problem.

2nd Class

1. **Assign teams.** Assign groups of students to work together on the organizer project. Explain that they will be working together for the remainder of the organizer project.

2. **Discuss the definition of the problem.** Ask the students to pull their chairs together around a table or into a circle so that they can compare their ideas about defining the problem. Tell them that they can add (or subtract) ideas from the preliminary list they made, in response to ideas from others. They should agree on a clear statement of the problem, and make a list of at least three criteria and three constraints. They should all have a final statement of the problem in their *Engineer's Notebook* before leaving class.

3. **Discuss the strengths of team members.** Ask the students to fill out the table on page 43 in which they list the names of the other students on their team, and one or two strengths each student is willing to declare. Remind the teams of the *Nightline* "The Deep Dive" video that showed how important it is to have team members with diverse skills. Ask students to think of one skill they have that would be helpful in designing things to share with their teammates.

    Note: Team formation can be difficult, and you might have your own reasons for assembling students into certain teams. The idea of having students identify their strengths is for them to become aware of their individual contributions and responsibilities to a group. It will also help to get the whole group focused toward a similar goal if they know what each person "wants" to focus on based on his or her personal strengths.

4. **Have students read about teamwork on page 44.** After they've finished reading, invite students to comment on the "Teamwork Guidelines." Are there any guidelines they think will be difficult to follow? Do they recommend any changes? Discuss the behaviors of good team members at the bottom of the page. (Teamwork guidelines are brought up again at the beginning of Projects 2.0, 3.0, and 4.0.)

5. **Assign homework: Chapter 5.** Ask students to read Chapter 5 in their textbooks, and to answer questions at the end of the chapter. Tell them that the main theme of that chapter is the importance of teamwork in business.

6. **Materials for scale models and prototypes.** On page 45 students are asked to list the materials they'll use for scale models and prototypes. If you know the materials that the students will be using, now is also a good time to show them the materials, tell them what quantity each team can use, and what tools they can use. If you don't have these answers yet, you can come back to this page later.

7. **Conclude Task 1.4** by discussing the focus questions:

   • What is the problem you're trying to solve?
   • How will we know when you've solved it?
   • How do changes in technologies affect people's lives?
   • Why are design teams more effective than lone inventors?

8. Have the students answer questions in the Benchmarks quiz on page 46.

9. Ask the students to tear out Task 1.4 so you can look it over. This is an easy way of finding out how well they understand the lessons concerning technologies, organizers, and teams.

Assessment

Collect one copy of page 42 from each team and read carefully to see if there are any ambiguities in the problem definitions, misuses of the terms "criteria" and "constraints," or cases in which solutions are incorporated in the problem definition. You can check each team's accomplishments in their papers.

Evidence of each student's ideas will be found in their responses to the Benchmark questions on page 46. Following are possible answers to the questions.

Answer Key

EN Page 46: Benchmarks
1) A city organizes buildings, roads, cars, trains, buses, people, and much more. This organization helps people know where to go to get the services and products they need.

2) What would you call these organizers?

   Books—bookcases
   Socks—bureau, or drawer
   Shirts and pants—closet, bureau, or drawer
   Money—wallet, bank
   Dishes—cupboard, drying rack
   Papers—file cabinets, desks, wastepaper baskets
   Electronic information—computers, cell phones, digital music players
   Cars—garages, parking lots

3) Teams—Acceptable ideas:
- Include people with diverse ideas and perspectives.
- Bring together people with different skills.
- Encourage critical discussions though not everyone will agree.
- Provide more research, more different ideas, and more fun!

Background and Further Suggestions

The engineering design process is at the heart of what engineers do. Even though most engineers do not follow this process step by step, it nonetheless provides a pathway for thinking, just as the inquiry method does for scientific thinking. The following chart illustrates that scientific inquiry and engineering design are parallel processes, but are not exactly the same.

Scientific Inquiry	Engineering Design
Formulate a question.	Define a problem.
Research how others have answered it.	Research how others have solved it.
Brainstorm hypotheses and choose one.	Brainstorm solutions and choose one.
Conduct an experiment to test the hypothesis.	Create and test a prototype.
Modify hypothesis based on results.	Redesign solution based on test results.
Draw conclusions, write paper.	Finalize design, make drawings.
Communicate findings orally and in writing.	Communicate design in words and drawings.

Another important distinction is that, unlike the work of scientists, artists, or poets who may work on projects that only they and their peers think is important, engineers must take into account the needs and interests of many more people.

To keep your students focused on the engineering design process, tell them that when they start each new task they should notice the tiny icon in the lower-right-hand side of the box at the top of the page. Think of the wheel as a kind of mental map of where you are in the design process.

Criteria and constraints can be challenging for students and adults to decipher. You should think ahead to what your list might look like and why you would put something like "material selection" in constraints but "must be made of pine" in criteria. A good rule of thumb for separating these ideas is to think of criteria as indicators of success, while constraints are limits that help you decide which solutions are feasible and which are not.

Look ahead to the rubric for this project on page 74 of the *Engineer's Notebook*. You may want to share this rubric with your students, or use it as a guide to develop your own.

Task 1.5:	Research the Problem

Overview
Teams begin market research on organizers, guided by their *Engineer's Notebook*. Each team member chooses a different group to survey (e.g., students, teachers, football players, and so on) and develops a set of questions to find out what kinds of organizers that group uses, what improvements are needed, or what new kinds of organizers might be marketed to that group. The students conduct their research individually and then meet as a team in class to share results and decide on an audience for their team product.

Five Es
Explore the many ways that people organize the technologies that they use every day; **Explain** the difference between mass markets and niche markets; **Emphasize** the process of conducting research by planning, implementing, and summarizing the results of a survey.

Time Frame
3 class periods

Focus Questions
- What kinds of organizers do people use?
- How would they like their organizers to be improved?
- What new kinds of organizers would they like to buy?
- What is the competition doing?

Objectives
Students are able to:
- Explain what is meant by market research, and why it is important
- Give examples of how human decisions have driven changes in technology
- Give examples of how new technologies have affected people's lives
- Value their teammate's diverse skills and talents

Materials
For every two students:
    1 home shopping catalog that includes organizers (gardening, kitchen equipment, furniture, home improvement, storage and organizing, office or school supplies, tools, art supplies, etc.)
    or a computer connected to the web

Preparation
Decide in advance whether you'd like your students to research organizers sold by the competition in class using home shopping catalogs, on computers using the web, or as a homework assignment. If using a school- or community-focused project, you may want to set up an interview with the "customer" to learn more about their needs.

1. **Discuss the homework: Chapter 5.** This chapter provides an insider's view of the industrial design firm IDEO, which was featured in the Nightline video shown in Task 1.1. Students should come away from this discussion with a few key concepts:

   - Good teamwork is essential to good design. It means that team members listen to each other thoughtfully and respect different viewpoints and skills of other team members.
   - Good design brings together art, science, math, and the ability to observe people and understand their needs.
   - Although human factors specialists and artists are important on design teams, engineers of various kinds are also important. (Industrial, mechanical, electrical, and software engineers are mentioned in the chapter.)
   - Some products, like wallets and televisions, are designed for a *mass market*, which means a great diversity of people would be interested in buying them. Others are designed for a *niche market*, which refers to a smaller group of people with a special need, such as surgical instruments for doctors.
   - *Innovation* refers to the improvement of existing products, which is what designers and engineers do most of the time. *Invention* refers to the creation of new products.

2. **Introduction to research.** Explain that the second step in the engineering design process is to research the problem. There are many kinds of research, including:

   - *Laboratory research* to test new materials, chemicals, or machines
   - *Library research*, using books or computers, to find out how others have tried to solve the same problem
   - *Market research*, which is the process of learning about consumers' thoughts and attitudes about products

3. **Ask students what they know about market research.** Ask the students about the market research they saw in the *Nightline* video. What did the researchers do? (They observed how people used the technology, and they talked with consumers and with experts who have a lot of experience with the technology.) Ask students if they know of any other market research.

4. **Describe Task 1.5.** Tell the students that they will do two kinds of market research to develop an organizer that will save the company. The first kind is to find out what competitors are selling, to whom, and at what price. Then they will interview people to find out what their needs for organizers are.

5. **Hand out catalogues, or direct students to computers.** Ask students to work on their own to browse the catalogs (or surf the net) to find organizers. They should list the data they find in the table on page 47, using three columns to indicate the type of organizer, customer group that would buy the item, and how much it costs.

6. **Research the competition.** Provide 15–20 minutes for students to search for organizers. When they have several items on their lists, ask them to meet with their teams and share what they've found.

2nd Class

1. **Mass markets and niche markets.** Ask the class to read page 48. Each individual should answer the questions and fill in the chart at the bottom of the page on their own, listing various mass markets and niche markets. (Note: You may be asked whether a particular group, such as people who deliver the mail, should be classified as a mass market or a niche market. This question is not always easy to answer because the terms are not absolute, but rather ends of a spectrum. However, as a rule of thumb, if a group is defined by a particular interest or occupation, it should be considered a niche market.)

Answer Key

EN Page 48

1) **A mass market** has the advantage that there are lots of possible customers. Most clothing, food, and even expensive items like cars and houses target mass markets. A disadvantage is that there is lots of competition.

2) **A niche market** usually has the advantage of less competition. The obvious disadvantage is fewer potential customers.

Mass markets might include men, women, children, teenagers, people in the military, tourists, and so on.

Niche markets would include more restricted groups: trumpet players, surgeons, basketball coaches, history teachers, tour guides, and so on.

2nd Class
Continued

2. **Choose a market to survey.** Ask the team to discuss the various possible markets; ask each individual on the team to volunteer to gather information from people in one of the groups. It's okay if two or more people want to research the same market, as long as they interview different people.

3. **Generate questions.** On page 49, each person should write the name of a group, and make a list of possible questions to ask people from that group.

4. **Compare notes.** Ask the students to meet in their groups again to share ideas about the questions they plan to ask, and for each individual to make a final list of questions. They should number the questions.

5. **Homework: Conduct surveys.** Ask students to interview 8 or 9 people, and to record the answers on notebook paper, using numbers to indicate which responses go with which questions. Tell the students to summarize their findings by answering these questions:

    *   What does this group need or want?
    *   What organizer product might best meet this group's needs?

3rd Class

1. **Summarize results.** Ask students to spend a few minutes writing down the results of their surveys on the bottom of page 50 of their *Engineer's Notebook.*

2. **Decide on a market.** Have the students meet in their teams and share their results. Each team should decide together which of the markets provides the best opportunity to develop a profitable organizer for the ACME Organizer Company.

3. **Redefine the problem.** As soon as the team decides on a market, they should plan a more precise description of the problem. For example, the problem might now be "Design an organizer for art supplies that will meet the needs of art teachers." The team should closely examine the results of the survey for that group to identify criteria and constraints. All students should write the team's decisions on page 51.

4. **Conclude Task 1.5** by discussing the following focus questions:

    *   What kinds of organizers do people use?
    *   How would they like their organizers to be improved?
    *   What new kinds of organizers would they like to buy?
    *   What is the competition doing?

5. **Assign homework: Chapter 6.** Ask students to read Chapter 6 and to answer the questions at the end of the chapter.

6. **Have students write their answers to the benchmark questions** on page 52. You may want to have your students tear out pages for Task 1.5, staple them, and hand them in for your review.

Answer Key

EN Page 52: Benchmark

1) Which are designed for niche markets and which for mass markets?

    Eyeglasses—could be either niche or mass market; for people with poor eyesight, but a lot of people wear them

    Pots and pans—mass market; the majority of people use them

Engineering the Future Teacher Guide
©2008 Museum of Science, Boston

Violins—niche market; only violin players will purchase these

Ties and belts—mass market; the majority of people wear them

Surgical instruments—niche market; just for surgeons

Drafting tools—niche market; just for people who do engineering drawing

Hammer—mass market; most people buy a hammer at one time or other

Books—could be either mass market (in the case of popular novels and nonfiction) or niche market (for people with special interests)

2) Why do some companies focus on niche markets?

Possible answers:
Niche markets usually have less competition.

A company gets to know its customers better and develops a reputation.

3) Again, many answers are possible. Students might focus on barriers people perceive in maintaining and improving their own health. For example:

What do you do to maintain your health now?

What do you see as your greatest challenge in maintaining good health?

What could help you overcome this challenge?

Assessment

You will be able to gauge what students have learned from their in-class discussions or responses that they write in their *Engineer's Notebook*.

Responses to the benchmark questions will reveal any misconceptions that students may have about niche markets and mass markets, and the process of market research.

You want to look for evidence that students understand the phases of the engineering design process. In this case, when they "Research the Problem," they are conducting a special kind of research, called **market research**.

Background and Further Suggestions

The term "marketing" has a poor reputation among some educators who may associate the term with unscrupulous sales people. However, the concept of marketing can be applied broadly to any situation in which a person or organization aims to provide products or services that people really want and need. Recalling Chapters 1–3 of the *ETF* textbook, for example, Amy Smith's team of engineering students must conduct some form of market research when they go to a new country, or they'll end up developing technologies that nobody wants or can afford. As your students will see in Chapter 6, Araceli Ortiz explains how important it is for car designers to take into account the full diversity of men and women who purchase and use automobiles.

There are, of course, other forms of research, and if there is time you may want to end this chapter by having your students refer to the text for other examples of research. For instance, Jamy Drouillard described the research his team was conducting to design a camera-carrying helicopter to monitor basketball games. His research included:

- Making detailed measurements of the dimensions of basketball courts
- Researching other technologies that have been used to track players with a camera
- Purchasing and analyzing toys that may possess possible solutions to the problem
- Learning about the physics principles that underlie a machine's operation
- Running computer simulations
- Conducting experiments with mock-ups and prototypes

Task 1.6:	Develop Possible Solutions

Overview
Moving on to the third step of the engineering design process, the students learn techniques for generating creative solutions for the problem that has now been defined and researched. They do this by using various methods to generate creative ideas on their own, then sharing ideas with their teammates, and going through a "brainstorm process" to synthesize their best ideas and identify the top three or four solutions.

Five Es
Elaborate by developing several alternative solutions to the problem; **Evaluate** the alternative solutions using a Pugh chart.

Time Frame
2 class periods

Focus Question
• How do you come up with *great* ideas?

Objectives
Students are able to:
• Use various methods to generate creative solutions on their own
• Engage in effective group brainstorming and synthesis
• Work with teammates to identify the best solutions

Materials
For each team:
1 roll of masking tape
Small Post Its® or sticky dots (three per person)

Optional:
1 newsprint pad or butcher paper
Set of various-colored felt markers for each team

Preparation
Provide spaces where teams can work together—maybe near a wall or other surface where they can post their sketches with masking tape.

If you have a large pad of newsprint or butcher paper, set aside 2–3 large sheets and a set of colored felt markers for each team.

1st Class
1. **Discuss the homework: Chapter 6.** Ask the students to describe the kind of research conducted by Araceli Ortiz and why that research was valuable to the Ford Motor Company. Allow time for the students to answer and express their ideas about market research. You may want to defer a discussion of the history of manufacturing until later, and focus instead on the importance of meeting customers' needs, as an introduction to Task 1.6.

2. **Introduce Task 1.6.** Ask students to read the introduction to Task 1.6 on the top of page 53. Tell them that the process will be a lot like the team brainstorm session they saw in the video at the start of the course. The goal of these class sessions is to generate some good ideas for organizers that the target audience just can't wait to buy.

3. **What's the problem?** Ask the students to read the rest of page 53 before they start listing ideas. Call attention to the three tips at the bottom of the page, and ask some questions to generate discussion about these ideas. Keep the focus on defining the problem better rather than coming up with solutions yet.

4. **Individual Brainstorming.** Tell the students that groups come up with more creative ideas if they spend time brainstorming as individuals first, before they work as a team. Ask them to take out a piece of notebook paper or graph paper and start thinking and jotting down ideas and sketches. Tell them not to spend too much time developing just one idea, but to try to come up with several different ideas. Answer any questions they might have, and then allow them about 15 minutes to work quietly. It is best not to permit talking so that students who need silence to think can have that personal space for reflection.

5. **Guidelines for Brainstorming.** Call the class's attention to the guidelines for brainstorming on page 54. Tell them to start by giving each member of their team time to share his or her ideas. Go over the other ideas on page 54. Ask if the students have any questions. Emphasize that it is very important that team members speak respectfully to each other, and that they do not object to any ideas during the discussion. There will be time to focus on the best ideas later; for now, the wilder the better!

6. **Prepare for brainstorming.** Ask teams to form semi-circles near a wall or someplace where they can post sheets of notebook paper (or newsprint or butcher paper). Give each team a roll of masking tape so that they can post their ideas and sketches on the wall. If you have large sheets of newsprint or butcher paper and markers, distribute these to the teams now.

7. **Begin brainstorming.** Tell the teams to list all ideas on these large sheets of paper. Allow the students the rest of the period to brainstorm ideas for the organizer that will save the company.

Engineering the Future Teacher Guide
©2008 Museum of Science, Boston

2nd Class

1. **Team Brainstorming Continues.** Invite teams to continue brainstorming as a group. Let them know that in about 20 minutes you'll want them to shift gears and start narrowing down the best ideas, rather than generating new ideas. Remind them to keep these things in mind:

   - Try to find opportunities to combine two or three good ideas.
   - Be sure everyone who wants to speak can do so.
   - Do not put *down* each others' ideas. Put them *up* on the wall, as even wild ideas may suggest something that's innovative and practical.
   - After the team runs out of fresh ideas, shift to the final stage: picking the best ideas out of those generated so far. Explain why you think those ideas are the most likely ways to solve the problem. New ideas may still come up at this stage!
   - Vote when you're ready. (Hand out sticky dots or Post-Its®.) Use the votes to choose the top three or four ideas.

2. **Circulate** around the room during the discussion, helping whenever needed. Ask groups which phase of brainstorming they are in—still listing new ideas without evaluation or discussing which are the best ideas and why. Make sure that all groups have selected the top 3–4 ideas before the class ends.

3. **Conclude Task 1.6** with an opportunity to report on their top 3 or 4 ideas. Follow the team reports with a discussion of the focus questions. What are the best methods you found to come up with *great* ideas?

Assessment

Pay close attention to the small group discussions, noting who participates and who does not, who tries to take others' ideas into account, who doesn't listen to others' ideas, and so on.

Also pay attention to whether teams are having difficulty separating the two phases of brainstorming: 1) generating new ideas and listening to each other respectfully; and 2) evaluating ideas that have been offered so far, combining different ideas, and voting to determine which are the top three or four ideas.

If following these guidelines for brainstorming seems to be a problem with more than one team, call the class's attention and explain why it is so important to refrain from evaluating too soon (because it squelches good ideas) and why it's important to listen to each other during the evaluation phase (so the team can find the best solution as a whole).

Background and Further Suggestions

One of the most difficult challenges students will encounter may be to "let go" of their own ideas, and to focus on the needs of the group. This process takes place during Tasks 1.6 and 1.7 as students provide their personal input to the decision-making process, then step back from advocating their own ideas to participate in a group process to choose the best organizer possible. Alerting students to the difficulty of putting their own ideas aside may help them get over this hurdle.

There is considerable research on effective problem-solving both alone and in groups. Two excellent references are below, but there are many more. In brief, the research shows that groups generate the greatest number of different ideas when individuals have a chance to work alone for a while. Students should write down their own ideas before they work as a member of a group.

References and Resources

Paulus, P. B. and Brown, V. (2003). "Ideational creativity in groups: Lessons from research on brainstorming." In Paulus, P. B., & Nijstad, B. (Eds.) *Group creativity: Innovation through collaboration.* (pp. 110–136) New York: Oxford University Press.

Wellner, Alison Stein. "A Perfect Brainstorm." *Inc. Magazine,* October, 2003, page 31. Also available online at http://www.inc.com/magazine/20031001/strategies.html.

Task 1.7:	**Choose the Best Solution**

Overview   Each team creates a Pugh chart to rate the alternative organizer designs based on the criteria and constraints of the problem. They select the best choice to refine further.

Five Es   Students **Evaluate** the alternative designs using a Pugh Chart; **Evaluate** their own performance as team members.

Time Frame   1 class period

Focus Question   • How can people decide on the best solution?

Objectives   Students are able to:
- Demonstrate how to select a design that best meets the criteria and constraints of the problem, based on an organized thought process

Materials   No special materials other than pencils and *Engineer's Notebooks*

Preparation   If some teams have been slower than others in choosing the top 3–4 solutions, decide how to move them along more quickly, and what the teams who finish early should do. You might ask early finishers to write a few paragraphs or create a flow diagram showing how their final idea developed and the process of selecting it as their top choice. Alternatively, you might ask them to start thinking of how the product might be marketed, and the qualities that would make it a blockbuster product for the ACME Organizer Company.

Be sure to take time to check your supplies and workshop area for building the scale models or prototypes, which will begin during the next class session.

1st Class
1. **Introduce Pugh Chart.** Tell the students that today they'll learn a method often used by engineers to choose from among the top 3–4 solutions to a problem. It's called a "Pugh chart."

2. **Pugh chart example.** Ask students to read page 55, which describes Pugh charts, and figure out which digital music player was chosen based on the Pugh chart at the bottom of the page.

3. **Meaning of the Pugh chart.** Ask for students to explain what the Pugh chart says about *why* "Giga-Play" is the best digital player. (Giga-Play stores a lot of MP3 files, it is easy to use, durable, and looks terrific. Unfortunately, it cannot be used on a Mac and PC and is more costly than Micro-Music.) Invite discussion about what other factors, aside from overall score—might affect the choice. (For example, if the person buying the MP3 player has a PC, and

the Giga-Play will only run on a Mac, that might determine his or her choice.) Emphasize that a Pugh chart can be very helpful in organizing your thoughts and taking everything into account—but it does not make a decision for you.

4. **Teams make Pugh charts.** Ask the students to turn to page 56 and make up a Pugh chart for the organizer solutions they've thought of so far, using the blank chart on that page. Or, if they wish, insert a sheet of notebook paper at that point in their *Engineer's Notebook*.

5. **Individual and Group Work.** Remind students of the instructions in their *Engineer's Notebook*:

   • **The team** works together to create the chart and decide on values for each criterion and constraint.
   • **Individuals** use the chart to rate the top solutions and come to a tentative decision.
   • **Team members** compare notes to see whether they all agree. If not, they discuss the choices and come to consensus; or if they cannot all agree, they vote on the best solution.

6. **Teams report in.** In the last 15–20 minutes of class, have a spokesperson from each team describe what problem they decided to solve, and give a brief summary of the chosen solution. They should address each of the following items briefly:

   • Their customer audience
   • What needs they were trying to meet
   • The criteria for a good solution
   • Their constraints
   • Their chosen solution and why they think it's the best one

7. **Conclude Task 1.7** by discussing these focus questions: How can people decide on the best solution? Why is the Pugh chart helpful?

8. **Assign homework: Chapter 7.** Ask students to read Chapter 7 in their textbook and to answer the questions at the end of the chapter.

Assessment

You can assess what students have learned by looking at their work on the Pugh charts, as well as their team reports.

Students need to be able to interpret the results of a Pugh chart by explaining the decision in their own words. For example, suppose the students are making an organizer for a card collection. Saying "It got the highest points" is not sufficient. A much deeper understanding would be evident in a statement such as, "We chose this solution because it will organize the most trading cards, it will make it easiest to divide the cards into categories, and it's the lightest of all the possible solutions, which will make it easy to ship or carry home from the store."

This is also a good time to observe teamwork dynamics and have the students assess their teams and their own performance on the team. Forms for this purpose are included in the Assessment Tools section in this Teacher's Guide.

Background and Further Suggestions

Many of the Field Test Teachers have told us that their students find Pugh charts to be very interesting and helpful.

Pugh charts are commonly used by engineers, and various ways of using Pugh charts are described on a number of web sites.

References and Resources

Teamwork and Individual Assessment rubrics were previously drawn from Lemelson Center, MIT InvenTEAMS web site.

The Lemelson Center for the Study on Invention & Innovation, "Resources." http://invention.smithsonian.org/resources/.

For additional resources and educational materials, see the Smithsonian National Museum of American History.

Task 1.8:   Create a Prototype

Overview   Students start by looking at the rubric on page 74 to see how their work
on Project 1.0 will be judged. Then they make engineering drawings of
their organizer designs, create scale models and parts lists, and redesign
their ideas as necessary. Depending on available facilities, students will
build mock-ups, scale models, and/or prototypes of their top design.

Five Es   **Engage** students in building a prototype; **Explain** the different types
of models; and **Elaborate** on the top design by creating engineering
drawings, parts lists, and a scale drawing and/or prototype.

Time Frame   5–9 class periods

Focus Questions
- How will your performance on Project 1.0 be judged?
- Why is it helpful to make engineering drawings, scale models, and parts lists before fabricating a prototype?
- What safety rules and emergency procedures should you know about before using tools?

Objectives   Students will be able to:
- Explain why engineering drawings, scale models, and parts lists are helpful in the engineering design process
- Identify proper safety rules and emergency procedures.

Materials   For each team:
For scale models:
   2–3 sheets 16 × 20 of corrugated cardboard or foam core
   1 utility knife
   1 cardboard, wallboard, or plywood sheet to protect desks or tables
   1 carpenter's square, ruled "T" square, or yard stick
   pencils
   1 container of paper glue or glue gun (with extra glue sticks)

For prototypes:
Materials will depend on facilities and materials budget.

Preparation **Important: All teams should construct scale models, whether or not it is possible for them to go on to fabricate prototypes.**

Plan to discuss this with your students:

1) What kinds of models they'll make and what materials they'll use
2) Where the students will work, and where they'll store their models
3) What tools they will use and what safety instructions need to be given
4) Any additional constraints on the building process

Safety

A **safety briefing** is an important part of any class in which students will be using tools to build. Each classroom has a different set of equipment and rules that you will want to highlight. Students should be made aware of any special instructions for your particular room.

Prepare safety briefings in advance for the use of power tools, large machine tools, smaller tools such as utility knives or hot glue guns, fumes from paints, and inhalation of dusts.

Students should also be aware of the **emergency equipment** around the room such as fire extinguishers, exits and evacuation maps, eyewashes, and communication procedures in the event of an emergency.

Some teachers have students and their parents sign a **safety contract** that lists the tools the students will be using, the safety rules, explains why it's important for students to act responsibly, and what actions will be taken should students fail to follow the rules.

1st–2nd Classes

1. **Discuss the homework: Chapter 7.** Tell students that the ideas of systems analysis will be very important in designing manufacturing processes for their organizers.

2. **Introduce three kinds of models.** Ask students to read about the three kinds of models on page 57. After they've had time to read the page, ask whether there are any questions.

   Compare a mock-up and scale model. Ask the students to explain their understanding of the difference between a mock-up and a scale model. (A mock-up is a rough model that does not accurately represent all dimensions. A scale model is more carefully constructed so that dimensions are scaled in proportion to the full-size design.)

   Compare a scale model and a prototype. Ask the students to explain their understanding of the difference between a scale model and a prototype. (A scale model is made of a material that is easy to cut and tape or glue so it's easy to change. And it may be smaller or larger than the design, as long as it is made to scale. A prototype is the first of its kind. It's usually made full size, using the same materials intended for the manufactured product.)

   When are these model types used? Ask your students why they think all three kinds of models are helpful. (Mock-ups are very easily changed, so they are helpful in the early stages of design. Scale models are most helpful when a design is nearly complete, to see what it will look like in 3-D, but while it is still easy to change. Prototypes are valuable just before manufacturing starts, to be sure that the look and feel is right, and to design the manufacturing process.)

3. **Explain what happens next.** If time, budget, and facilities allow, the next steps will be for the students to make orthographic drawings and parts lists (two days), then to construct scale models (two days), followed by building of prototypes (up to five more class periods). *Explain that teams may build mock-ups if they want, but if the designs are well developed, they can start with scale models.*

4. **Project Rubric.** Have the students turn to page 74 to see how their entire project will be evaluated at the end of the quarter. Point out that five aspects of their individual work will be judged: defining the problem, researching the problem, creating and testing a prototype (which they are about to do), communicating their design, and preparing a written report and project outline. Ask if there are any questions about this rubric.

5. **Refine Designs.** Ask the students to read page 58 to see what they will be doing in the next few days. The team should then discuss their chosen design. What size and shape should it be? Can they suggest any improvements? Teams should discuss their plans in enough detail so that every team member is confident of being able to draw the design.

6. **Decide on a scale for model.** The appropriate scale for the models will depend in large part on the thickness of material used for the scale model and for the prototype. If the students will be using 3/8-thick foam core for the model, and 3/4-thick wood for the prototype, then they should build a 1:2 scale model. If they are using 1/4 cardboard for the model, and 3/4 wood for the prototype, then they may wish to build a 1:3 scale model. Assuming they have little prior experience of these materials, it might be difficult for the students to consider the final size of their model, so you may want to give them the appropriate scale.

7. **Decide on a scale to use for orthographic and isometric drawings.** Ask the students a few questions: "How big do you want the finished product to be? How large is a sheet of paper?" If the longest dimension of the model will be 30 and the longest dimension of the paper is 11, then a scale factor of 1:3 is appropriate. (That is, 1 on the drawing is equal to 3 on the finished product, and there will still be a little room around the drawing.)

8. **Make orthographic drawings.** As students finish their discussions, encourage them to start making orthographic drawings of their selected design. Explain that *each student is to make his or her own orthographic drawings*, showing at least three views of the team's organizer. Individuals may also make isometric drawings if they wish, but orthographic drawings are absolutely necessary to go on to the next stage. Drawings should indicate the scale of the design in a title box at the bottom right of the page.

9. **Teams compare their drawings** and select the best design to build a scale model. (Each student should insert their drawings into the *Engineer's Notebook* whether or not their design is used to make the scale model.) Explain that *each team will make one model.*

10. **Make parts lists.** Ask teams to look at the example of a parts list on page 58, and to create a parts list for their organizers. Depending on the size of their organizer, they should decide if they want their scale model to be full scale or a smaller scale. (If they are designing a really tiny organizer, they may want to build a larger scale model.)

11. **Give safety instructions.** It is best to give safety instructions on the day *before* the students will be working with tools. This is especially important if you will be giving the students a contract to share with parents.

3rd–4th Classes

1. **Start scale models.** When teams finish their orthographic drawings and parts lists, inspect their work carefully to be sure the plans are feasible. A **common mistake** is for the students not to take into account the thickness of materials in calculating the sizes of parts. When you approve their plans, give the team the materials that they will need to make one scale model.

2. **Help teams as needed.** Whether using cardboard or foam core, students rarely have experience building with these tools. They may need help in the safe use of tools, cutting techniques, and methods of gluing and holding materials in place until glue dries. Replace damaged parts if needed.

3. **Collect tools before end of class.** If utility knives are being used, you should collect the tools at the end of class. This is easier if there is just one utility knife per team.

4. **Store models.** Store the models in the classroom between class periods.

5. **Make improvements.** When teams finish their models, have them meet to examine the model and determine what changes might be made to improve it. They should consider questions such as the following:

   • What did they learn from making the scale model?
   • Were there any errors in the drawings or parts list?
   • How can the design be improved to better meet customers' needs?
   • Can the shape be changed to make it more attractive?
   • Are there ways to use fewer materials?
   • How could the organizer be changed to make it lighter?

1. **Modify drawings and parts list.** If you have the facilities and the time to have the students go through the prototyping stage, they should change their drawings or make new drawings and parts lists to represent modifications as a result of their work with the scale model. These may be inserted into their *Engineer's Notebook*.

2. **Start prototypes.** Prototypes should be full scale (1:1) unless the organizer is too large to be built from given materials. When teams have made whatever changes are necessary in their drawings and parts lists, they can get your approval to proceed to the prototype stage. Be sure to ask them what they learned from making their scale models and what changes they decided to make.

3. **Build Prototypes.** Begin by reviewing safety rules. Provide each team with the materials that they'll need, and provide teams with some tips for using the tools and materials. For example, if cutting wood, tell students to:

   • Take into account the width of the saw blade so that when they are marking a measurement they should indicate clearly which side of a line they should cut along
   • Measure out all pieces before they begin cutting
   • Measure three times and cut once

4. **Circulate** around the room and help teams as necessary. Be especially alert to potentially unsafe practices.

5. **Project for early finishers.** You will want to have a meaningful "going further" activity for groups that have made all of their revisions and are waiting for the other groups to finish before they can start making their prototypes. You may have them develop an advertising campaign and create a jingle or video about their product. They might think about:

   • What kinds of activities would appeal to this audience?
   • What would capture their attention on television or in a magazine ad?
   • What are the advantages of the product?
   • How would purchasing the product improve people's lives?

   After discussing these, the team can sketch some ideas for advertisements that could be print ads or storyboards for television.

6. **Students summarize what they have learned.** When teams finish their prototypes, have them first discuss what they learned from the scale model and prototype building, then add a page summarizing that discussion to their *Engineer's Notebook*. Questions to spark discussion may include:

   • What problems did you encounter?
   • What changes did you make?

- How does the product reflect results of your market research?
- What might you do different next time?

7. **Conclude Task 1.8 by discussing the focus questions:**

   - How will your performance on Project 1.0 be judged?
   - Why is it helpful to make engineering drawings, scale models, and parts lists before fabricating a prototype?
   - What safety rules and emergency procedures should you know about before using tools?

8. **Homework: Bring in materials to test prototypes.** Tell the students that in the next class they will need to test their prototypes. The team should meet to see who can bring in materials. If they built a scale model, they'll need to find or make objects at the appropriate scale. (Modeling clay may be helpful for this.)

Assessment

Making scale models and prototypes is engaging, but it can be very challenging for students who have had little or no experience building with their hands. Assess students' abilities to construct scale models and prototypes by observing and helping them work through the activities on this project. The models themselves will provide evidence of their developing skills.

Background and Further Suggestions

Understanding scale is very important in mathematics and science, but challenging for many students because it involves a ratio (Arons, 1990). Encourage students to think about scale when they are deciding what scale factor to use in creating drawings and models and, when measuring, to make their drawings and models. The students may begin to grasp the concept of scale by visualizing different scales as they decide which scale to use, and creating drawings and models of different scales.

References and Resources

Arons, Arnold B. *A Guide to Introductory Physics Teaching.* Especially "Chapter 1 Underpinnings." New York: Wiley, 1990.

Task 1.9: Test and Evaluate

Overview

Students evaluate their design by using the prototype to see whether it will store things the way its designers intended and by comparing the product with the criteria and constraints of the problem. Then they consider how different materials will affect the weight of the product and how the final version of the product will be manufactured.

Five Es

Students **Evaluate** their prototypes in light of the criteria and constraints of the problem; **Explain** how the concept of density can be used to estimate the weight of an object made of different materials; and **Elaborate** their understanding of key concepts by developing a manufacturing process and conducting a life cycle analysis of their product.

Time Frame

3–4 class periods

Focus Questions

- Will this design solve the problem they set out to solve?
- How does the density of a material affect the total weight of a product?
- How should they manufacture it?
- What will be its impact on the environment?

Objectives

Students will be able to:
- Describe two ways of testing a prototype
- Use information on density to calculate the change in weight of an object due to a change in material
- Sketch a possible manufacturing sequence
- Diagram a system of related technologies
- Conduct a life cycle analysis

Materials

For the class:
   Appropriate scale for obtaining the mass of the prototype
   Set of density cubes and a scale (suggested)

For each team:
   Calculator
   Prototypes (or scale models if they did not build prototypes) for Task 1.9

Preparation

This task is quite rich in learning experiences. Your students will learn to do calculations involving density, learn about different manufacturing processes, and conduct a life cycle analysis of their product.

Density is a very important concept in science and engineering; it is also one of the more difficult concepts for many students to learn. It is presented here in the context of a related problem: to calculate how much the organizer will weigh if it is manufactured from a different material.

Take time to look over the pages in which students are asked to calculate the difference in the weight of their product if they decide to use a different material for manufacturing. Make the relevant calculations yourself and decide how you will approach it with your students.

Engineering drawing takes practice. That is why the students are asked to make a final set of drawings for the manufacturing plant.

Manufacturing processes is yet another important set of ideas in this task. Simply reading about these processes is not enough. Your students should have opportunities to plan a manufacturing process for their organizers or some other object. Following the suggestions below, the students will do this on graph paper first and then create a team version to share with the rest of the class.

Life cycle analysis. The last substantive topic presented in Project 1.0 is considered by many people to be the most important: how humans are affecting natural systems. Depending on the material your students decide would be "ideal" for the finished organizer, this will affect the life cycle analysis. Life cycle analysis is a practical application of systems analysis, and it is presented in the last part of Chapter 7 in the textbook.

1st Class

1. **First test.** Have students read the first page of Task 1.9, on page 59. Invite the teams to try storing things in their organizers and discuss how well they work, whether or not improvements are needed, and, if so, what they might do to improve the design. They should write a summary of what they want to include in their final report.

2. **Second test.** Have the students start the second test, in which they reconstruct part of the Pugh chart that they used to choose this solution. (This is a nice opportunity to point out the value of keeping good records, as they can just look up the Pugh chart from earlier in the book.) If it is not obvious to the students, tell them to do the following:

   - **In the 1st column,** list criteria and constraints for this problem.
   - **In the 2nd column,** give the maximum value for each specific criterion and constraint depending on its importance to the overall product.
   - **In the 3rd column,** the students should list a rating value for each criterion and constraint and why they gave it that value. Team members should do their ratings separately before comparing notes.

3. **Third test.** Have students talk to others outside their team. If possible, they should talk to people who might want to purchase these products. Ask them how they think the product might be improved and how much they might be willing to pay for the product.

4. **Materials choice.** Explain that manufacturing design often begins with a final decision about materials. The material that is selected affects the beauty and durability of an object, as well as its weight and cost. Selection of a material often involves trade-offs. Have the students read about different materials on page 60 and answer the two questions at the bottom of the page.

2nd Class
(If students have a difficult time understanding density, this could require two class periods.)

1. **The meaning of density.** Explain that the density of a material is one of the most important chacteristics in deciding what material will be best for mass production. Start by discussing the meaning of the term "density."

   A. Ask the students for their definition of density. (The precise definition is "mass per unit volume." Look for similar ideas, such as "weight for a given size." It is not important for your students to learn a precise definition, but rather that they can distinguish density from the weight.)
   B. Ask the students what makes one material denser than another. (Some may think that less dense materials have air bubbles, or that the atoms and molecules of dense materials are heavier or spaced farther apart. In fact, all of these are true of different materials.)
   C. (Optional) If you have a set of density cubes and an equal arm balance, you can demonstrate the idea of density by showing the students two cubes that are different volumes but weigh the same, and two cubes that weigh the same but have different volumes.
   D. Have your students read page 61 and work on their own to fill in the blanks. This will be a good way to assess whether some students need additional explanations and practice with the density concept.

2. **Measuring density.** Tell your students that their next task will be to find out how much their organizers would weigh if they decide to produce it from a different material. The density calculation is a valuable experience whether or not they decide to change the materials they will use. You may also point out that the calculation assumes that the design will be exactly the same, but of course the students could change the thickness and shapes of the pieces so that it would weigh less, even if they used a denser material.

3. **Find the material volume of the prototype.** Have the students read and fill in the table on page 62 to find the volume of all the material in their prototype.

4. **Find the density of the prototype.** After students find the volume of the material in their prototype, ask them to weigh their prototype. They then find the density by dividing the weight by the volume, resulting in a density value in units of "ounces or pounds per cubic

inch." (Note: strictly speaking, density is mass per unit volume, not weight per unit volume. On Earth, these are equivalent and represent a sufficient level of understanding for this introductory course.)

5. **Weight with different materials.** Figure out what the organizer would weigh if it were made from a different material. Have your students fill in the table on page 63. Each box in the "volume" row will have the same value, found on page 62. Then have them answer questions 2, 3, and 4. (See Answer Key below.)

ERROR: On page 63, question 2, the Zip code for Boston, MA, should read 02114.

6. **Decide on a material.** Have teams read and discuss the questions on page 64, then make a decision about what kind of material would be best for their organizer. Each student should write his or her team's decisions in his or her own *Engineer's Notebook*.

Answer Key

7. **Homework assignment: Chapter 8.** Ask students to read Chapter 8 in the textbook, and to answer all of the questions. As they read the chapter, they should think about how engineer Christine Epplett tests prototypes, and how her process compares with their own.

EN Page 61: Understanding Density

1)

$$\rho = \left(1\frac{\text{lb.}}{\text{in.}^3}\right) \qquad \rho = \left(1\frac{\text{lb.}}{\text{in.}^3}\right)$$

$$\rho = \left(1\frac{\text{lb.}}{\text{in.}^3}\right) \qquad \rho = \left(1\frac{\text{lb.}}{\text{in.}^3}\right)$$

$$\rho = \left(1\frac{\text{lb.}}{\text{in.}^3}\right) \qquad \rho = \left(2\frac{\text{lb.}}{\text{in.}^3}\right)$$

$$\rho = \left(1\frac{\text{lb.}}{\text{in.}^3}\right) \qquad \rho = \left(2\frac{\text{lb.}}{\text{in.}^3}\right)$$

2) =, right arm moves down, right arm moves down, =

EN Page 63: Weight with Different Materials

Answers in the table and question 2 will depend on the students' particular organizers. Following are answers for questions 3 and 4.

3) If all dimensions of a product are doubled, the volume, and therefore the weight, will increase by a factor of 8.

4) The moon has one-sixth the gravity of Earth. So the weight simply needs to be divided by six. For example, an organizer that weighs 36 pounds on Earth would weigh just 6 pounds on the moon.

1. **Discuss the homework.** Focus especially on the manufacturing processes and the manufacturing system as a whole, since the students are about to design a manufacturing system for their organizers. Also review the ideas from Chapter 7 concerning systems, with inputs and outputs, as well as the idea of a life cycle analysis.

2. **Develop a sequence of manufacturing processes.** Start by asking the students whether their product is something that will be mass produced or hand-built to provide a custom product for a niche market. Then ask the students to read the top half of page 65 and to design a manufacturing process for their organizers. Give teams time to work together. You may want to have each student individually sketch the manufacturing process, or have the team collaborate and draw their ideas on a large sheet of newsprint or butcher paper to share with the other teams as part of their report to the rest of the class in Task 1.10.

3. **Conduct a Life cycle analysis.** Ask students to read the bottom half of page 65 and to create a life cycle analysis for their organizer. It is only in recent years that engineers have begun to take into account the impact of new technologies on the environment. While it may not seem as though a single organizer has much of an impact on the environment, it becomes more obvious if the company is successful and sells millions of them, and if all the other competing products are taken into account as well. There will also be interesting comparisons to make between organizers that are made of wood, versus plastic, when you consider what inputs and outputs there are in the life cycle of the product.

   A complete life cycle analysis might include a diagram and/or description of the entire system of technologies needed to obtain the raw materials, transport the materials to the factory, construct the organizers, transport them to stores or directly to people's homes, and then eventually dispose of them when no longer needed. Each part of the design process could be shown in a box, with arrows showing the flow of energy and/or materials. The life cycle analysis would include arrows to show the inputs as energy and materials and outputs as products and wastes.

4. **Conclude Task 1.9** by discussing the focus questions:
   - Will this design solve the problem they set out to solve?
   - How does the density of a material affect the total weight of a product?
   - How should they manufacture it?
   - What will be its impact on the environment?

Background and Further Suggestions

Although everyone uses manufactured products every day, students rarely have a chance to learn much about how manufacturing is done, even if they have had a chance to visit a factory. Chapters 6, 7, and 8 of the textbook are intended to provide background material, but if your students are really going to understand these ideas, they will need to apply what they learn by designing a manufacturing system for their organizer or some other object.

The concept of density is presented here because it underlies many of the other ideas that will be developed in this course, as well as in other science courses. The concept of density as a property of a material is difficult for many students who confuse the density of a material with the weight of an object. If your students seem to have difficulty with this, you may want to write these two questions on the board and discuss them:

- What weighs more, a pound of lead or a pound of feathers? (A pound is a pound—they both weigh the same.)
- What weighs more, a cup of lead or a cup of feathers? (A cup of lead weighs more, because lead is much denser than feathers.)

References and Resources

An excellent web site, listed below, is "How Everyday Things Are Made." It includes more than 40 virtual factory tours. Students can be referred to this web site as a homework assignment, and asked to make a report on one or more manufactured items or manufacturing processes and systems.

Understandings of Consequence Project, The. *Causal Patterns in Density: Lessons to Enable Deeper Understanding.* Cambridge, MA: Project Zero, Harvard Graduate School of Education, 2005.

Alliance for Innovative Manufacturing at Stanford. "How Everyday Things Are Made." http://manufacturing.stanford.edu/.

Task 1.10:   Communicate the Solution

Overview

Students report what they have discovered as they have gone through the engineering design process to design the "best organizer in the world." Before they present their final solution, they will also make a cost estimate for the manufacturing, shipping, and distribution of their product. Depending on your resources, you may ask the students to make commercials, poster presentations, or PowerPoint presentations. This is a time for the team to show some more creativity and another chance for students to be graded individually (including drawings, organization, and written reports, as well as group work).

Five Es

Students **Explain** how the product they developed will meet the requirements of the problem; and **Elaborate** with a mathematical analysis of costs and a compelling presentation about their product.

Time Frame

4–5 class periods

Focus Questions

- Will this product sell?
- What have they accomplished so far; and what will they recommend to the Acme Organizer company?

Objectives

Students will be able to:

- Communicate how they have followed the engineering design process, and what they have learned as a result
- Make a convincing presentation about their engineering ideas and recommendations

Materials

For each team of students:
    Prototype (and/or scale model)
    Newsprint or butcher paper
    Colored markers

or

Computers with PowerPoint software and LCD Projector

Preparation

Timing. As this task comes near the end of the semester or quarter, you will need to think about how much time you can allow for each presentation so that the students have sufficient time to finish Tasks 1.10 and 1.11 without rushing their oral presentations. Think of a way to warn a group when their time is nearly up (such as holding up a sign with the number of minutes) so they can come to a conclusion.

Determine the costs of materials the students used to build their prototypes (or scale models if they did not build prototypes). Decide if you want your students to look up this information as part of the class assignment, or if you want to give it to them. If you intend to give them the information, prepare a sheet on actual materials costs, or post the information on the board. If you want the students to research the answers, tell them how best to get the actual prices (online? By calling the store or lumberyard?)

Determine shipping costs. As with the costs of materials, you will need to decide whether you want to get a summary of shipping costs from a post office or the U.S. Mail web site, or if you want to have students look up this information themselves.

Audio-Visual Aids: Provide your students with newsprint or butcher paper and colored markers, so they can present their key findings, sketch ideas that didn't work, or show their cost calculations. Or, if students have computers and a projector available, they can prepare PowerPoint presentations. Be sure to remind them to use their models and prototypes to demonstrate what they did and what they learned.

1st Class

1. **Prepare to communicate your team's ideas to the ACME Board of Directors.** Ask the students to read page 67, which summarizes what they are about to do. Emphasize that their report should be honest. If they have found problems with their organizer, these should be presented as well as the positives. Engineers should never try to make their proposals look better than they are, because the result could be disastrous. Tell the students that their grades will depend on the quality of their presentation, not on whether they have the best organizer design. (You may want to quote from the rubric on page 74, in particular the first box in the row marked "Communicate the Design.")

2. **How much will it cost?** Each team should conduct a cost analysis of their organizer design by following the steps on page 68. You may want to remind them of finding the cost to make their cell phone holders. If the students in your class find such problems challenging, call the class's attention and work out a sample problem on the board. Pause at appropriate times so the students can do the calculations. For example:

   Suppose the cost of 6 pine boards is $0.75 per foot, and 1/4 plywood is $10 for a 4× 8 sheet. Assume that you can get wood for four organizers out of a single sheet of plywood, and you can get wood for two organizers out of a single 10'-long pine board. How much will it cost for the wood for 100 organizers?

   Plywood: 25 sheets × $10 = $250

   Pine: 50 boards × $7.50 = $375

   Cost for material: 100 organizers = $625; cost for 1 organizer = $6.25

   Estimated cost of labor and overhead: 3 × $6.25 = $18.75

Total production cost: $6.25 + $18.75 = $25

Calculated manufacturer's markup: 10% of $25 = $2.50

Wholesale price: $25 + $2.50 = $27.50

Shipping and handling: $5.00

Store's cost = $27.50 + $5 = $32.50

Retail price = 2 × $32.50 = $65.00

3. **What will customers pay?** Discuss with the class how they will show their prototype to members of the target audience, as described on page 69. If it is difficult to transport the organizer and/or to reach the target audience, ask the team to come up with a plan for overcoming this. (For example, they could call people in the target audience and describe the product, or take a picture of the organizer and show it to people in the target audience.) Not every member of the team needs to interview eight people—they can split up the work. However, each team member should write in the results and note who conducted the interviews.

4. **Will it save the company?** Ask the students to read page 70 and to draw conclusions about their product. Again, emphasize that honesty is most important. The Board of Directors may well prefer a team of engineers who determined that certain ideas would not work over another team that is trying to sell an idea that will never work.

5. **Assign homework: Chapter 9.** The last chapter in the first unit of the textbook is a very strong finish. While the chapter is relevant to the upcoming task of deciding what materials to use when manufacturing the organizers, the more important message is what motivates some engineers to do what they do. Also important is Saul Griffith's willingness to recognize when there's an even more important problem to solve than the one he's been working on. Ask the students to answer the questions at the end of the chapter and to be prepared to discuss their own ideas about it.

2nd–3rd Classes

1. **Discuss Homework: Chapter 9.** Start with the most important question mentioned in the *Engineer's Notebook*: "What would you say is the most important message of this story?" (There are several good answers to this question, such as the importance of good materials and design, always being willing to recognize that you're trying to solve the wrong problem, the motives that drive engineers, and so on.) Tell your students that this is the last chapter of Project 1.0. All of the engineers that they read about are actual practicing engineers, and all of the stories are true.

2. **Presenting your product.** Have students read the instructions for preparing an oral report on pages 71 and 72. After reading the instructions, urge the students to make a team outline of the ideas they want to present, and to be sure that each person on the team

has an active part in the presentation. Then, each individual should make an outline of the ideas that he or she will present as his or her part of the presentation. Emphasize that an outline, or at least a list of ideas, is important to be sure nothing critical is left out. However, they should not write out exactly what they will say because it's boring to listen to someone read a speech.

3. **Checklist.** Near the end of the third class, call everyone's attention to summarize the expectations for this report. Each person's report should include:

   - A description of the target audience and what these people need/want
   - A definition of the problem
   - Demonstration of the prototype
   - Results of the tests to determine whether this is a good solution
   - Density calculations with conclusions
   - A decision about what material to use in manufacturing the product with a rationale for why that was chosen
   - A diagram showing a sequence of manufacturing processes
   - A cost analysis
   - A life cycle analysis

Tell the students that their report will not be complete without each of these parts, and that if one of the parts is not finished, they should do that for homework.

4. **Time to prepare.** You should give the students a full class period to go over their work, coaching individuals and teams as needed. This is an excellent time for the students to reflect on their work, and see where it shined and where it was lacking. You will want to provide time and assistance so that the students can re-draw or otherwise revise their earlier work, now that they have a better understanding of what was wanted.

4th–5th Classes

1. **Setting up for group presentations.** Either the teacher can play the role of the Acme Company President, who will facilitate the discussion and ask for Q&A after each presentation, or a student can be appointed to play the role of President for the day. The rest of the class can play the role of "Board of Directors." Tell the students how much time they will have for their presentations, and how much time you can allow for questions and answers.

2. **Student presentations.** Invite teams to come up to the front of the room one at a time to make their presentations. If you have appointed one of your students to act as "President," you can sit at the side or back of the room and coach as needed. After the presentation, invite questions from the Board of Directors, and add your own questions if you wish.

3. **Conclude Task 1.10** by discussing the focus questions:

- Will this product sell?
- What have they accomplished so far; and what will they recommend to the Acme Organizer company?

Note: We do not recommend that you have the students vote for the best organizer, as that sets up students to be "winners" or "losers." The important thing is what students learn from the process. If this were an actual presentation by several teams to a Board of Directors, each presentation would be scrutinized as a possible solution to the problem, and the Board may decide to implement one, none, or all of the ideas.

Background and Further Suggestions

Although engineering competitions are exciting and engaging for many students, the arguments against emphasizing classroom contests are compelling. According to a research review and field study of students in grades 5–9 (Sadler et. al. 1995), engineering contests began at top-flight engineering schools, such as MIT, and were then adapted for high schools and middle schools. Observations of such contests have shown that student competitors only rarely apply science, focusing instead on the narrow goal of winning the competition. And when winning becomes the goal, student teams do not share what they've learned. Competition also tends to favor boys' inclination to compete, versus girls' preferences for cooperative modes of learning.

Sadler and his co-authors recommend that the focus of open-ended engineering challenges be on frequent public trials in which students learn from each other, and in which all teams are competing against the constraints of nature rather than against each other. We favor this approach in these teaching materials.

References and Resources

Miller, C.M. *So Can You Build One? Learning Through Designing—Connection Theory with Hardware in Engineering Education.* Doctoral Dissertation. Cambridge, MA: MIT, 1995.

Coyle, Harold P., Sadler, Philip, and Schwartz, Marc. "Engineering Competitions in the Middle School Classroom: Key Elements in Developing Effective Design Challenges." *The Journal of the Learning Sciences.* Vol. 9, No. 3, pp. 299–327.

Task 1.11:	Redesign

Overview   Students consider how they would redesign their organizer if they were going to make it again. This should be a part of their final presentation, or you might have them write it as a reflection after they have seen all the presentations from the class.

Five Es   Students **Evaluate** their product to see how it might be improved; and **Evaluate** their work on the entire project using a rubric at the end of their *Engineer's Notebook* for Project 1.0.

Time Frame   1 class

Focus Question
• What changes do you want to make in your product?

Objectives   Students will be able to:
• Suggest redesign ideas based on test results and feedback from peers

Materials   For every team:
1 or more calculators
Newsprint or butcher paper
Colored markers

Preparation   **Extra-credit projects.** In most cases, the school year requires that students complete the first quarter of their work, pass in a major project, and/or take a test, and move on. If so, this is a good time to end this unit. However, if you want to provide an extra-credit opportunity, students can be given the chance to redesign their organizer, provide new engineering drawings, or a new scale model or prototype.

Written Report. The *Engineer's Notebook* does not assign a written report, although it is referred to in the rubric on page 74. This is to allow for teachers to customize the assignment. For some students, the oral report provides a sufficient opportunity for the students to reflect on their work and for the teacher to assess the teams' and students' accomplishments. Also, your students may have tired of the project and may want to go on to the next project.

However, students in a rigorous academic program should be tasked to write a detailed final report of their project, including what they accomplished during each step of the engineering design process, and a thorough description of the final product and how well it performed in various tests.

To prepare for this last class, you will need to decide in advance whether or not you want to give a final written assignment, and, if so, whether it will be a team or individual report, and exactly what you want your students to do.

Test. After concluding this Task, you may want to give the end-of-project test, found near the end of this Teacher's Guide, as a final exam.

1st Class

1. **Why redesign?** Tell the students that the final step of the engineering design process is called "Redesign." Have the students read page 73 in their *Engineer's Notebook*. Explain that for many professional engineers the job is just beginning when they get the go-ahead from their client based on the prototype tests. Actually developing the manufacturing process may suggest new ideas for reducing waste or improving the product. And the first few products that are sold may have problems that result in an expensive "recall."

2. **Plan your work.** Tell the students that they will not be asked to undertake a major redesign (unless you plan to offer that as an extra-credit alternative). However, they should give some thought to how they might redesign it, and write these thoughts in the box at the bottom of page 73. Suggest that they take some of the ideas from the Q&A following their oral reports as a source of ideas for creating a "new and improved" organizer.

3. **Final Report.** If you plan to assign a final report, this is a good time to do so. Have them look at the rubric on page 74 so that they will understand how their reports will be evaluated.

4. **Test.** If you assign an end-of-project test, tell students to prepare for the test by going over their *Engineer's Notebook*. You may also want to hold a special class to answer their questions in advance of the test, and to go over any concepts or skills that you know have been difficult for them.

5. **Conclude Project 1.0** by asking your students what they have learned about technology, about engineering, and how they felt about the various activities. You might also ask them if they have any suggestions for how you will plan and present Project 2.0.

Background and Further Suggestions

Typically, students are not fond of the redesign phase of the engineering design process. Most students are used to doing something once, then moving on to something else. However, engineering is not like that. It's not normally a quick-and-easy process. To "engineer" something means to produce something (a product or a process) that solves a problem and does not create more problems. Anyone who has purchased something that functions poorly knows what problems can be caused by engineers who cut corners. The results can be disastrous for the companies that hire those engineers if everyone is dissatisfied with their products. Our compromise is to address the issue of redesign, but to keep it brief so students do not "burn out."

Finally, the teaching suggestions that we offer in this last task are purposefully vague. For example, whether to end with an oral report alone or to require a written report from every student is a major decision, and it depends both on the teacher's goals and on how much time is left for Project 1.0.

Finally, the suggestion that students be asked for their input is an important one that some teachers have found exceptionally helpful. Even if students' ideas cannot be accommodated practically, many students appreciate the opportunity to be heard. Often, students' suggestions are practical and may improve the experience for them, and therefore for the teacher. Student input may also provide one more source of data for planning Project 2.0.

Project 2.0: Design a Building of the Future:
Construction Technologies and Thermal Systems
Project Guide

Central Hong Kong, China (Image courtesy of Wikipedia)

Project 2.0: Design a Building of the Future introduces students to some of the problems of today's cities: urban sprawl, lifeless urban centers, underdevelopment of mass transit systems, and a lack of public meeting spaces. These problems have led to degradation of the environment and of the quality of life in the 21st century. In Task 2.1 students are introduced to "New Urbanism," a movement among city planners, architects, and engineers working to foster sustainable development of cities and towns. New Urbanists believe that the creation of mixed-use structures, enhanced public spaces, and improved mass transit systems can revitalize urban centers by increasing urban density, thereby reducing sprawl and traffic congestion. Students are challenged to work in teams to design a mixed-use, energy-efficient structure that can be used for housing and at least one other function, such as office space, retail shops, or manufacturing facilities. The project draws to a conclusion in Task 2.9, when students make drawings, construct a model, and evaluate their buildings.

In tasks 2.2–2.8 students develop the knowledge and skills they will need to accomplish the major challenge. They learn about live loads by designing, building, and testing a model deck. They construct towers and analyze modes of failure. They test materials for tensile and compressive strength, investigate the mechanical properties of various construction materials, and practice making scale drawings. An essential part of the project involves learning about how thermal energy transfers through walls and windows, and how to minimize energy losses to accomplish efficient heating and cooling. In the final activity, the students apply all that they've learned to design and model a building of the future.

Below is an example of a **Gantt chart**, which is used by engineers to break a large project down into smaller tasks with time estimates. Each column represents five 45-minute classes and each bar is an estimated number of classes per task. This chart also lists the corresponding text chapters to the tasks in the last column.

Project 2.0: 45-Minute Class Periods	5	10	15	20	25	30	35	40	Text Chapter
Task 2.1: Define the Problem Students examine the problem of urban sprawl and possible solutions.	▓								10
Task 2.2: Identify the Loads the Building Must Support Students learn how to calculate live and dead loads, and explore how loads are transferred through the members of a structure.		▓							11
Task 2.3: Use Failure Analysis to Design a Safer Building Students design and then load a tower to analyze the forces that affect a structure.			▓						12
Task 2.4: Test Construction Materials for Strength Students test materials and compare their strength under tension and compression.			▓						13
Task 2.5: Describe Mechanical Properties of Materials Students examine the properties of a variety of construction materials.			▓						14
Task 2.6: Experiment with Concrete Students test the compression strength of concrete samples.				▓					
Task 2.7: Make Your Building Energy Efficient Students are introduced to energy concepts through thermal systems and energy transfers in a structure.					▓				15, 16
Task 2.8: Make a Scale Drawing of Your Building Design Students review scale and scale factors by drawing plan views of their classrooms and homes.						▓			
Task 2.9: Design a Building of the Future! Students present a plan and a model of their multi-use building. The plan will include important considerations for structural design and energy efficiency.						▓			

Engineering the Future Teacher Guide
©2008 Museum of Science, Boston

Preparing to Teach Project 2.0

Introduction

In a sense, Project 2.0 is an extension of Project 1.0—buildings can be viewed as large organizers, and cities as organizers of buildings. Project 2.0 builds on the skills that students developed in Project 1.0—using the engineering design process to solve problems that meet peoples' needs, creating scale drawings and models, organizing the environment so that the technologies they need are close at hand, and minimizing negative impacts on the environment. Project 2.0 differs from Project 1.0 in that it introduces structural engineering concepts (calculation of loads, forces, failure modes, and materials testing) and science concepts (energy transfer in thermal systems).

Urban sprawl. Prepare for the first task by reading Chapter 10, "Redesigning America," in the textbook *Engineering the Future*, in which Peter Park describes how new urbanism combats urban sprawl and promotes sustainable development. Then, take a tour of the areas where your students live to see what aspects of urban sprawl you can find that they might recognize. Keep in mind that evidence of urban sprawl is not only found in cities. Suburban areas may have widely separated residential areas, malls, and industries that require residents to drive long distances daily, and rural areas may have new housing developments that are threatening to reduce forest or farmland. If you can relate the ideas in this project to the students' local environment, you will have much greater success in engaging their interest and communicating the importance of the topic.

Selecting teams. Prior to the first class session, you may want to think about how you will assign teams. Students assigned to a team should work well together and have complementary strengths. You may prefer to have the same teams work together throughout the project. However, most teachers like to assign different teams to work on the various tasks. The most important team is the one that will work together during Task 2.1. They should be the same group that meets during Tasks 2.8 and 2.9, to design and model a "Building of the Future." In planning those teams, some teachers like to have students write a confidential note concerning what they perceive their own strengths to be, with whom they would like to work, and who they do not want to work with, before assigning those teams. Some teachers prefer same-gender groups while others prefer to mix boys and girls. However, after the teams are selected for the major design project, you can mix students for Tasks 2.2–2.7 if you wish.

Quantitative analysis. Project 2.0 increases the cognitive demand on students by introducing additional quantitative analysis as they calculate live loads in Tasks 2.2 and 2.3 and test construction materials in Tasks 2.4, 2.5, and 2.6. We advise you to try the activities described in these tasks before starting the project to be sure that you can obtain the required materials and are prepared to help students if they encounter problems doing the tests or analyzing the results.

Concrete testing. Building the "concrete crusher" in Task 2.6 (and described on the next two pages) will involve some simple carpentry. If it is not possible to construct the concrete crusher, or if time is short, Task 2.6 can be skipped. However, it reinforces standards introduced in the earlier tasks, so it should be included if at all possible because most students appreciate the opportunity to test materials actually used in construction.

Energy concepts. In Task 2.7 students are challenged to apply science concepts related to designing heating and cooling systems for the building that they have been asked to design. The fundamental concepts of thermal energy transfer introduced in this task are very important in laying the foundation for energy transfer in fluid systems like they will learn about in Project 3.0, as well as electrical systems in Project 4.0. In brief, the key ideas that students will learn about in this part of the course are as follows:

1. **Energy is like a substance, but it is *not* a substance.** Energy can be measured and it can flow from one place to another, but it does *not* consist of matter.
2. **It takes a difference to make a difference.** In order to maintain a warmer temperature inside a building on a cold day, there must be a continuous input of energy (such as a furnace or space heater). Similarly, in order to cool a building on a hot day, there must also be a continuous flow of energy (an electric air conditioner removes thermal energy from a room).

    Difference drives change. If the air inside a building is warmer than the air outside, thermal (heat) energy will flow out. The bigger the temperature difference, the greater the flow of energy will be. When the temperature difference disappears, thermal energy will stop flowing.

3. **Resistance slows the rate of energy flow.** Insulation slows the flow of thermal (heat) energy through walls and windows. The more effective the insulation, the more efficient the heating and cooling of the system.

These ideas will appear again in the context of fluid and electrical systems, but they are easier to understand in the context of thermal systems. Be certain to spend enough time on Task 2.7 so that students will have an easier time when they encounter energy-transfer concepts in the more abstract contexts of Projects 3.0 and 4.0.

Engineering drawing in Task 2.8 builds on students' skills in making orthographic drawings, a skill they learned in Project 1.0. However,

Engineering the Future Teacher Guide
©2008 Museum of Science, Boston

when making scale drawings of buildings, they will encounter the additional challenges of measuring and estimating large areas as well as making drawings of buildings with much larger scale factors than when drawing small objects.

The culmination of Project 2.0 will be the design of a multi-use building. You will need to plan sufficient time—at least a week—for the student teams to make engineering drawings and models, and to present their ideas in class. Be sure to call the students' attention to the evaluation rubric for their final designs at the beginning of the week, so they will understand the quality of work that is expected.

As extra-credit projects, students might research architectural styles (Brutalism, Early Modernism, Futurism, International Style, Modernism, Post Modernism, Structural Expressionism) and brainstorm what the outside façade of their mixed-use structures might look like if they were to reflect the characteristics of these styles.

Students could also develop mini-projects in which they find ways to make energy-efficient designs support architectural ideas—for example, integrating green spaces and natural light into the building design.

Instructions for Building the Concrete Crusher
Designed by Fred Hopps, Beverly High School, Beverly, MA

Although student teams will make their own concrete samples, only one concrete crusher is needed for the class. You can construct it yourself or assign construction to students who have access to tools and adult assistance.

You will need the following parts (in addition to some nails):

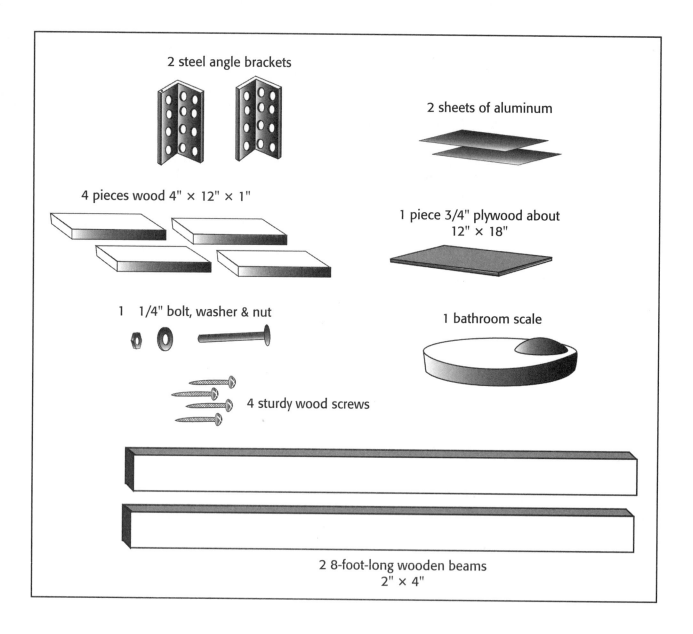

2 steel angle brackets

2 sheets of aluminum

4 pieces wood 4" × 12" × 1"

1 piece 3/4" plywood about 12" × 18"

1   1/4" bolt, washer & nut

1 bathroom scale

4 sturdy wood screws

2 8-foot-long wooden beams 2" × 4"

Step 1 Drill a hole for 1/4" bolt in one end of an 8-foot 2" × 4" wooden beam. Attach an aluminum sheet a few inches from the end, and nail plywood on opposite end. Note that the beam is placed with the narrow side down.

Step 2 Use wood screws to securely fasten steel angle brackets to one end of the other 8-foot-long 2" × 4" wooden beam. Space between brackets should be just wide enough for the other beam. Note that beam is placed wide side down.

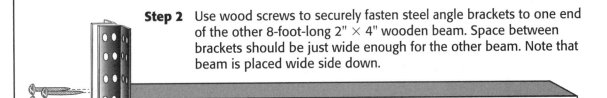

Step 3 Nail wooden pieces on bottom of beam to increase stability. Fasten second aluminum sheet to the beam with nails as shown.

Step 4 Use bolt, washer, and nut to fasten the upper wooden beam to lower wooden beam. The concrete crusher is now complete.

Bolt pivot

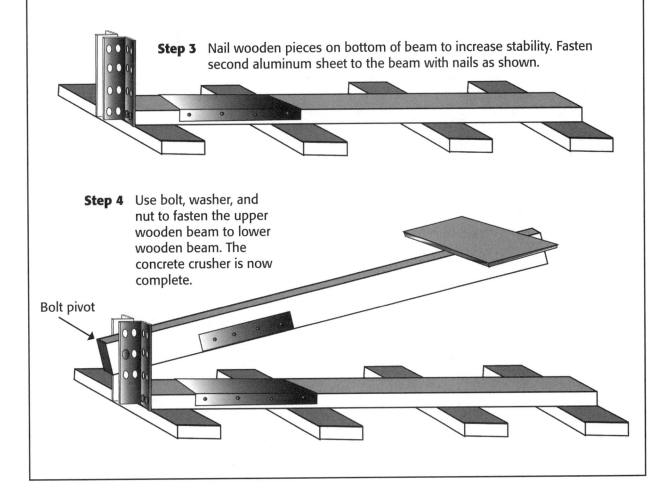

Task 2.1:   Define the Problem

Overview

Students start by considering the problem of urban sprawl and recognizing where it is happening around them. They are guided in this effort by questions in the *Engineer's Notebook* and by Chapter 10, "Redesigning America," of the textbook, in which Peter Park describes how *new urbanism* intends to combat urban sprawl and promote sustainable development.

A key concept in understanding urban sprawl is usage density, or the amount of space allocated for different purposes. Students learn to measure areas and calculate usage density using a simple estimation method.

At the conclusion of Project 2.0, teams are challenged to design one possible solution to urban sprawl: an energy-efficient, mixed-use structure where people will live and work. At the end of Task 2.1, the students define the problem more precisely by identifying criteria and constraints for a successful solution. Tasks 2.2–2.7 will provide them with the knowledge and skills they will need to design the building, for which they'll construct engineering drawings and a model in Tasks 2.8 and 2.9.

Five Es

Engage students in thinking about how urban sprawl applies to their own city or town; **Explore** how space is allocated for different functions; **Explain** the concept of population density.

Time Frame

3 class periods

Focus Questions

- What is urban sprawl?
- Can you find signs of urban sprawl in your community?
- What are some ways to meet people's needs while preserving the natural world?

Objectives

Students are able to:
- Identify what urban sprawl is and what its consequences are
- Estimate area and calculate usage density
- Distinguish between building codes and zoning laws
- Identify criteria for a successful new urbanist structure (e.g., mixed-use, proximity to transportation and public spaces)

Materials

For each student:
    1 *Engineer's Notebook*

For each pair of students:
    1 calculator
    1 yard stick, tape measure, or roll measure

Preparation

Preparation

Read Task 2.1 in the *Engineer's Notebook* and Chapter 10 in the textbook to be sure that you're prepared for any questions the students may ask.

Tour the areas where your students live to see what aspects of urban sprawl you can identify. Also, look for examples of projects—such as apartment buildings near public transportation, or development of neighborhood centers—that reduce or prevent urban sprawl.

1st Class

1. **Welcome students** to Project 2.0, in which they will learn how to design a building of the future.

2. **Hand out Project 2.0 of the *Engineer's Notebook*** for the students to insert in their 3-ring binders. Tell the students that as they work through each page of the *Notebook* they should write their names at the top and, when finished, initial and date it at the bottom.

3. **Explain the project expectations and timeline.** Ask the students to read the top of the page, which introduces the challenge of Project 2.0. As with Project 1.0, the goal here is to complete the entire project by accomplishing each of the tasks, one at a time. Like real engineers, the students will be asked to complete the tasks on schedule so that the entire project will be finished on time.

4. **Point out the Teamwork Guidelines and Engineering Design Process on page 6.** Students should be familiar with these ideas from Project 1.0, but you may mention that because they have more experience with teamwork and the engineering design process, you will expect them to perform at an even higher level.

5. **Introduce the concept of urban sprawl** by asking students to read the first page of Task 2.1, on page 7 of their *Engineer's Notebook*, and to given an example from the city or town where they live or one they've visited. If the concept is new to them, point to the definition of urban sprawl in the middle of page 7, and give your own local examples to further define it.

6. **Measure length of step.** Explain that one of the first things architects and engineers need to consider in designing a building is how big it should be for the number of people it serves. They will start by analyzing existing structures. To do that they will need to estimate the length of their "pace," or "step." Have the students read page 8 and measure the length of their pace. Each team of two students will need a yardstick or tape measure for this.

7. **Find the area of the classroom.** Once the students know the length of their pace, have each student measure the area of the classroom by pacing off the length and width and multiplying the two numbers. Information for how to do this is given on the bottom of page 8 and the top of page 9.

8. **Compare findings.** Gather students' attention and have them share their measurements of the area of the classroom floor. Write answers on the board to show similarities and differences and to emphasize units (ft.²).

9. **Calculate usage density**, which is defined on page 9 as the number of square feet of a given space divided by the number of people who use it at the same time. As an example, calculate the usage density of the classroom using an average value for the square footage measured by your students and the number of students in the current class. (Note: the concept of room *usage density* is intended to introduce *population density*, which students will read about in Chapter 10.)

10. **Invite questions.** Students may come up with excellent questions or comments at this point, such as how the estimate for usage density would change at night when the classroom is empty. As used here, the term refers to high-usage times of day.

11. **Assign homework.** Assign students to measure the area of their bedroom and other rooms, either at school or at home, and then find the usage density of these spaces by dividing the area (number of square feet) by the number of people who use them at any one time.

2nd Class

1. **Analyze space.** Have your students write their answers to the questions on page 9, then compare notes with other students. Lead a class discussion about the homework, in particular any insights that students may want to share about the differences in how space is allocated for different uses. Tell the students that when they design their buildings they will need to estimate usage density for each part of the structure.

2. **Location, location, location.** The questions on page 10 encourage your students to think about how the layout of a city or town affects the lives of the people who live there. You may want to have students work together in pairs to write answers to the questions, or have students write their individual answers and then discuss them in small groups. You may want to add questions that help students become aware of how their own community is laid out.

3. **Large-class discussion.** Ask small groups to report the highlights of their discussions. If there is time, raise a few broad questions about urban sprawl: "Did it always exist? When did it come into existence? Are there some advantages to urban sprawl, or only disadvantages?" This discussion will help students prepare for what they'll be reading about in their textbook.

4. **Assign homework from the textbook.** Ask the students to read Chapter 10, "Redesigning America," and to write their answers to the questions at the end of the chapter.

3rd Class

1. **Discuss the homework reading.** Ask students for their answers to the questions at the end of Chapter 10. Encourage discussion when answers differ. When possible, ask the students how a response to a question might be applied to their own community. Spend most of the class time on the last questions, under "What Do You Think?" These ideas apply to their next assignment. You may want to collect homework papers for grading.

2. **Form teams** who will work together to design a multi-use structure. As previously stated, it's best for the teacher to assign the team, rather than have students choose. Assign teams to read page 11 and meet to share ideas about the "criteria" and "constraints" that are needed to define the problem clearly. Tell them that everyone should record the group's ideas in their *Engineer's Notebooks*, so they can refer back to this problem definition at any time. Ask students whether they have questions about the assignment.

3. **Let teams define the problem.** Walk around from group to group to help them get started. If some groups have difficulty getting started, you might ask the following questions to help them identify **criteria**:
   • What is important to people when they buy a home or rent an apartment?
   • What would you like to find in a place where you live and work?
   • What about surroundings and location?

   To help students identify **constraints**, you might ask:
   • What might limit your choice of a house or apartment?

4. **Reducing urban sprawl.** As groups finish defining the problem, ask students to work individually to come up with an initial idea for such a building and to sketch it in the space on page 12. Tell the students to add enough information about their idea to show how it would function to reduce urban sprawl, and how many people it could accommodate.

5. **Conclude Task 2.1 by discussing the focus questions:**
   • What is urban sprawl?
   • Can you find signs of urban sprawl in your community?
   • What are some ways to meet people's needs while preserving the natural world?

Assessment

Infer student understanding of objectives through discussion, activities, and answers in the *Engineer's Notebook*.

The final activity on page 12 is intended as an open-ended embedded assessment to see whether your students understand the challenge, and whether they have learned some of the ideas about estimating usage density for a building. Ask your students to tear out these pages after completing them and pass them in so you can look them over. Watch for patterns among the responses and plan the next day's activity accordingly.

For example:
- If students tend to overestimate or underestimate the number of people who can occupy a building, plan to revisit ideas on usage density.
- If students fail to include multiple uses of the building, prepare to revisit the ideas of urban sprawl and new urbanism concepts.
- If students seem to have a good grasp of the key ideas in Task 2.1, prepare to go on to Task 2.2 the next day, possibly with different team arrangements.

Background and Further Suggestions

You may want to tell your students about the Vermont Smart Growth Collaborative, which is an example of an institution successfully combating urban sprawl. Between the years 1982 and 1997, developed land in Vermont grew by more than 30 percent while the state population grew by 13 percent. Ten organizations came together to form the Collaborative in order to:

1. **Influence public policy** at the federal, state, regional, and local levels to ensure that they follow smart growth, or sustainable development, principles.

2. **Build public awareness** of the problems of sprawl and the opportunities for smart growth through educational activities that move citizens to action.

3. **Advance community-outreach strategies and demonstration projects** to promote smart growth.

The first step is educating the public about urban sprawl and how it can be avoided. Ask your students how *they* think the public can be educated, and what messages could be part of that education.

Extension Activity: Zoning Laws

Urban planners must abide by city zoning regulations when designing structures and landscapes. Zoning regulations in each municipality dictate how land can be used. For instance, an area zoned for shopping and dining would be designated as "commercial," an area designated for both shopping and apartments would be a "residential-commercial" mixed district, and an area that allows for a factory would be designated as "industrial." By contacting the city planning office, you or your students can obtain local zoning maps. Some zoning regulation maps are available online.

If you can obtain a zoning map for your locality, make copies of the map and have your students work in pairs to answer questions such as:

- How is land use divided for each district?
- Are there any green spaces in the district?
- What symbols are used on the maps for roads, highways, green spaces, and so on?
- Where do you live on this map? Where is your school?
- Are there any industries, stores, or offices in the district? Where?
- Where are the residential districts?

- If you stand at one point on the map, what would you see when you look around?
- What are the different "codes" that designate permitted land use?
- What sort of problems (traffic, pollution) do you think exist in the area?
- In what ways do these zoning regulations encourage urban sprawl?
- In what ways do these regulations tend to reduce urban sprawl?
- If you could change the map to improve living conditions for people in your community, how would you do it?

Task 2.2:	**Identify the Loads the Building Must Support**

Overview

Task 2.2 is intended to provide a fun and engaging activity in which the students design a structure to transfer a load from a surface to the building supports. Students also learn how to estimate live and dead loads and apply that knowledge to design specifications. Finally, they learn about the importance of such specifications in building codes and permits.

In this major open-ended activity, the students work in teams of two to design and build a model deck. You will give them dimensions and materials (straws, cardboard strips, paper, and tape), and a minimum load that their model decks must support. After testing their structures, they learn construction vocabulary and apply the terms to their model decks. Students can also check their understanding of live loads and safety factor by solving a problem at an aquarium. Finally, the students look at building codes and a sample building permit to see what they would need to know to get permission to build a deck.

Five Es

Engage the students by having them design and build a deck; **Explore** various ways of building a model of the deck so that it will support a load; **Explain** dead load, live load, and total load; **Elaborate** on these concepts by applying them to a problem at an aquarium and by examining building codes.

Time Frame

3–4 class periods

Focus Questions

- What are the components of a deck and how do they distribute a load?
- How should structural components be arranged for maximum strength?
- What information would you need to calculate the total load of a deck?
- What is a safety factor and why is it important?
- What is a building code?
- What is a building permit and when do you need one?

Objectives

Students are able to:
- Visualize how decks or floors are constructed
- Name some of the structural members used in decks and floors
- Design a structure to transfer a load from a surface to the building supports
- Describe ways to maximize strength by the positioning of structural members
- Calculate total load as a sum of dead and live loads
- Define "safety factor" and explain why it is important in structural design
- Describe the purpose of a building code and a building permit

Materials

Each team will need:
1 pair of scissors
1 sheet of copy paper
6 1" × 11" strips of cardboard (or tag board)
2 plastic straws (preferably straight; provide 3 if bendy straws are used)
1 12" strip of masking tape

For each student:
Internet access or city building codes

Preparation

Read Task 2.2 in the *Engineer's Notebook* and Chapter 11, "Bridging the Future," in the textbook to become familiar with the concepts of live loads and dead loads.

Because the purpose of the activity is not to teach the students "the right way" to build a deck, but rather to give them some hands-on experience in designing a structure, you do not need to know a lot about how decks are traditionally built. Nonetheless, if you have never constructed a floor or deck before, you may want to use the Internet or a do-it-yourself book to become familiar with typical procedures. Then try the model deck project yourself before introducing it to your students.

Look up your local building code, either on the Internet or in person at the City Clerk's office. Find out what specifications are given for how much load a deck or floor must support (usually given in pounds per square foot), and make copies for your students.

Decide how you will divide class into teams of two. This is a good opportunity for students to work with others rather than their usual teams.

Students may be more conscious about conserving their supply of building materials if the paper, cardboard, and tape are pre-cut and handed out as a package. Prepare a kit of materials for each team of two students.

1st Class

1. **Introduce this activity** by explaining that their multi-use buildings will all have floors, and that the simplest version of a floor built above ground is a deck. Ask the students if any of them have any experience building or helping to build a deck, porch, or wooden floor. Invite them to talk about their experiences.

2. **Why is it important to calculate loads?** Ask the students to read page 13, which introduces Task 2.2. To further illustrate why it's so important to calculate loads correctly, you might ask the students if they know of any serious engineering failures that caused loss of life. You could also show them some engineering disasters from

the web. For example, a video clip of the famous Tacoma Narrows bridge failure is available at http://www.enm.bris.ac.uk/research/nonlinear/tacoma/tacoma.html.

3. **What's under the floor?** Ask students to imagine that they can look through the floorboards to see how the floor that is now supporting them is structured, and to make a sketch of what they imagine is holding up the floorboards. They can do this in the small space at the bottom of page 13, or on a separate sheet of paper. Allow just a few minutes for the students to do this, and then ask them to compare their drawings in groups of two or three.

4. **The deck challenge.** Ask the students to read the design challenge on page 14 before they start. Show them the materials that they will be allowed to use; ask them to list ideas and make sketches to show how they might meet the challenge.

5. **Define the task.** Allow time for your students to ask questions after reading pages 14 and 15. To be sure they understand the challenge, ask them how large their model will be. (Answer: given a scale of 1:12, the model will be 8" × 11" × 3" high.) The deck must support its own weight (dead load) and the people and objects listed (live load). It should be strong enough to support twice as much weight as the maximum weight it is likely to experience (safety factor of 2) and limited to the materials given (as inexpensive as possible).

6. **Show students the load their model deck must support.** For example, one book will be heavy enough to make an impressive load but light enough so that all teams can succeed. Tell them that their task is to build a deck to support that *live load* with a minimum of materials.

7. **Divide the class into teams of two or three.** Tell the teams that they must come up with three or four different sketches before they receive their materials kits.

8. **When teams have sketched at least three different designs,** provide each with one piece of copy paper, six 1" × 11" strips of cardboard (or tag board), two plastic straws, and a 12" strip of masking tape. The paper is intended to represent the decking; the cardboard (tag board) or straws can be used for girders, joists, or posts; and the tape is the fastening system. As you give them materials, ask them which design they prefer and why. (The listed materials and material amounts are suggestions and may be altered to accommodate your classroom.)

9. **While students are working** on their models, circulate around the room to:
    - Ask students to describe what they are trying to accomplish.
    - Provide tips to help students with cutting (separating), joining (combining), and drawing.
    - Ask students "What happens to a flat piece of cardboard when you hold the ends and place a weight in the middle? How could you address this in your design?"

2nd Class

1. **Prepare to test.** It's best to wait until all of the students have finished their model decks. Tell the students that:
    - The maximum live load will be represented by one book. If it holds twice the maximum weight, it has a safety factor of 2; if it holds three times the weight, it has a safety factor of 3; and so on.
    - By adding weights until the deck fails, students can see the weak points and decide how to strengthen it.
    - As engineers, their job is to learn which kind of structures are the strongest, so they can design a safe building at the end of the project. Students can learn as much from studying someone else's deck as they can from their own.

2. **Test the models.** Have each group test their model to see if it holds the required live load. After each test, ask the students, "How and where did it fail? What did you learn from this model?"

3. **Analyze your design.** Have each student answer questions about their decks in his or her *Engineer's Notebooks* on page 15.

4. **Communicate the solution.** Ask the students to read page 16 and to create a drawing of their final deck design, given what they have learned about how to build strong decks. Tell them to use the vocabulary shown on page 16 to label the different parts of their deck design and to explain how their original deck performed when tested. Drawings can be finished as homework.

5. **Redesign.** Conduct a class discussion about how to build a strong deck or floor. Tell students that engineers are considered successful if they meet the criteria of the problem—in this case, to support the maximum weight times two (a safety factor of 2). But they may want to go beyond the specifications of the problem and design a structure that will do even better. Ask the students to describe their redesigns and how they felt about the design and testing process.

3rd Class

1. **The Aquarium Design Challenge.** Tell the students to read the problem on page 17, and then to solve it by answering the questions on pages 17 and 18. They should imagine that they are structural engineers who have been asked to resolve the dispute between the curator and the director of City Aquarium. Following are the correct calculations that your students will need to make to solve the problem. Note that the water does not go to the top of the tank. The tanks are filled until the **water level is 1 ft. from the top.** So:

Answer Key

The volume of water in the LARGE tank is 8 ft. × 8 ft. × 4 ft. = 256 ft.^{3}

The large tank holds (7.5 gal/ft.^{3}) × (256 ft.^{3}) = 1,920 gal of water.

Water in the large tank weighs (8.34 lb./gal) × (1,920 gal) = 16,012.8 lb.

The volume of water in the SMALL tank is 6 ft. × 6 ft. × 4 ft. = 144 ft.^{3}

The small tank holds (7.5 gal/ft.^{3}) × (144 ft.^{3}) = 1,080 gal of water.

Water in the small tank weighs (8.34 lb./gal) × (1,080 gal) = 9,007.2 lb.

	Large Tank 8 ft. × 8 ft. × 5 ft. deep	Small Tank 6 ft. × 6 ft. × 5 ft. deep
Weight of tank (pounds)	400 lb.	300 lb.
Weight of fish (pounds)	15 lb.	15 lb.
Weight of water (pounds) (tank filled up to 4 feet)	16,012.8 lb.	9,007.2 lb.
Total live load (pounds) (tank, fish, water)	16,427.8 lb.	9,322.2 lb.
Area of platform (ft.²)	64 ft.²	36 ft.²
What are the minimum pounds per square foot (psf) that the platform must hold?	$\frac{16,427.8 \text{ lb.}}{64 \text{ ft.}^3} \approx 258.95$ psf	$\frac{9322.2 \text{ lb.}}{36 \text{ ft.}^2} \approx 258.95$ psf
With a safety factor of 3, how many psf must the platform be built to hold?	≈ 770 psf	≈ 777 psf

The conclusion is that the platform does not have to be any stronger to support the larger tank. The curator was right when she said, "Yes, the big tank will be heavier, but the load is spread out over a larger area, so the platform will not have to be stronger."

2. **Introduce building codes and permits.** If your local building codes are on the Internet, have students look up the specifications for building a safe deck or floor. If not, provide copies to your students. You can ask them to fill out the sample building permit as though they were asking permission to construct their final deck design. Note that some areas will remain blank, as they do not apply to obtaining a deck permit. Alternately, have your students look at the sample building permit on page 19 and answer the question about it at the bottom of page 18.

3. **Conclude** by discussing the focus questions:
   - What are the components of a deck and how do they distribute a load?
   - How should structural components be arranged for maximum strength?
   - What information would you need to calculate the total load of a deck?
   - What is a safety factor and why is it important?
   - What is a building code?
   - What is a building permit and when do you need one?

4. **Have the students answer the benchmark questions** on page 20. They could do this as homework if you run out of time.

5. **Assign homework.** Ask the students to read Chapter 11, "Bridging the Future," in the textbook and write answers to the questions at the end of the chapter. Discuss the students' answers to the questions the next day. Reflect on how the answers relate to deck-building activity.

Answer Key

EN Page 20: Benchmark Questions

1) The live loads, which should be circled, are Desk, Pictures, Medical Equipment, Telephone, Coat rack, Stethoscope, Chairs, and Patients. (The following are dead loads: Roof, Flooring, Walls, and Windows.)

2) A safety factor is the number of times greater than the maximum total load a structure is designed to support. Safety factors are important to avoid failure in cases where there are unusual loads nobody had anticipated.

3) Research can help to define the problem or provide suggestions for solutions, or even uncover solutions that someone has already found.

4) A building code is a series of regulations about how buildings must be constructed so that they will be safe. A building permit is a written statement by appropriate city officials allowing for the construction of a building according to submitted plans, on a particular lot, and in accordance to local building codes.

5) There are a number of things someone could do to strengthen the deck frame. The most important thing to notice, however, is that the frame is not strong enough as designed, so just strengthening the girder may not work. It will need either an additional post in the middle, or angle supports that distribute the weight from the center of the girder to the posts.

Assessment

The primary goal of Task 2.2 is for the students to realize that the strength of a structure depends, to a great extent, on how the structural members are arranged. You can assess their understanding of this main idea by observing the structures that they design, the improvements that they make as they redesign their decks, their discussion, and their responses to the benchmark questions.

Collect the benchmark papers and look them over to see if there are ideas that many of the students have missed; for example:

- Identifying dead and live loads
- The meaning and purpose of safety factors
- The value and possible uses of research
- How to arrange structural members to maximize strength
- Recognizing how loads are transferred through structural members to the ground
- Uses of building codes, zoning laws, and building permits

Be prepared to spend part of an extra period on these ideas, if necessary.

You can also ask students to revisit the question at the start of this task: "Imagine you can look through the floor to see the supports underneath. What would you see?" Ask them to draw the supports they envision, and look for evidence that they learned about how decks (floors) are usually constructed.

Background and Further Suggestions

It may seem trivial to design a deck; it's simply a flat surface built above the ground. However, the activity introduces students to the types of loads and the kinds of supports needed to distribute the load on a floor. Consequently, designing a deck is basic to almost all building design because nearly all buildings have floors. Multiple-story structures have the same problem, except the need to minimize the number of large supports is even greater than in designing a deck that sits on the ground.

This activity also introduces your students to structural engineering—a very broad field of engineering that is required for any structure—not just houses, boats, and bridges, but also cars, trains, and airplanes. The structural engineer's responsibility to design a safe structure is as important as the design principles. Additionally, the fact that the engineer depends on mathematics to determine what is safe is also a very important lesson.

Students often wonder about the difference between an architect and a structural engineer. The main difference is that the architect's job is to design a beautiful structure that meets people's needs, and the engineer's job is to make sure it is sufficiently strong to stand up under all conceivable conditions. Some of the most successful architects are also trained as structural engineers.

Extension Activity: How much weight does each post need to support?
Students who finish early can be challenged to find out how much each post needs to support by adding the live and dead loads, and then divide by the number of posts. (Center posts would actually support more weight than the corner posts, but that can be ignored for this estimate.)

To do this, students would need to consider a deck with timbers instead of straws and cardboard. They would need to determine how many timbers are needed and their dimensions, then calculate the total volume of wood in cubic feet (ft.^{3}). To find the weight of the structure, they would need the density of wood. Southern pine at 12 percent moisture content is commonly used for deck construction, and it has a density of about 36 lb./ft.^{3}

Once the students find the total weight of the structure, they would add the estimated live load (people, furniture, etc., that would be on the deck at any one time) to the dead load and divide the total load by the number of posts.

References and Resources

Fisette, Paul. *Calculating Loads on Headers and Beams*. Department of Natural Resources Conservation–Building Materials and Wood Technology at the University of Massachusetts, 2005. Also available online at http://www.umass.edu/bmatwt/publications/articles/calculating_loads_on_headers_and_beams.html.

Fisette, Paul. *Understanding Loads and Using Span Tables*. Department of Natural Resources Conservation – Building Materials and Wood Technology at the University of Massachusetts, 2003. Also available online at http://www.umass.edu/bmatwt/publications/articles/understanding_loads_using_span_tables.html.

McVicker, Scott. *Single Family Residential Construction Guide*. "Itemization of Loads." May, 2005. Half Moon Bay, CA: McVicker Associates, Inc. Also available online at http://www.mcvicker.com/resguide/page012.htm.

Task 2.3:   Use Failure Analysis to Design a Safer Building

Overview

Students will build a tower from paper, straws, paper clips, and masking tape, and then load it with weights until it fails. This activity encourages students to "optimize" the design by creating the strongest possible structure with a minimum of cost.

The primary emphasis is on the detailed analysis of failure to identify weak points and the kinds of forces that caused the failure using appropriate vocabulary, so as to strengthen the design. This activity's key message is that by studying failures in the lab, engineers can reduce the chance of catastrophic failures in actual structures.

The students are also asked to prepare a detailed report on their failure analysis and to evaluate their own work using a rubric.

Read Task 2.3 in the *Engineer's Notebook* and Chapter 12 in the textbook to be sure that you're prepared for any questions students may ask.

Five Es

Engage the students in a quick-build project that complements the deck project; **Explore** methods to shape and join materials to build a tall tower; **Explain** the value of failure in engineering, and the various forces and failure modes; **Elaborate** on these ideas through textbook reading about the work of structural engineers; **Evaluate** their design projects by testing them to failure.

Time Frame

4 class periods

Focus Questions

• How can you build a tall tower so that it will be structurally sound?
• What shapes and materials will you use to handle the loads?
• How can you keep cost to a minimum?
• What kinds of forces cause structures to fail?
• How can catastrophic failures be avoided?

Objectives

Students will be able to:
- Identify static and dynamic forces that act on structures
- Explain the difference between tension, compression, bending, torsion, and shearing forces
- Understand how connections or fasteners allow the members of a structure to work as a whole
- Explain how to compare designs by using a benefit/cost ratio
- Recognize that failure is not necessarily bad

Materials

For the entire class, you will need (at least):
   500 straws (straight straws preferable)
   100 sheets of construction or copy paper
   2 rolls of masking tape
   100 paper clips

Preparation

Read Chapter 12 to review how modern skyscrapers are constructed and what the governing factors are in skyscraper design. You may also want to do your own research on how the frame of the skyscraper is designed, how the space is oriented inside the structure, where the elevators are, and how the building is analyzed for potential failure.

Decide how you want to divide students into teams of two or three. You may want the same teams that worked on the deck together, or you may want to give the students opportunities to work with others. Assign the teams at the start of the second class rather than the first, so that the students start out thinking about the tower problem on their own.

Set up a station where you (or a student you appoint) will "sell" the construction materials to the teams when they are ready to start building. You will need to keep track of how much of each material each team purchases. (Some teachers place either a monetary limit or an item limit on the amount of materials each team can use. This is up to you.)

Decide on any alterations to the original list of criteria and constraints that you would like to make. Decide what minimum weight you'll use to test the compressive strength of the towers, and prepare to explain how the towers will be tested.

You will need space to store the towers between the second and third classes. Find a safe place where the towers will not be damaged.

1st Class

1. **Instruct the students to read the introduction to Task 2.3 on page 21.** After they've read the page, explain how their towers will be tested. For example, if they will be tested by placing books or other objects on top, the towers will need to have a flat place to hold the weights. Invite students to ask questions to be sure they understand the task.

   The criteria state that the minimum tower height must be 2 feet. Some teachers have found that they prefer to change this height due to time or material constraints. A shorter minimum height of 15–18 in. also works well.

   Actual weights are not needed to run this activity. Depending on the designated structure size, teachers have run the activities using weights, soda bottles filled with water, books, marker boxes, or Tupperware dishes filled with sand. Also, designating items with predetermined whole-number weights may make the calculations easier for students. (For example, declaring that each textbook weighs 1,000 lb. makes summing easier.)

   The materials listed are easy to find and work well. However, a variety of other materials have been used for construction. Teachers who could not find straight straws have used bendy straws with success. In some classrooms, paper is at a premium while newspaper can be found easily. Please adapt this and all activities as needed.

2. **Introduce the terms "compression" and "tension,"** as described on page 22. Ask the students to read the page and fill in the blanks at the bottom. Invite students to compare answers with their neighbors and discuss the answers as a class to ensure that everyone understands how to determine whether an element of a structure is under tension or compression.

3. **Have the students read about bending** on the top of page 23. Discuss how bending involves both compression (on one side of the beam) and tension (on the other side of the beam).

4. **Ask the students to start sketching ideas** for their towers, after they read the list of considerations on the bottom of page 23. The process of sketching will engage their thinking about the problems they will encounter, and prepare them to share their own ideas with the team in the next class session. Remind students that they are looking for the tallest structure that holds the most weight, for the least amount of money. You might even have students refer to the benefit/cost ratio formula on page 26.

5. **As a homework assignment**, ask the students to research skyscrapers on the Internet or in books to get ideas for designing their towers. Tell them to think about the forces that act on skyscrapers that are not important for decks and floors.

Answer Key

EN Page 22: Tension and Compression
   YZ is under tension
   XY is under tension
   XZ is under compression

2nd Class

1. **Assign teams.** Tell the teams that they will have five minutes to share their ideas. Warn them not to decide which idea is best until they've heard everyone's ideas.

2. **Choose a final design.** Call the class's attention to the top of page 24 in their *Engineer's Notebook*, with a set of questions to help them decide on the best solution. Tell the teams to spend the next ten or fifteen minutes deciding on the best solution. Urge them to combine the best ideas from each design, if possible, and to remember how the towers will be tested. They should also decide how much of each material they will need.

3. **Draw designs and request materials.** Explain that each student on the team should draw a sketch of what he or she envisions the final design to look like. When each has done so, the team can "purchase" materials from you. (You may want to ask to look at their drawings before giving them the materials.)

4. **Students begin construction.** Help students as needed. Encourage them to redesign their structure as they go if they feel it will improve the tower. Be prepared for them to request additional materials. Be sure to record what materials they take and remind students to do the same. (Some teachers allow students to sell back unused materials, some do not.)

5. **How tall? What did it cost?** If there is time, have the students measure the height of their towers and calculate the cost to construct it. If there is not enough time, students should just make sure to measure height and calculate cost before testing. Set aside the towers for testing during the next class. Have each team write their names on their tower.

3rd Class

1. **Introduce forces.** Before you begin testing the towers, call your students' attention to the list of forces on page 25 of their *Engineer's Notebook*: Tension, Compression, Bending, Torsion, and Shear. Define each of these and tell your students to watch for which of these forces cause their towers to fail when they surpass their load limits.

2. **Test the towers.** Before testing each tower, have team members reflect upon their design. Ask students how they came up with their design, and what their thoughts were behind it. Have students reflect upon how their design may fail.

    It's most fun if the towers are tested one at a time, with members of the team first placing the minimum load on top, and then adding more weights until the tower fails. (Using larger, inflated weight values and measuring the tower height in inches will keep the benefit/cost ratio greater than 1.) Before going on to the next tower, ask the team to analyze quickly where and how their tower failed using appropriate terminology (compression, tension, bending, shear, and torsion). Ask the team how they might change their design. Invite other students to join in if they see something else.

3. **Record the results.** After all of the towers have been tested, have students complete page 26 of the *Engineer's Notebook*: "Safety Analysis" and "Benefit/Cost Analysis." Go around the room and help students as needed.

4. **Ask each student to write a report** on his or her team's tower project, according to the outline on page 27 of the *Engineer's Notebook*. Tell students that they can work together in discussing the ideas in their reports, but that each student should write his or her own summary of what the team did and what he or she found out. This would make a good homework assignment, as well.

1. **Discuss results.** You should take time for the teams to share their findings with the rest of the class. If necessary, continue the next day. Ask each team for their tower's safety factor, and to describe how their tower failed and what its weak points were. If they have any ideas about how to strengthen the tower, they can share that too. Finally, be sure to discuss the benefit/cost ratio. Although the students may think of the monetary aspect of the project as a game, you can point out that in real life costs are essential. If two companies present equally good designs with evidence of a high safety factor, then the company with the lowest cost estimate will almost always win the contract.

   Following are some additional questions you might use to guide discussion and review the key concepts:

   • Were there similarities in the way that the towers failed?
   • How does failure of one member contribute to failure of the entire tower?
   • In what ways does location determine the forces a building must withstand?
   • Did the tower behave as you expected? If not, what surprised you?
   • How is designing a tower different from designing a deck?
   • What would you do differently if you were to build the tower again?

2. **Invite the students to evaluate their own reports** using the rubric on page 28, and add their self-evaluation before you collect their papers. Use the same rubric to evaluate and grade the reports. You may want to give some credit for the work of the team as a whole, in addition to providing feedback on the report itself.

3. **Assign homework in the text.** Ask the students to read Chapter 12, "Tower in the Sky," in the textbook, in which Bill Baker describes how he designed a multi-use skyscraper, which would be the tallest building in the world, to withstand the live loads of people and wind. Ask your students to write answers to the questions at the end of the chapter. Discuss their answers the next day. Ask them to reflect on how the answers relate to the failure analysis activity.

Assessment

A rubric for the tower challenge project and report is included in the *Engineer's Notebook*. Look for evidence in their discussions and written assignments that your students understand the key idea in this task—that systematic and detailed failure analysis is an essential aspect of engineering.

If many of the students are not able to identify different kinds of forces or explain the ideas behind systematic failure analysis, spend some additional time leading them to reflect on the two recent activities—building and testing a deck, and building and testing a tower—to consider the different forces that act on these structures, where and why failure occurs, and how prototype testing of this sort can help to save lives.

Background and Further Suggestions

This task focuses on how the elements in a structure work together to form a system. Connections are what make the parts work together as a whole; this is something that should be emphasized in the lesson. While failure can often be isolated to one particular location in a structure, it is generally related to how elements are positioned and connected together. In structures, both members and systems take on forces. For example, we may say that a beam in the structure bends, or we can say the entire structure bends. The concept of bending is still the same whether applied to an individual member or to a system of members. When a beam or system bends, compression will exist on one side, tension on the other.

Many students expect to receive better grades if their projects have been "successful." In engineering, honesty is far more important than success in testing any given prototype because the purpose of the test is to find potential problems before they cause any harm. In the case of bridges, dams, and buildings, the cost could be human life. Unfortunately, there are examples in which completed structures failed, causing many fatalities and injuries. In such cases, the reason for the failure is investigated. Results often show that the tests were inadequate, calculations were wrong, or the people doing the construction did not follow directions and/or cut corners. That is why honest testing and clear communication are so important for engineering.

Extensions

If some teams finish early while others are still working, you can challenge the early finishers to consider how engineers might secure a skyscraper to the earth. What does this connection look like? How is it made? What could happen to a skyscraper if this connection were not secure? How does location affect foundation design?

References and Resources

Macaulay, David. *Underground.* Boston: Houghton Mifflin, 1976.

Macaulay, David. *Unbuilding.* Boston: Houghton Mifflin, 1980.

Petrosky, Henry. *To Engineer Is Human: The Role of Failure in Successful Design.* New York: First Vintage Books Edition, 1992.

At http://www.emporis.com/en/, Emporis gives an outline of different types of foundations as well as links to other building and engineering topics.

Task 2.4:   Test Construction Materials for Strength

Overview

Failure analysis continues in this task, in which students test different materials under various loads. In the first activity, students test two materials—a plastic straw and construction paper—to see how they behave under tension. Using weights makes it possible to compare the samples quantitatively.

The second activity is a qualitative test of how materials behave under compression and bending forces. The way an object behaves when subject to these forces depends both on the type of material and how it's shaped. In the last activity, students think of ways they could test how materials behave under shear and torsional forces.

The fundamental concept uniting these activities is that it is important to test materials and components of structures before they are built.

Simple testing devices are recommended for these activities, but there are alternative ways to test these materials, depending on the equipment you have available. Keep in mind that an important part of engineering is coming up with creative ways to test things, so feel free to innovate or follow up on students' suggestions.

Five Es

Engage students in testing materials to failure; **Explore** the properties of various materials when they are stressed; **Explain** how to use precise definitions to characterize the behavior of a material under different forces. If time allows, **Elaborate** on these concepts by testing additional materials; **Evaluate** materials for different uses in construction.

Time Frame

3 class periods

Focus Questions

• Why do you need to test material under a variety of loading conditions?
• What is the engineering definition of stress and strain?
• What can be done to make a material stronger—i.e., handle more load?

Objectives

Students are able to:
  • Observe how materials behave under tension and compression
  • Observe and record different types of failure
  • Give examples to illustrate that the strength of a structural component depends on its composition and shape

Materials

Each team will need:
  2 squeeze clamps (or vice grips)
  2 flat wooden rulers
  1 small piece of sandpaper
  1 roll of tape
  3 plastic straws
  3 pieces of construction paper
  1 6" length of kite string

2 cardboard tubes from paper towels or toilet paper

1 pair of scissors for every two teams

Various scale weights (3 100-gram weights, 3 500-gram weights, **and** 5 1-kg weights. If scale weights are not available, other items can be measured with a scale. A small bucket of sand or a 2-liter bottle of water with recorded amounts could be substituted.)

Preparation

Decide what weights your students will use. If you do not have standard laboratory weights, one solution is to use a 2-liter bottle with water. One ml of water weighs approximately one gram, so students can create a 100-gram weight by adding 100 ml of water to the bottle using a graduated cylinder or measuring cup.

Perform the tension and compression tests yourself before asking the students to do them.

Organize the class into teams of 2–4 members.

Set up lab stations with materials for tension testing. Use a sharp utility knife to slice open a plastic straw lengthwise for each team. (Depending on the size of straw and available scissors, students may be able to cut the straw with a scissors.)

Read Task 2.4 in the *Engineer's Notebook* and Chapter 13 in the textbook to be sure that you're prepared for any questions students may ask.

1st Class

Tensile Strength Testing

1. **Ask students to read the introduction to Task 2.4** on pages 29 and 30. When the students have finished reading, ask if they have any questions about the "Basics of Failure Analysis," or "Tensile Strength," which review the ideas presented in Task 2.3, but with an emphasis on materials rather than whole structures.

2. **Demonstrate tensile strength testing.** Have students follow along in their *Engineer's Notebooks* while you demonstrate how to use the apparatus shown on page 31.

   1) **Samples.** Have students carefully cut 3"-long × 3/8"-wide samples of paper and straw with a scissors. Point out the sample plastic straws you've already cut to form strips of plastic.

   2) **Show how to set up a sample** for testing using two clamps according to the picture in the *Engineer's Notebook*. Samples will be clamped on both ends; the top clamp holds the material (supported by two rulers) and the bottom clamp pulls down on the sample.

    3) Add weight slowly. Weights are hung from a string that is tied around the bottom clamp. (Stop short of actually hanging a weight, so that students see the first results from their own experiments.)

    4) Have students record what the failure of the paper looks like in their *Notebooks,* as well as the failure (maximum) loading for the paper sample.

    5) Should the sample slip from clamps, use sandpaper, as described below.

3. **Tell the teams to test the paper and the straw.** Show them how to use sandpaper to create enough friction to keep the straw from slipping. Have students cut a 2" × 1" piece of sandpaper, fold it four times, stick the straw in the middle fold, and clamp it tight. Both the straw and the clamp must be in contact with the rough side of the sandpaper.

4. **Ask students to note the behavior of the straw** and how it compares with the failure of the paper. They should describe any changes in shape or appearance and also note the maximum loading before breakage in their *Engineer's Notebook.*

5. **Have teams conduct the tests** with the paper and plastic straw, then record their findings on pages 31 and 32 of their *Engineer's Notebook.* Help teams as needed.

2nd Class

1. **Have students share the results** of their tensile strength tests. Write the results of each team's tests on the board so the students can see how their findings compared with other students' findings.

2. **Ask the students to read page 33 in their *Engineer's Notebook* on "Compressive and Bending Strength."** Since the testing process is considerably simpler than the test for tensile strength, the directions may be clear enough for them to proceed. Or, if the students have a lot of questions, you may demonstrate the qualitative tests for compression and bending.

3. **Have the students prepare the four samples and conduct the tests as described in the *Engineer's Notebook.*** Students should have a standard method of rolling the paper for each exercise to eliminate variables. Ask them to sketch what each sample looks like when it fails and to judge how much compression each sample will take before failing. (The paper will be crushed, buckling from compression, and the straw will pinch in the middle from bending.) Help teams as needed.

4. **Ask students to summarize their results,** using the table for tension, compression, and bending tests on page 34, and to answer the questions below the table.

5. **Lead a discussion,** starting with reports from each team on which materials better withstand tensile and compressive forces.

6. **Shape and material are both important.** If it does not come up in the discussion, call attention to differences in strength when the same piece of paper is rolled the short way versus when it's rolled the long way. Ask the students why they think this is the case. If they do not recognize it, point out that a design element that is relatively thicker and shorter has greater compressive strength than an element that is tall and slender. In other words, *shape and material* are both important in designing a strong structure. Tell the students to keep this in mind when they design their multi-use building.

3rd Class

1. **Test for shear strength and torsional strength.** Have the students read pages 35 and 36. Assess their understanding by asking them to come up with other examples in which a material has to resist these forces. For example:

   - **Shear forces:** Pushing a desk or table across a rough floor will put shear forces on the legs of the table; an airplane flying at a high rate of speed experiences strong shear forces where the wings meet the fuselage.
   - **Torsional forces:** The drive shaft of a car or propeller, the beater in an electric mixer, or wet clothing being rung out before it is put out to dry.

2. **Devise a test for torsional and shear strength.** You may want students to work on this individually or in pairs to come up with ideas for devices to test materials and see how well they stand up to shear and torsional forces. It will help them to think of a particular application, such as one of the examples mentioned above or in the *Engineer's Notebook.* You might suggest that they keep in mind the tests they just did. They will need:

   - A way to hold the sample
   - A means of exerting a greater and greater force (torsion in one case, shear in the other)
   - A way to measure the amount of force before failure

3. **Invite students to share** their ideas with the rest of the class. Highlight similarities and differences and innovative ideas.

4. **What's happening inside the materials?** Most students have learned about the particle theory of matter in middle school. Although the theory of atoms and molecules is not emphasized

in this course, materials testing provides an excellent opportunity for students to apply what they've learned. Lead a discussion using questions like the following:

- What do you think is happening to the molecules and how they are connected when a material is under stress?
- How do molecules behave differently in the case of a paper strip, which tears, compared with a plastic straw, which stretches?
- How might your observations during this activity affect your choice of building material for your final design?

5. **Conclude by emphasizing the main point of the class:** failure testing of materials is just as important as failure testing of entire structures; a structure can be no stronger than its individual components and how they are joined together. In addition, the strength of a given material may be different depending on how it is shaped, as well as other conditions such as temperature or the presence of water.

Extensions

Teams that finish early can make predictions about how they could make the same materials even stronger by changing the shape. They can then test their ideas.

Assessment

Assign homework in the text. Ask the students to read Chapter 13, "Home Sweet Home," in the textbook, in which Prity Rungta, a construction manager in Toronto, Canada, describes the complexity of building a house on time and on budget. Ask your students to write answers to the questions at the end of the chapter. Discuss their answers the next day.

References and Resources

Wikipedia, The Free Encyclopedia, "Hyatt Regency walkway collapse." http://en.wikipedia.org/wiki/Hyatt_Regency_walkway_collapse—The Hyatt Regency walkway collapse in Kansas City, Missouri, in July 1980, provides an example of failure analysis. It also emphasizes the importance of testing designs before construction.

Task 2.5:   Describe Mechanical Properties of Materials

Overview

Choosing the material for a new building—or any design, for that matter—involves more than determining whether it will fail and how it will fail under a load. Materials have other properties that make them suitable for some things more than others. Students are already aware of obvious properties such as weight or cost, but there are other important properties as well. In Task 2.5 they learn about types of materials and four different ways that they can be characterized: elastic, plastic, brittle, and malleable.

To begin, students conduct an activity using elastic bands from which they create a graph very similar to a stress-strain curve, which is an extremely important conceptual tool used by structural engineers. After learning about elastic deformation, students learn about plastic deformation by testing plastic from a produce bag. The most important concept students need to learn from this activity is that the relationship between stress and strain is different for different materials.

Five Es

Engage in new laboratory activities; **Explore** the way various materials change (strain) in response to different levels of force (stress); **Explain** this relationship in terms of a graph; **Elaborate** by testing additional materials; **Evaluate** the use of various materials for construction.

Time Frame

2 class periods

Focus Questions

- What do you expect from a material that is elastic? Plastic? Brittle? Malleable?
- What is the engineering definition of stress and strain?
- How does the relationship between stress and strain differ for different materials?

Objectives

Students are able to:
- Create and interpret a graph showing material properties
- Give examples of materials whose mechanical properties are elastic, plastic, brittle, or malleable
- Describe the relationship between stress and strain

Materials

Each team will need:
3 rulers
1 roll of tape
1 12" piece of kite string
1 marker
2 elastic bands
2 samples from a plastic vegetable bag from the grocery store
Various scale weights (3 100-gram weights, 3 500-gram weights, and 5 1-kg weights. If scale weights are not available, other

items can be measured with a scale and used. A small bucket of sand, or a 2-liter bottle of water with recorded amounts could be substituted.)

Preparation

The testing apparatus for elasticity is very simple: just two rulers making a strong bridge between two tables or desks, with an elastic band hanging from the center. Weights are hung on the elastic band and the students measure and graph the elongation of the elastic band as a function of load. Although the activity is quite simple, you might want to do it first to anticipate the data the students will get with the elastic bands and the weights you will give them to work with.

Although many materials reach an "elastic limit" (also called the "yield point") beyond which the material is stretched but will no longer return to its original shape, elastic bands tend to stretch less and less with more weight and then finally break. The graph is nonetheless interesting for students to interpret.

Prepare thin strips of plastic bags from the produce department of a grocery store. These materials tend to reach an elastic limit sooner, and will make a nice comparison with the elastic band curves. Samples can be provided by using scissors to make cuts across the bag after it has been removed from the roll, but before it is opened. The samples then unfold into a loop like a large rubber band.

Read Task 2.5 in the *Engineer's Notebook* and Chapter 14 in the textbook to be sure that you're prepared for any questions students may ask.

1st Class

1. **Ask the students to read the introduction to Task 2.5** on page 37, and fill in the blanks on the bottom half of the page based on what they already know about these materials. (See answer key on the next page.) The purpose of this exercise is for students to add the engineer's definitions of these terms to their vocabulary, so you may want to encourage them to work together in small groups to share their ideas about the best answers to the questions.

2. **Introduce the "Measuring Elasticity" activity on page 38.** Start by telling the students that a great many materials are elastic, even steel. Since it's difficult to observe the elasticity of steel without heavy equipment, however, the students will measure how elastic bands behave under tension. (Strictly speaking, they will be measuring the elongation of an elastic band, not its elasticity. The term "elasticity" is a qualitative term that means a material will change shape under a load and then return to its former shape when the load is removed.)

Engineering the Future Teacher Guide
©2008 Museum of Science, Boston

3. **Ask the students to read pages 38 and 39 and follow the directions.** Tell them to be sure to mark *two places* on their elastic bands so that they can measure the changing distance between the two points as they add weights. (You might show them how to do this on the chalk- or whiteboard.)

4. **Tell students to write their measurements in the table** on page 39 as they add each additional weight. They should also be sure to remove all weights after each trial to see if the band snaps back to its original length. Help teams as needed.

5. **When teams have added all their weights,** or their elastic band breaks or does not expand when more weights are added, they should graph the data, following the directions at the bottom of page 39. This is a graph of load versus elongation.

6. **Teams should go on to answer questions on page 40,** "Analyzing Elasticity," as soon as their graphs are finished.

7. **Have your students test a strip of thin plastic bag** using the same method, as indicated on the bottom half of page 40. Give them additional paper to keep track of the data and to graph load versus elongation.

Answer Key

EN Page 37: Types of Materials

1) Fill in the blanks:
   A. Copper is more **malleable** than steel.
   B. Steel is more **elastic** than concrete.
   C. Concrete is more **brittle** than steel.
   D. Rubber is more **elastic** than plastic.
   E. Melted plastic is more **plastic** than hard plastic.

2) Fill in the blanks (many different materials can be used):
   A. A **diving board** is more elastic than **a chalkboard**.
   B. **Taffy** is more plastic than **chocolate**.
   C. **Chocolate** is more brittle than **chewing gum**.
   D. **Aluminum foil** is more malleable than **paper**.

2nd Class

1. **Conduct a class discussion** in which all teams share the findings they recorded on pages 38–40. If people found different results, ask why that might be the case.

2. **Ask the students why it is important** to know about how much a material elongates when under tension, and why it may be necessary to learn if a material has an elastic limit. (Airplane wings are an especially good example because they frequently encounter huge forces in flight. There is no problem as long as the wings spring back to their original shape, but if the forces are so great that they exceed the elastic limit of the material, the wing will be misshapen and provide less lift than the plane needs to keep flying.)

3. **Ask the students to read the page 41 on stress and strain.** These two terms are not intuitive; they have different meanings in everyday language, and the words sound similar, so it's easy to mix them up. Ask students to share their own ideas on how to remember the difference.

4. **Point out that the concept of stress is very much like load,** except that it is divided by the area of the object on which the load is placed. In the case of the rubber band tests, area refers to the cross-sectional area of the elastic band. Strain is how the rubber band deforms or elongates.

   [Note: As is customary in math and science, we ask students to plot weight (the independent variable) on the x-axis and elongation (the dependent variable) on the y-axis. However, in preparing stress-strain curves, engineers plot stress on the y-axis and strain on the x-axis. This may confuse students when they see stress-strain curves in Chapter 14. Prepare to explain that engineers often choose to do things differently than scientists and, once a convention is established, it is not easy to change.]

5. **Ask the students to write their answers** to the questions on page 41. Be aware that their elastic band tests may not have reached an elastic limit, so the students may not be able to answer some of the questions. However, the elastic bags probably do reach an elastic limit, so it may be easier for them to answer the questions about the bag strip rather than the elastic band.

6. **Have the students answer the Benchmark questions** on page 42.

7. **Assign homework in the text.** Ask the students to read Chapter 14, "From the Ground Up," in the textbook, in which geotechnical engineer Cathy Bazan-Arias explains why engineers need to understand the materials they are using and the land they are building on. Ask your students to write answers to the questions at the end of the chapter. Discuss their answers the next day.

Answer Key

EN Page 42: Benchmark Questions
1) Engineers build models or create computer simulations and test them to failure in order to identify the weak spots, so they will know how to improve their designs.

2) Many answers are possible. Here are some examples:
   • Tension: The ropes of a swing are under tension.
   • Compression: The legs of a chair are under compression.
   • Torsion: When wringing out a wet rag, you apply a torsion force.
   • Shear: Scissors (also called shears) cut with a shearing force.

3) Point B is under greatest stress. It is being bent, and could crack along its top surface.

4) AC: bending; BD: compression; AD: torsion or tension

5) More than one answer is possible, depending on how students interpret the question. If the force acts uniformly over the entire bridge tower exposed to the wind, it will undergo bending; it will experience tension on the side facing the wind and compression on the side away from the wind. However, the point at which the tower is anchored at its base will undergo a shearing force.

6) If the member is made of a plastic material, it would develop a permanent twist.

Assessment

The most important and challenging concept in this task is that the relationship between stress and strain is different for different materials. To understand this complex idea, students must first understand the definitions of stress and strain and how a stress-strain curve is generated. It may be too much to expect all students to grasp these ideas in a relatively short sequence of activities, but it would be worth asking students to define these terms, and to interpret a graph of load versus elongation like the one they created.

A secondary goal is for students to learn the vocabulary terms "elastic," "plastic," "brittle," and "malleable" to describe the mechanical properties of different materials. Observing how well they use these terms in class during discussions will be a more meaningful assessment of their understanding than asking them to memorize definitions for a quiz. You will also be able to assess learning by checking their sketches and answers in their *Engineer's Notebooks*.

Finally, collect the students' Benchmark questions to see how well they do on test-type questions related to the key concepts of the unit. Plan an extra class if students have difficulty with any of the questions. You can have teams work on the problematic questions together as one way to get them to grapple with the central concepts.

Background and Further Suggestions

Materials engineers test materials and publish tables of their results, so structural engineers do not need to do the tests themselves. Most engineers typically look up stress-strain curves in books or on the web when they are designing something. In this class, we have students do materials testing and design additional tests so that they can understand where this information comes from. We also want them to understand that the process of testing is not mysterious. It's a pretty straightforward case of controlled experimentation.

Most teachers think of controlled experiments as a "scientific" method rather than an engineering design skill. In fact, it is both. If the goal is to modify nature to meet human needs or wants, it is **engineering**. If the goal is to test a hypothesis about the natural world, it is **science**. However, some universities use the term "engineering science" to indicate the process of developing new knowledge about engineering.

Our decision to have students plot the results using a scientific rather than an engineering convention may be worth further discussion. Because this is a course in engineering, we have generally followed engineering conventions. However, because we recognized that most students will be taking simultaneous classes in math and/or science, we did not want to create an unnecessary conflict, especially because many science and math teachers consider the proper uses of the x- and y-axes to be very important. If students bring up this distinction, you might ask them for their opinions about why engineers sometimes have different conventions than scientists, and what would be the best course to follow. If they have a chance to change the rules someday, what would they do?

Engineering the Future Teacher Guide
©2008 Museum of Science, Boston

Task 2.6:	Experiment with Concrete

Overview

This hands-on experience with concrete will give your students a chance to experiment with actual building materials that have a very long history. A form of concrete was used by the ancient Romans to build aqueducts and such famous buildings as the Colosseum and the Pantheon, which have survived for 2,000 years. Today concrete is everywhere. Whether it is formed into columns, bricks, or laid as slabs, it provides structures with tremendous strength at low cost.

The most important concept for students to learn in this task is the method of controlled experimentation for investigating how to make concrete that is as strong as possible with cement, water, and aggregate. Failure analysis will again play a major role; the students can watch how and where their concrete samples fail.

These activities are also intended to help your students see concrete in a new light, to realize that there are hundreds of different concrete formulas that are used for different purposes, from bridges and dams to skyscrapers and boats.

Five Es

Engage students in testing a common construction material: concrete; **Explore** the properties of concrete by making samples under controlled conditions and testing them to failure; **Explain** why it is necessary to control variables in such tests; **Elaborate** by making additional concrete samples; **Evaluate** different recipes for concrete when used for different parts of a construction project.

Time Frame

4 class periods

Focus Questions

- For what applications is concrete best suited?
- What roles do the constituents of concrete play?
- What happens if you change the standard formula?
- How can the formula for concrete be changed to meet different needs?

Objectives

Students will be able to:
- Predict how changes in the formula for concrete will affect its compressive strength
- Explain what the different constituents of concrete do
- Perform controlled experiments to test and compare the compressive strength of actual construction materials

Materials

For the class:
    1 concrete crusher (see directions in the beginning of the Teacher's Guide for Project 2.0)

Each team will need:
    1 pound of portland cement
    1 dish for mixing

1 plastic spoon
2 3-inch lengths of half-inch (inside diameter) foam pipe insulation
Samples of aggregate (fine sand, rough sand, small pebbles)
Access to water
SAFETY—Gloves, masks, and goggles should be used for handling cement and testing samples

Preparation

This task requires more preparation than any of the others because you will have to build a concrete testing apparatus and gather various materials so students can make samples of concrete for testing. However, it is well worth the effort because your students will enjoy the opportunity to work with real construction materials.

It is important to construct concrete samples yourself and to try out the testing apparatus a few days before this class, so that you can make necessary modifications. One of the problems to anticipate is that if the students' samples do not fail with the crusher you have built, the tests will not be meaningful. **You might want to limit the amount of water used in each sample to no more than 1 part water for 2 parts cement.** Another way to avoid this problem is to **limit setting time to no more than 2 days.** Samples that set up for a week or longer may become so strong that they are impossible to test.

In the method we recommend here, one student pushes down on a bathroom scale that puts pressure on the concrete crusher while a second student watches the bathroom scale to note when it reaches the highest point before the sample fails. A third student (wearing goggles) will need to watch the sample and call out just when it begins to fail. In other words, you will need at least three volunteers to test each sample.

As with other test equipment in this course, you should feel free to develop better ways of testing the concrete samples. For example, one teacher used a hydraulic jack to put direct pressure on the sample.

Set up stations around the room for students to mix their concrete samples, label them, and set them aside to dry. Find a place in the classroom where the students will use the concrete crusher.

1st Class

1. **As an introduction, ask students** to identify something they have seen made out of concrete. Ask them to list the different ways they have seen concrete used. You should point out that an important property of this material is how easily it can be shaped, and the fact that it can be mixed and poured on site, reducing its production cost.

2. **Have the students read page 43,** which introduces Task 2.6 in their *Engineer's Notebooks,* and lead a discussion about the components of concrete and what each component does.

3. **Introduce the challenge.** Explain to students that they will experiment to find out how changing the recipe for making concrete will affect its mechanical properties. A recipe for baking a cake or making anything else has two parts: a list of ingredients and a description of the process for making it. Teams will have an opportunity to choose what part of the concrete recipe they want to experiment with. Each individual on the team should keep his or her own notes because all students will be asked to write a report about their team's experiment.

4. **Have the students read through pages 44–46 in their** *Engineer's Notebook*. Before they mix their samples, have each team share with the class what variable they have chosen to experiment with, and to explain how they intend to make their samples. If the students resist the idea of changing just one variable, ask them what conclusion they would be able to draw if Sample A or Sample B were stronger. You can approve the experiment if their tentative conclusion makes sense.

2nd Class

1. **Instruct the students to make the concrete** following the instructions on page 46 by mixing the cement and water in a paper or plastic dish or cup until it is smooth and an even consistency. (To ease crushing, limit the amount of water used in each sample to no more than 1 part water for 2 parts cement.) Then have them add the aggregate and mix just before putting it into the mold.

2. **Samples should all be made in one day** so that they have the same amount of time to set up. The samples should be tested the next day or the day after to be sure they are not too strong to be crushed in the concrete crusher.

   SAFETY—Be sure the student mixing the concrete sample wears gloves, as concrete can be very caustic and irritate the skin. All students should wash their hands after this activity.

3rd Class

1. **Test and evaluate.** One at a time, have teams test the samples as described on page 47, while the other teams watch. Each team should announce what variable they are testing, and predict whether Sample A or B is stronger, and say why. During testing, emphasize the importance of pushing the top beam down squarely onto the sample, so it doesn't wobble. Also, be sure that someone is standing by to read the scale.

2. **Have the students record the results** of the experiment on page 47 of their *Engineer's Notebook*. Call attention to how the sample looks when it starts to fail, and have students from each team sketch the sample's appearance after failure.

3. **Help students calculate mechanical advantage** of the concrete crusher, as shown on page 48. It's important that students realize that their testing apparatus is a lever—one of the simple machines. Like a nutcracker, it amplifies force. So the force exerted on the sample is many times greater than the force indicated on the bathroom scale. The calculation of mechanical advantage is not difficult, but students may need you to work out an example for them.

    For instance: Suppose a sample started to fracture when the bathroom scale read 50 pounds. If the center of the scale is 60 inches from the bolt on which the concrete crusher pivots and the sample is 6 inches from the same bolt, the mechanical advantage is 60 in./6 in. = 10, and the force on the concrete sample is 10×50 pounds = 500 pounds.

    The force exerted on the concrete crusher is the live load. The weight of the beam itself is the dead load. So the total load on the sample is the sum of the live and dead loads.

    Have your students do their calculations and fill in the results on page 48.

4. **Ask the students to discuss the Redesign questions** on the bottom of page 49 with their teammates, and to fill in the answers to the questions.

5. **Have each student write a report** on his or her team's experiment with concrete, as described under "Communicate" on the top of page 49. Ask them to be sure to include any conclusions about redesigning the recipe for concrete in their report. You can collect and read these as a means to assess students' understanding of the problem, the experimental process, and calculation of mechanical advantage.

4th Class

1. **Have each team report on their results.** Ask all the other students in the class to record the results in the table included for this purpose in their *Engineer's Notebook* on page 50. For each experiment they should record what variable each team was testing, the force it took to crush each sample, and the results. After each report, ask the class if they have questions for the team that is presenting. Each student should write his or her conclusions at the bottom of the table after all groups have reported.

2. **Have the teams who will be designing multi-use buildings meet** to decide what they learned from the class's presentations. They may discuss how they should use concrete in their building (if at all), and what recipe they would require the contractor to use in preparing the concrete.

3. **Conclude** with an all-class discussion about the focus questions:

- For what applications is concrete best suited?
- What roles do the constituents of concrete play?
- What happens if you change the standard formula?
- How can the formula for concrete be changed to meet different needs?

Assessment

Observe students' abilities to control variables when they bring you their plans and justify the concrete samples that they plan to make. If students seem to be more interested in changing everything that might make a difference, use the opportunity to communicate the idea of a fair test. *The goal, you might tell them, is not to create the strongest sample of concrete in the class, but rather to learn something important about how to make concrete that will support a building.*

Listen to their ideas during discussion to determine whether they have learned that concrete is a material that can have widely different properties depending on how and with what materials it is made.

Read the students' reports on their experiments. By now they should be familiar with the kind of laboratory report you expect. Critique the form of the report as well as the substance. As always, watch for patterns of errors across the class to determine whether you need to conduct an additional class on common problems.

Background and Further Information

Concrete is probably the most widely used material for construction purposes. It is simple to make, workable, easy to transport, and inexpensive. Concrete simulates the properties of rock. It is a combination of aggregates—normally sand, gravel, or crushed rock—held together with a paste that is activated by water. It has two main states, fresh and hardened. As it is transitioning from one state to the other, it stiffens and starts to gain strength.

Early forms of concrete were used by the ancient Assyrians, Babylonians, and Egyptians, and later by the Romans. Portland cement, still used in concrete today, was invented by Joseph Aspdin in 1824. Reinforced concrete, in which steel is embedded in concrete, was invented in 1849 by Joseph Monier. Reinforced concrete combines the tensile strength of steel with the compressive strength of plain concrete.

New uses of concrete are being developed constantly. Engineers in London have developed a "building-in-a-bag," which consists of a sack of cement-impregnated fabric. When water is added to it, the material can be manipulated into a small structure, dried, and used! This technology is designed to meet the need of relief workers who are trying to erect strong and durable housing quickly for refugees in war-torn areas. More information on this invention is available at http://www.concretecanvas.co.uk.

The method of testing concrete in this task—controlled experimentation—is more often associated with science than with engineering. Historically, however, controlled experiments were used to optimize the design of devices and manufacturing processes long before the development of modern science. Since the students' goal in this activity is to improve a technological process, not to investigate the natural world, it is clearly in the realm of engineering.

References and Resources

Concrete Canvas. "Concrete Canvas – The Building in a Bag." http://www.concretecanvas.co.uk.

Robertson, Sirion. *Science in Africa*, "Concrete: Hard Facts. Durable Structures," April, 2002. http://www.scienceinafrica.co.za/2002/april/concrete.htm.

The Portland Cement Association web site has background information on cement and concrete, further teaching ideas, an introductory quiz, and it guides students through an activity in which they learn about the chemistry of cement and the hydration process by creating samples of concrete and weighing them before and after hydration. They will see that the samples lose no weight through evaporation because of the chemical reaction between cement and water.

Portland Cement Association. "Cement & Concrete Basics." http://www.cement.org/basics/concretebasics_lessonfive.asp.

Extension Activity: Composite Materials
Demonstration of Composite Material
Materials: 2 baking trays, water, newspaper, hammer

The following activity demonstrates that composite materials, such as concrete, have greater strength than materials made of just one substance.

In one baking tray, freeze only water. In the second tray, freeze a small amount of water, mixed with shredded newspaper. Invite students to help you demonstrate how easy it is to break a block of pure ice, and how difficult it is to break the newspaper/ice combination. The newspaper greatly increases the strength of the material. This is analogous to reinforced concrete, which is a common construction material.

Task 2.7:   **Make Your Building Energy Efficient**

Overview

We live in a society that uses a high percentage of the world's natural resources for energy. We have made great technological advances, yet we have not seen dramatic improvements in energy efficiency. Our students will be the ones making decisions about energy policy in the future. Therefore, understanding how energy moves and how to avoid wasting it will better help them make good decisions.

Task 2.7 presents three key science concepts that students need to understand in order to design an energy-efficient structure:

1. **Thermal (heat) energy is like a substance—but it's *not* a substance.** Thermal energy can be measured and it can flow from one place to another by conduction, radiation, or convection; but it does *not* consist of matter.

2. **It takes a difference to make a difference.** If the air on one side of a wall is warmer than the air on the other side, thermal (heat) energy will flow from the warm side to the cool side. The bigger the temperature difference, the greater the flow of energy. When the temperature difference disappears, thermal energy will stop flowing.

3. **Resistance slows the rate of energy flow.** Thermal conductors allow energy to flow rapidly. Insulation slows the flow of thermal energy through walls and windows. The more effective the insulation, the more efficient the heating and cooling of the system.

These key concepts are presented visually and in a logical sequence to help the students develop a mental model of thermal (heat) energy. Self-test items are included to help you help your students understand how to apply these concepts. In the last part of this task, students will consider how to apply what they learned to the multi-use building they are designing.

Five Es

Explain the difference between thermal (heat) energy and temperature and describe other thermal energy concepts; **Elaborate** on these ideas in the context of a new building design; **Evaluate** the pros and cons of the various ways to conserve energy in buildings; **Explore** all of these ideas by designing a thermal box to test students' ideas.

Time Frame

4 class periods

Focus Questions

- What is the difference between temperature and thermal energy?
- What causes energy to move?
- What are the differences between conduction, convection, and radiation?
- What is an R-value, and how is it used in energy-loss calculations?

Objectives

Students will be able to:
- Give an example to illustrate the difference between thermal energy and temperature
- Explain the conditions and variables that affect how energy moves
- Describe how energy moves by conduction, convection, and radiation
- Identify materials that reduce energy movement, such as insulation and weather stripping

Materials

For each team of two students:
 1 set of colored pencils or thin markers, including red, orange, yellow, green, and blue
 1 piece temperature-sensitive paper (liquid crystal)
 Samples of materials with different conductive values (coins and plastic buttons and / or metal, wood, plastic, fabric, etc.)

For each team of four students:
 1 cardboard box (all teams should get the same size box)
 1 thermometer (either liquid crystal or glass)
 1 roll of tape
 1 dimmer switch
 1 light bulb and socket (same wattage for all teams)
 1 pair scissors
 1 piece of clear plastic
 Samples of various insulation materials (rock wool, fiberglass, cellulose, foam, etc.)

Preparation

Read Task 2.7 in the *Engineer's Notebook* and Chapters 15 and 16 in the textbook to prepare yourself for questions students might ask.

There are a lot of concepts concerning energy in this task. Address them one at a time, and have students discuss their answers to the self-test questions so you can help them clarify and correct their understanding as needed. These energy concepts are introduced in this section as they relate to thermal systems, but they will be presented again in the context of fluid systems in the next project, and in the context of electrical systems in the final project. Consequently, you should lay a firm foundation in this task.

Prepare the materials that you'll need for the various parts of this activity, and have them ready for the students to pick up or to place in stations around the room.

The challenge on page 61, in which students test insulating materials, does not specify what students should compare. If you can get the same size box and light for each group, they can compare the results of their tests with other groups.

Engineering the Future Teacher Guide
©2008 Museum of Science, Boston

1st Class

1. **Introduce the topic of energy by brainstorming how students use energy.** Guide the discussion toward energy use in their homes and school. Remind them of their multi-use building and that it must be energy efficient.

2. **Ask the students to read page 51, which introduces Task 2.7.** Invite them to ask questions. Tell them that they will need to understand these three big ideas about energy in order to make their buildings energy efficient.

3. **Have the students read page 52, "1. Thermal Energy Is Like a Substance."** The main purpose of the ideas on this page is to help students distinguish between the concepts of "thermal (heat) energy" and "temperature."

4. **Conduct a discussion of how thermal energy is "substance-like,"** but only after the students can distinguish between thermal energy and temperature. Start by asking the students what it means to them to say thermal energy is "substance-like." (It can flow from one place to another, you can feel it, and you know it's gone when something cools off.) Ask them to explain why thermal energy is not an actual substance (You can't see it, it doesn't take up space or have weight, and you can't hold it in your hands.) Finally, ask why temperature is not substance-like. (Temperature does not depend on amount. [You can have a pitcher of water at 90°C and a tiny drop of water at 90°C. They both have the same temperature, but you know there must be more thermal energy in the pitcher than in the drop.])

5. **Have the students answer the self-test questions** at the bottom of the page to see how well they understand the concepts presented above.

6. **If you can, set up a quick demonstration** using the three cups of water while the students write in their answers to the questions at the bottom of the page. Have the students predict the temperature in cups A, B, and C, and then actually pour half the contents of cups A and B into C to see if they were right.

Answer Key

EN Page 52: Self-Test
  A. Cup B
  B. 75°C
  C. Cup B
  D. Cup C
  E. Cup C will have half of the energy of the original cup B plus half of the energy of the original cup A. Since cups A and B only have half the energy they had before being poured into cup C, each one must have less energy than cup C.

2nd Class

1. **Ask the students to read page 53, "Flow of Thermal Energy."** This page describes three ways that energy can flow from one place to another. Ask the students to work with a partner to consider the questions at the bottom of the page for each of the three scenarios.

2. **Lead a discussion about the ways thermal energy flows.** Allow students about 10 minutes to discuss the scenarios, then lead a large-group discussion about each scenario, guided by the questions. Take the time to be sure the students understand how the three different ways thermal energy flows explain the way that thermal energy flows in these three situations.

3. **It takes a difference to make a difference.** Invite the students to read the top half of page 54. The key idea here is that energy will flow whenever there is a difference in temperature. A bigger difference means a bigger energy transfer. This means that energy will flow from an area of higher concentration to lower concentration as long as there is this imbalance. The transfer will continue until there is no difference anymore. In other words, transfer will occur until equilibrium is reached.

4. **What's a system?** Discuss the idea of a system. The word "system" has many different meanings in everyday language. The main idea here is that in engineering it's helpful to define a system that has a boundary and inputs and outputs. Ask the students to come up with other systems to see if they understand the idea.

5. **Direct the students' attention to the use of arrows in the illustrations at the top of the page.** Ask them to describe what the arrows are illustrating in the diagrams. (They show which direction thermal energy is flowing.)

6. **Ask the students to draw their own arrows in the pictures at the bottom of the page.** Remind them that the arrows always go from the warmer place to the cooler place. Invite students to work in teams of two on these questions.

Answer Key

- **Cup of hot tea:** arrows go from the tea to the surrounding air in all directions.
- **Glass of iced tea:** arrows go from the air into the tea.
- **Room-temperature tea:** no arrows because there's no difference in temperature.
- **Popsicle:** arrows go from air into the Popsicle.
- **Parked car:** There could be no arrows because the car is at room temperature; students may realize that the inside of the car will heat up (due to a greenhouse effect), in which case the arrows will go out from the car.
- **Car with its engine running:** arrows go out from the hot engine to the air, especially through the exhaust pipe, where hot gases escape.

7. **Colors and arrows.** Ask students to read page 55. It's ideal if your students have colored pencils or pens to fill in the boxes and then color code the self-test at the bottom of the page.

8. **Explain color coding,** which is a way to visualize the difference in temperature—which determines the direction and magnitude of the energy flow. (Later in the course, your students will color code fluid systems to show differences in pressure as well as electrical systems, to show differences in voltage. In these more complicated systems, the color coding will make it easier to visualize what's happening.)

9. **Have your students complete the diagrams on the self-test, following the example.** Use the key at the top of the page to relate the shades of gray shown in the *Engineer's Notebook* guide to colors. In the example, the box representing the bowl of soup is red and the surrounding air is yellow. In the other boxes, your students should draw the following:

   • The Popsicle is blue, and the surrounding air is yellow or orange. Medium or large arrows show energy flow.
   • Frozen ice cream is represented by a blue box, and the surrounding freezer is also blue. There are no arrows.
   • The hot cup of coffee is represented by a red box, and the surrounding air is green or blue. Medium or large arrows flow from the coffee to the surrounding air.

10. **Discuss the diagrams in the self-test with the whole class. Invite students to share their ideas.** Ask them to visualize the actual situations depicted. For example, how quickly does a cup of coffee cool off on a hot day versus on a cold day? Would they expect energy to be flowing within a freezer after everything in it is frozen solid? How about the Popsicle on a hot day: would it melt faster than on a cold day? Not everyone needs to come up with exactly the same answer. The important thing is that the students use the colors and arrows to represent their ideas about how the differences in temperature drive the flow of energy.

3rd Class

1. **Resistance to thermal energy.** Ask the students to read page 56, "Resistance Slows the Rate of Energy Flow." This section is key to a quantitative understanding of insulation. First, however, ensure that students understand the qualitative idea that some substances conduct thermal energy better than others. To do so requires overcoming a common misconception that some substances, like metals, are "cold" while others, like blankets and sweaters, are "warm." The penny and button problem in the middle of the page helps with this misconception.

2. **Give each team of students a room-temperature penny and a button or bit of plastic.** (Do not take coins right out of your pocket, or they will be at 98.6°!) Ask the students to touch the metal and plastic object and to report which feels colder. (They should report that the penny feels colder.) Tell them that both objects have been in the room for a while, and because they know that energy stops flowing when temperatures are equal, they should all be at room temperature. Why, then, does the penny feel colder? Write their explanations on the board.

3. **Hand out a piece of temperature-sensitive paper and do the following:**

   Ask the students to touch it with a finger and see what happens. (It will change color where they touched it; when they remove their finger, the color will eventually fade.) Explain that this material changes color with differences in temperature.

   Ask the students to put the coin and plastic on the temperature-sensitive paper and see what happens. (There will be no color change.) Ask them what this means. (The coin and plastic are both at room temperature.)

   Next, ask the students to touch the coin for a minute and see how it affects the temperature-sensitive paper, and to explain what they see. (It turns green under the penny because the thermal energy from your body flows into the coin and then into the temperature-sensitive paper.)

   Then ask them to do the same with the button. (Color change under the button or plastic is slight, if at all, because it does not conduct energy well from your finger to the temperature-sensitive paper.)

   Now ask the students again why the penny feels colder than the button.

   If students do not come up with the explanation, you can offer the idea that what you really feel when you touch metal is thermal energy leaving your finger. The button or plastic resists the flow of thermal energy, so it does not feel cold.

   Keep in mind that the belief that metals are "cold" and plastic, wood, and other substances are "warm" is deeply ingrained, so it may be difficult to change. Do your best!

4. **Equation for rate of flow.** Point out the equation at the bottom of the page that gives a quantitative expression for the rate of thermal (heat) energy flow:

$$Q = \frac{A\,\Delta T}{R}$$

The questions at the bottom of the page are intended to get students to think about the relationship of the variables in this equation:

    1) If ΔT increases, Q increases.
    2) If R increases, the Q decreases.
    3) If A increases, Q increases.

5. **R-Value.** Have teams of two read page 57, which introduces the R-values of various insulating materials. (R-value is pronounced "R value," not "R minus value," as this is a hyphen, not a subtraction sign.) Have each student consider a possible wall design for his or her multi-use building by finding the total R-value, following the instructions at the bottom of page 57.

6. **Find the R-value of two walls.** Have the students read page 58 and find the R-value for the two walls at the top of the page. Answers are as follows:

    1) Wall A: $R_T = 0.80 + 3.70 + 0.77 = 5.27$
    2) Wall B: $R_T = 0.44 + 1.00 + 0.77 = 2.21$
    3) Wall A has a greater R-value, so it will do a better job of slowing the rate of thermal energy through it than Wall B.

7. **Relate R-value to rate of energy flow.** Have the students read the bottom half of page 58 and calculate the rate of energy flow through the two walls as follows:

    1) For Wall A: $Q = 10\ \text{ft.}^2 \times 60°F\ /\ 5.27 \approx 113.9\ \text{BTU/hr}$
    2) For Wall B: $Q = 10\ \text{ft.}^2 \times 60°F\ /\ 2.21 \approx 271\ \text{BTU/hr}$

8. **Assign homework in the text.** Ask the students to read Chapter 15, "Building Green," in the textbook, in which architect Chris Benedict describes the problems with conventional heating systems and explains how she designs energy-efficient buildings. Ask students to write answers to the questions at the end of the chapter. Discuss their answers the next day.

4th Class

1. **Discuss the homework.** Concepts presented in Chapter 15 are intended to reinforce the concepts presented in Task 2.7, and to provide a real-world context for learning about energy. Discuss the students' answers to the questions and encourage discussion when there are differences of opinion.

2. **Develop an energy plan for your building.** Ask students to get together in their teams for designing a multi-use building. Ask them to read "Designs for Energy-Efficient Buildings" and "More Energy-Saving Ideas" on pages 59 and 60, and to discuss what materials they want to use for the walls, and which of the strategies on pages 59 and 60 they might want to adopt. Tell them that they do not need to make firm decisions today, but to at least identify three or four good alternatives to keep in mind.

3. **Discuss insulation ideas.** Show the insulation materials you have collected and the other equipment needed for the design challenge on page 61. Tell each team that before they make final decisions about the walls of their structure, they should first conduct an experiment to see what combinations of materials work best. Because all teams are receiving the same size box and light bulb, they will be able to compare their results with other teams. Have students read pages 61 and 62 and come up with a plan to test a combination of insulating materials.

4. **Begin tests.** When a team has completed a plan, give them the materials that they will need to test the insulating materials. Ask them how they will record and display their results; you want to be sure they've thought about this.

5. **Establish a control.** Set up one box with no insulation. Either develop a temperature curve for the uninsulated box yourself (by noting the temperature inside the box every minute after the temperature is turned on) or ask a student to do so for you. Each team can then compare their results with this box to see how the insulation helped.

6. **Have teams run their experiments.** Each student should write a report on what his or her team did and what he or she found out. Directions for this written report are on the bottom of page 62.

7. **Have each group report on the results of their insulation experiment.** Write these results on the board. Suggest that everyone take notes so they can find out what the other teams have discovered about effective insulation. Teams should feel free to "borrow" the most effective insulating ideas from other teams. Remember, the goal is to find out which insulations are best, not to "win" the competition.

8. **Assign Homework.** Ask students to read Chapter 16, "A Race for the Sun," in the textbook and write answers to the questions at the end of the chapter. Discuss the students' answers the next day.

Engineering the Future Teacher Guide
©2008 Museum of Science, Boston

Assessment
You can gather evidence on whether or not your students understand and can apply the three big ideas about thermal energy flow from the class discussions, small group work, homework, and their reports on insulation experiments. If your students appear to understand the major thermal energy concepts and are able to calculate R-values and draw valid results from their energy experiments, then you are ready to move on. However, if your students are confused by these ideas, you may want to copy and hand out the two worksheets at the end of this task: "Color Coding & Insulation."

Have each student color code the diagrams and answer the questions. Pick up the papers so you can see how each student understands key ideas and the use of color coding at this point. If it appears that many students are still confused, hand the papers back the next day (without corrections), and have students compare answers and see if they can figure out what the best answers should be. You can then provide teams of two or three students with a fresh sheet so they can revise their answers. Finally, lead a large-group discussion to see if you can help clarify the big ideas.

Background and Further Suggestions
Following are more detailed descriptions of the mechanisms that allow thermal energy to move from one place to another.

Conduction: Transfer of thermal energy by direct contact. At a molecular level, thermal energy is the kinetic energy of moving molecules. The more rapidly the molecules are moving, the hotter the object feels. According to this model, thermal energy is conducted from one place to another when moving molecules bump into adjacent molecules, causing them to move faster too. These collisions cause the faster molecules to slow down and the slower molecules to speed up, so that thermal energy becomes more evenly distributed. Metals are generally good "conductors" of energy. Energy from the stove is conducted through metal pans to warm up food and/or water. Materials such as wood, air, and fabric resist the flow of energy, and can be used as insulators. Construction products are generally tested and rated with a "resistance value," or R-value, that specifies how effectively they block the flow of thermal energy.

Convection: Transfer of energy by the movement of liquid or gas. As fluids get hotter, they expand and become less dense (more buoyant). Most forced hot water heating systems use baseboard convectors to distribute heat—cool air near the floor flows past hot heat-exchanger fins, heats up, and rises into the room. Schools often use forced convection systems, where fans blow fresh air past hot pipes before it enters the classrooms.

Radiation: Transfer of energy by electromagnetic waves. Electromagnetic waves range from very short waves (gamma and x-rays) through ultraviolet and visible light, and longer waves (infrared, microwaves, and finally radio waves). All of these waves carry energy by radiation. Infrared is the most efficient means for transferring thermal energy because the speed of vibration (frequency) corresponds very closely to the natural vibration speed of molecules in many materials. The warmth you feel when lying in the sun is due to the infrared component of sunlight. And the warmth you feel when sitting near a campfire is mostly due to radiation, while a toasting marshmallow receives most of its energy from convection—the column of rising air just above the campfire.

The equation for heat flow used in the *Engineer's Notebook* is a simple version. The following equation might also be used:

$$Q = U \times A \times \Delta T$$

Where:

Q is the rate of energy transfer in BTU/hr,
A is the perpendicular surface area through which the energy flows in ft.^{2},
ΔT is the difference in °F between the temperatures on either side of a surface,
U is the thermal transmission coefficient (the inverse of the sum of R-values).

R-Values and U-Values

R-values are given to *single* components of materials to rate the energy efficiency of the material. R-values represent how much a material *resists* energy passing through it; therefore, a high R-value means that a material is a good insulator. Most buildings have more than one material between the interior and exterior environment, so R-values need to be added to calculate total R-value.

In building energy-loss calculations, U-values are used. U-values are also a rating of energy efficiency, but are usually listed for components such as double-paned windows, skylights, and exterior building components that are made up of more than one material. U-values rate how much energy is conducted through the combination of materials. So, where R-values rate how well the material resists the flow of energy, U-values rate how well a material *allows* energy to pass through it. Again, while a *high R-value* indicates good energy efficiency—R-19 is better than R-11— a *low U-value* indicates good energy efficiency—U-0.35 would be better than U-0.43.

We eliminated U to simplify the mathematical formula:

$Q = (A \times \Delta T) / R_T$ is equivalent to $Q = U \times A \times \Delta T$
$R_T = R_1 + R_2 + R_3 + \ldots$ $U = 1/(R_T)$
                                                                    $R_T = R_1 + R_2 + R_3 + \ldots$

Another reason we eliminated U is to emphasize the similarity of energy flow with the fluid flow through a pipe and the flow of electric current expressed in the following equations:

$Q_{thermal} = A\Delta T/R_T$ Thermal energy flow through a wall, where ΔT = temperature change

$Q_{fluid} = \Delta P/R_T$ Rate of fluid flow through a pipe, where ΔP = pressure change

$I_{current} = \Delta V/R_T$ Electric current flow through a wire, where ΔV = voltage drop

Engineering the Future Teacher Guide
©2008 Museum of Science, Boston

Color Coding & Insulation

To show how the temperature difference is causing a transfer of thermal energy (as represented by the arrows), color code the air inside the box and the surrounding air below:

Stage one: Bulb off, no flow of energy Assume that: Ambient air is "normal" and the box has been sitting in the room and there is no energy input from the bulb	
Stage two: Bulb on <u>low</u> setting Small transfer of energy	
Stage three: Bulb on <u>high</u> setting Large transfer of energy	

Case 2: Imagine that <u>insulation</u> is added to the box and the bulb is on a <u>high</u> setting.

Draw the arrows *and* color code.

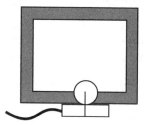

Case 3: Imagine that the box with insulation is placed outside on a cold winter day.

Draw the arrows *and* color code.

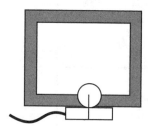

How do the arrows in cases 2 and 3 compare?

Questions to consider:
- In each example, when does the box reach a "steady state"?
- How is the steady-state box like the heating of a room of a house?
- How is it different?
- How can the steady-state box be applied to the heating of a large building?
- How can the steady-state box be used to learn about efficient energy usage?

Task 2.8:   Make a Scale Drawing of Your Building Design

Overview

Engineering drawings are an important tool in designing and analyzing space. In the previous project, students created drawings of solid objects using isometric and orthographic drawing techniques. Architects often use orthographic projections when drawing plans for buildings or spaces, including plan and elevation views. By looking at scale drawings, engineers can determine the size and shapes of elements in a space without actually being at the site.

In order to describe a three-dimensional space in two dimensions effectively, both a plan view (looking directly down on top of the space) and an elevation view (looking at the object from the front or side) are needed. In this exercise, your students will draw a plan view of the classroom and a room in their homes. Students may measure the distances by pacing or using a tape measure. A rubric for the scale drawings is provided for assessment. As an extension, students who finish early could be asked to sketch the elevation view(s) of their home and include approximate dimensions.

For students who learned how to do engineering drawings in Project 1.0, Task 2.8 will be mostly review.

Five Es

Engage in the design process as students bring ideas from all previous tasks to bear on the main challenge—to design a multi-function building of the future; **Elaborate** on the ideas using their engineering drawing skills; **Evaluate** and revise their design as they make detailed drawings.

Time Frame

2–3 class periods

Focus Questions

- What is the best way to represent a three-dimensional space in two dimensions?
- How do you use drawings to describe space?
- What tools do you need to make a scaled drawing?

Objectives

Students are able to:
- Use a ruler, triangle, and/or T-square as a drawing tool
- Use math skills (fractions, proportions, and so on) to create scale drawings
- Analyze horizontal and vertical space in terms of its scaled dimensions

Materials	For teams of 2–3 students:

Materials

For teams of 2–3 students:
- 1 12-inch ruler or architect/engineer scale
- 1 tape measure
- 2 pieces of paper, either poster size or smaller
- 1 right triangle or T-square
- 2–3 pencils with erasers
- 2–3 sheets of quad-ruled graph paper

Preparation

Obtain the above materials. Read Task 2.8 and answer the questions yourself so that you are prepared if students have questions.

Students do not need to be in their building design teams; Task 2.8 focuses on how to do engineering drawings of buildings and does not ask students to create their final design. That will happen in Task 2.9.

1st Class

1. **Discuss the homework.** Ask students for their answers to the questions after Chapter 16. This chapter provides further ideas for the students on how to design a building that is as "green" as possible.

2. **Ask the students to read page 63, which introduces Task 2.8.** Discuss how engineers and architects depict three-dimensional space in two dimensions. Introduce the "plan" drawing and the "elevation" drawing and how these drawings apply to their major project. You may want to show examples of a plan and elevation on the board, noting how walls and windows are depicted horizontally and vertically.

3. **Introduce the concept of a "footprint" as a plan showing the outer walls of the building.** Ask the students to interpret the floor-plan view on the next page, and to answer the Finding Dimensions questions by measuring the drawing. Students should be allowed to help each other.

4. **Have a large-group discussion about the answers to the questions,** allowing students to correct their papers and help each other.

5. **Call attention to the title box on the lower-right side of the drawing.** Explain that each of their drawings for the final project should have a title box.

6. **On page 65, have students make their own scale drawings** of an apartment with the dimensions given. The directions for the drawing are very simple; the layout of the rooms is the same as the drawing on the previous page. The key point in this activity is that after they have made an accurate scale drawing, they can use it to find the dimensions of the parts of the structure that weren't listed. Help individuals as needed.

Engineering the Future Teacher Guide
©2008 Museum of Science, Boston

Answer Key

EN Finding Dimensions: Page 64
1) Living room: 16 ft. × 24 ft.
2) Area of living room: 16 ft. × 24 ft. = 384 ft.^{2}
3) Dining room: 16 ft. × 16 ft.
4) Area of dining room: 16 ft. × 16 ft. = 256 ft.^{2}
5) Dining room table: 7 ft. × 3 ft.
6) Chair seats: 1 ft. × 1 ft.
7) Footprint: 32 ft. × 24 ft.
8) Dimension lines should show the dining room as 16 ft. × 16 ft. and kitchen as 8 ft. × 16 ft.

EN Make Your Own Scale Drawings: Page 65
A good scale for this drawing is 1" = 10' or 1:120.

2) A. Dining room is 2.5 in. long × 2 in. wide in the drawing.
    B. Dining room in actual apartment is 25 ft. long × 20 ft. wide.
3) A. Area of kitchen in drawing is 2" × 1.5" = 3 in.^{2}
    B. Area of kitchen in actual apartment is 20 ft. × 15 ft. = 300 ft.^{2}

2nd Class

1. **Ask the students to read page 66, "Your Classroom."** Have them work in pairs to measure the classroom and create a floor plan to scale. Give them quad-ruled paper, but do not tell them what scale to use. Determining what scale will fit on the paper is the main point of this exercise.

2. **Each student makes a scale drawing of the classroom,** sharing data and working with one other student to figure out a good scale.

3. **Call the students' attention to the rubric on the same page.** Ask them to self-rate the drawings they just made. Tell them that the drawings they make of their building design will be graded using this rubric.

Assessment

Use the rubric in the *Engineer's Notebook* to assess the students' drawings. Expect students to apply these skills to the final design project.

If, after finishing these activities, students are unable to interpret or create scale drawings, provide additional practice. For example, you can have students make scale drawings of their houses or apartments. They will need to take measurements and make sketches or tables for recording the information, find a scale that will work, and create a final scale drawing.

Background and Further Suggestions
Teachers may obtain samples of plan- and elevation-view drawings from an architect. Engineering drawings of the school would be especially interesting; the students would be able to locate their classroom and other familiar landmarks. As-built drawings of houses can be found online or at the library.

Task 2.9:

Design a Building of the Future!

Overview

For Task 2.9, students will work on the design team that was established to define the problem in Task 2.1. The challenge is to create an energy-efficient building of the future that will reduce urban sprawl. Design teams will give a presentation complete with plans, a front elevation view, floor plans, a report, and a scale model of the building.

Students are advised to designate specific titles to members of the team. For example, planner (investigates zoning and decides on building floor usage); engineer (designs structural system and determines materials); architect/draftsperson (researches building styles and puts ideas to scale on paper); and energy engineer (selects appropriate insulation and mechanical systems to maintain comfortable temperatures). However, all team members should participate in major decisions, and all team members must do his or her own drawings and write a report from his or her own perspective.

Teams will be asked to proceed through the engineering design process, starting by recalling their definition of the problem, and making any changes in light of what they've learned. All steps of the engineering process must be documented in each members' report.

Finally, it's very easy for this project to take up weeks of time. It's best to stick with the recommended schedule, if possible, so that there will be time for model-building and wrap-up.

Five Es

Engage students in creating a model of their final design; **Explore** different ways of communicating their ideas; **Elaborate** the pros and cons of the design for marketing; **Explain** their ideas to their fellow classmates; **Evaluate** each other's designs.

Time Frame

4–6 class periods

Focus Questions

- Where will the building be located?
- What are your criteria and constraints?
- What examples of mixed-use buildings already exist?
- What are the zoning laws in the area where you want to build?
- What will take place in the building, and what loads will it need to support?
- What materials should it be constructed from?
- How will it be designed to minimize energy use?
- What will it look like?

Objectives	Students are able to:

Objectives

Students are able to:
- Apply all previous learning to this culminating project
- Work on their own and as a group
- Communicate with peers to create a product
- Explain why teamwork is valuable in solving problems

Materials

For each team:
> Drawing paper and tools (ruler, T-square, right triangle, compass, etc.)
> Foam core or cardboard
> Tape, glue, or glue gun
> Straws
> Masking tape
> Utility knife and/or scissors

Preparation

Review the tasks in the *Engineer's Notebook* and Teacher's Guide to know what the project entails.

If possible, arrange for Internet access so students can research mixed-use buildings around the world. Conduct some research first, so that you can suggest web sites such as the Project for Public Spaces, "Mixed-Use Development," http://www.pps.org/mixed_use/.

1st Class

1. **Have the structure design teams read page 67, which is the first page of Task 2.9, and then review their earlier problem definition.** Ask team members to look back to Task 2.1 in their *Engineer's Notebooks*, where they listed criteria and constraints for a mixed-use building in their community. Do they want to stick with that problem definition, or change their plans? They should all agree on the same problem statement, criteria, and constraints, and add a page to their *Engineer's Notebooks* with this information.

2. **Ask teams to designate assignments, such as the following:**
   - **Planner** (investigates zoning and building codes, plans floor usage)
   - **Structural engineer** (calculates live and dead loads, proposes structures)
   - **Materials engineer** (chooses materials for different components)
   - **Architect** (researches building styles and sketches ideas)
   - **Energy engineer** (selects insulation, heating, and cooling systems)
   - **Draftsperson** (makes sketches and scale drawings)

   Explain that the person who is given an assignment will not do all the work—he or she will take the lead in doing research in a particular area, and bring proposals to the group to make final decisions. In the end, all students must understand everything about the project because they will all be asked to write their own report and make their own drawings.

3. **Suggest that the architect play the role of facilitator,** making sure that the team works together well, and that everyone's ideas are heard. Have students read through the rest of the design process steps on pages 68 and 69, and then plan who will conduct research on what area.

4. **Have the team reread "Research the Problem" at the top of page 68.** The team should gather research. All students should leave class with a clear research assignment. Students start their research.

2nd Class

1. **Conclude research.** Students finish their research and report back to their team on what they've found. Teams decide what is relevant to their project and what is not. The team will modify their criteria and constraints, if necessary, to take the research results into account.

2. **Develop possible solutions.** Continuing with steps in the engineering design process on page 68, students should spend at least 20 minutes on their own thinking about what kind of building would be the best solution and would reflect the research. Each student jots down notes and makes sketches of his or her ideas and puts them in his or her *Engineer's Notebooks.*

3. **Choose the best solution.** The team meets together to share solutions. Make sure teams go around the table to be sure everyone has their ideas out before discussing the pros and cons of each idea. If possible, synthesize the best ideas in two or three different designs to come up with something better than any individual could produce. Encourage students to use a Pugh chart to choose the best solution.

3rd and 4th Classes

1. **Create a prototype.** Students can work together or in twos or threes to develop various aspects of the building project. For example:

   - **Architectural sketches.** The planner and architect might work together to develop a short written description of the building and a sketch of what the building would look like in its surroundings.
   - **Engineering drawings.** Several students can work on scale drawings of floor plans and elevation drawings. These jobs can be divided up, with some doing plans of different floors or different sections of the building.
   - **Analysis and materials.** What loads must the building support? What materials should be used for the foundation? For the different floors?
   - **Energy efficiency.** What insulation will the building have? Where will it be located? What lighting will be needed? What heating and cooling system will be used? What other energy-saving qualities will the building have?
   - **Model.** After the above issues have been decided by the whole team, several students can collaborate on building a scale model using cardboard or foam core and glue.

Engineering the Future Teacher Guide
©2008 Museum of Science, Boston

5th and 6th Classes

1. **Test and evaluate.** When the engineering drawings and model are finished, the students look back at their problem definition and decide if there is anything that they want to change about the building they designed. Unless there is lots of extra time, they should simply make note of these changes on their drawings and notepads, and incorporate new ideas or redesigns into their reports.

2. **Communicate.** Each team member writes his or her own report, describing how his or her team went through each step of the design process. The report should describe what the writer did, and what other students on the team did. These can be done as homework over two or three nights. Tell the students to pay special attention to the rubric on page 70, which will be used to evaluate their report.

3. **Present.** When the reports are finished, each team makes an oral presentation to the rest of the class, describing how and why their design developed as it did, and why they think such a building would improve their community. Students from other classes, other teachers, or the school principal might be invited to see these presentations.

Final Class

Capture student feedback. Ask the students how they liked Project 2.0. What did they think of the text? The hands-on projects? The *Engineer's Notebook*? Would any of the students consider careers in any of these areas?

Assessment

1. **Test.** If your students are taking the end-of-project test, tell them to prepare for the test by going over their *Engineer's Notebooks*. You may also want to hold a special class to answer their questions in advance of the test, and to go over any concepts or skills that you know have been difficult for them.

2. **Portfolios.** You might also ask students to assemble a portfolio of their work, including some of the work in their *Engineer's Notebooks* in addition to the final project and report.

3. **Conclude Project 2.0** by asking your students what they have learned about technology, about the work that goes into designing buildings, and how they felt about the various activities. You might also ask them if they have any suggestions for how you should plan and present Project 3.0.

Project 3.0: Improve a Patented Boat Design: Fluid and Thermal Systems

Project Guide

Engineers often redesign existing products. Patents are meant to protect original ideas, but also make those ideas known to others, so that improvements can be made. That's what happened with the putt-putt boat, a toy invented in the late 1800s, and redesigned several times in the early 1900s. This toy is still manufactured today in India, and there are many patents available (viewable online) that date back as far as the original British design in 1891 by Thomas Piot.

In Task 3.1, students see a putt-putt boat in action, and receive their major challenge: to improve on the putt-putt boat design, and to write a patent application that describes their innovation. On the way to meeting this challenge, students learn about press- and brake-formed manufacturing, fluid dynamics, hydraulics, pneumatics, propulsion, heat engines, resistance in pipes, product quality improvement, patenting, and marketing. As in all of the other ETF Projects, students also have opportunities to improve their teamwork skills and their ability to innovate.

In Task 3.2, students learn about the importance of quality control as they manufacture a putt-putt boat to specifications. In Task 3.3, they learn about hydraulic and pneumatic systems, and then apply what they learn in Task 3.4 to produce a machine press for manufacturing boat hulls. In Task 3.5, the students turn to the question of propulsion systems, looking at various kinds of heat engines for comparison with their putt-putt boat. The idea of energy transfer in this section parallels the presentation of thermal energy in Project 2.0.

Because the putt-putt boat engine combines the function of a heat engine and rocket engine, the students explore the rocket effect in Task 3.6. They then explore the remaining part of the putt-putt system—what happens in the straws—in Task 3.7. At this point, students have all the background they need to articulate how the putt-putt boat works; to re-design it and prepare a patent application, which they do in Task 3.8; and, finally, to present their solution to the design challenge in Task 3.9.

In the following Gantt chart, each column represents five 45-minute classes and each bar is an estimated number of classes per task. This chart also lists the corresponding text chapters to the tasks in the last column.

Project 3.0: 45-Minute Class Periods	5	10	15	20	25	30	35	40	Text Chapter
Task 3.1: Putt-Putt Boats and Patents Students see a putt-putt boat in action and receive the project assignment.	▓								
Task 3.2: Manufacture a Putt-Putt Boat Students follow instructions and plans to make a replica of a toy boat.		▓							17
Task 3.3: Investigate Fluid Systems Students learn about the basic properties of air and water.			▓						18
Task 3.4: Develop a Manufacturing Press Students consider the properties of hydraulic and pneumatic systems in designing a syringe system that can operate a machine press.				▓					19 20
Task 3.5: Investigate Heat Engines Students learn how heat engines are heated and cooled to produce motion.				▓					21
Task 3.6: The Rocket Effect Students use a model of the boiler engine to understand how pressure difference, resistance, velocity, and volume flow rate are related.					▓				22
Task 3.7: Investigate Resistance in Pipes Students blow through different types of straws of different lengths, areas, and angle bends, in series and parallel, to learn about fluid resistance.					▓				23
Task 3.8: Redesign the Putt-Putt Boat Students design a change to some aspect of the boat, justify the change, and implement it.						▓			
Task 3.9: Present Your Patent Students write a patent application describing how the putt-putt boat works, their changes to the design, and the results. Finally, students present their results to the class.						▓			

Introduction

Build a Putt-Putt Boat. Putt-putt boats are the most popular of all the activities in this course. They are challenging to build, but it's tremendously exciting when you build one and it works! Figuring out how they work is also very challenging, but the challenge is just at the right level. After completing Project 2.0, students have a fairly good idea of how energy is transferred from one place to another, so it is not a great stretch to realize that chemical energy stored in the candle wax is released in the form of heat, and it transfers to the water in the boiler, which produces steam. However, after the first "putt," it's not so easy to figure out the mechanism that causes the boat to continue putt-putt-putting along. With the help you'll give students in understanding pressure change, they will eventually understand that the putt-putt boat is a heat engine with no moving parts, working in a cycle, that moves forward due to the "rocket effect." Students will learn these ideas through the carefully structured tasks in this project. But it all starts with building a putt-putt boat, so the students can see the mechanism that makes it work.

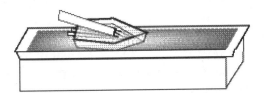 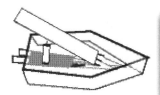

We strongly recommend that you build a putt-putt boat yourself before having your students build one. Full instructions are given in Task 3.2. Simply follow the directions, and if you're careful to *mix equal lengths of epoxy thoroughly* and *test the boiler to be sure it has no air leaks*, you should be successful in building a putt-putt boat that moves forward under candle power. You'll also be able to speak from experience in teaching the students how to use the epoxy to make the boiler, and how to mount the boiler in the hull.

One safety concern of putt-putt boat construction is cutting an aluminum soda can to make the boiler; the edges are sharp. We recommend wearing leather work gloves and eye protection while doing this to avoid cuts from jagged edges. Some teachers prefer to cut soda cans in advance of the class and trim the edges and corners, so that the students 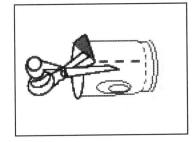 have a safer strip of aluminum to work with. Another option is to purchase and cut coiled aluminum shim stock into strips instead of using soda cans. We recommend having the students work together in pairs to make the putt-putt boats, so you'll need one strip of aluminum for every two students. (Variations include having each student make a boat, or configuring the class as a manufacturing team with task specializations.)

During early trials, we found too many students were unsuccessful in building functioning putt-putt boats. When field-test teachers recommended various steps to ensure success—perhaps, most important being testing the boiler for air-tight seams—we realized that the phrase for such processes in industry is "quality control." We urge you to use both the recommended quality-control methods and the phrase itself, so that students understand the care that must be taken when manufacturing products. Even with rigorous quality control, there will still be observable differences in boat performance, and possibly some failures, presenting ample opportunities to analyze, remanufacture, and learn.

Hull construction—Why two methods? In Task 3.2, students make hulls using two methods: a *brake forming process* and a *hydraulic machine press*. Both methods are commonly used in manufacturing; one reason students are asked to use these two methods is simply to become aware of manufacturing methods. A second reason is the opportunity for them to learn about the use of hydraulic mechanisms in industry, and to compare hydraulic and pneumatic systems. A great many industrial, and even residential, systems use hydraulics and pneumatics, so understanding such systems is an important component of technological literacy. An additional reason is that the putt-putt boat's engine is a thermal-fluid system, so by learning about hydraulics and pneumatics, students are also preparing to understand the putt-putt boat's engine at a deeper level.

Syringe activities. In Task 3.3, your students will investigate pneumatic and hydraulic systems using syringes and various tubes and connectors. The materials and sources are listed in the Materials List section of this Teacher Guide, and in Tasks 3.3 and 3.4. Be sure to do these activities before presenting them to your students. Pay special attention to the different characteristics of pneumatic and hydraulic systems. For example, pneumatic systems are good at storing energy, while hydraulic systems are good at transferring energy rapidly from one place to another.

Engineering the Future Teacher Guide
©2008 Museum of Science, Boston

If there are local examples of pneumatic or hydraulic systems, you might want to identify these before Task 3.3, so you can point them out to your students. Here are two examples.

A jackhammer is a **pneumatic** device used to break up hard materials such as concrete or asphalt. In this image, a pneumatic hose leads from the air compressor to the jackhammer. (Image courtesy of Josh Parris, via Wikipedia.)

This earth mover, like most heavy equipment, uses **hydraulic** cylinders to transfer energy from one place to another and multiply force. You can see two hydraulic cylinders here. (Image courtesy of the U.S. Bureau of Land Management, via Wikipedia.)

Instructions for Making a Hydraulic/Pneumatic Press and Die Set

In Task 3.4, students create a machine press (choosing between hydraulics or pneumatics) to construct boat hulls from soft aluminum sheets, like the material used to produce disposable pie pans. If your students have access to a wood shop, they may be able to construct simple press frames and dies out of wood. Or, if students do not have access to the tools, you can make one press frame and die set for the class, to demonstrate how it works.

Following are instructions for making a simple pneumatic or hydraulic machine press and die set from wood and two syringes. To make such a press, you will need the following:

1 wooden board 1" × 6" × 36" (Note: a 1" × 6" board is actually ¾" thick and 5¾" wide.)

1 wood saw

1 ruler or carpenter's square

1 small syringe

1 large syringe

1 4" length of tubing and connectors to the syringes

1 electric drill

1 drill bit to make a hole just the right size for the large syringe

1 small drill bit to make pilot holes for the nails

screws or nails and glue

screwdriver or hammer

coarse sandpaper or wood rasp

safety glasses or goggles

Directions

1. Cut four pieces of wood to make the frame as shown. Measurements are not critical. The frame should be approximately 6" square on each side.

2. Drill a hole in the top center of the frame so that a large syringe fits snug into the hole. The syringe should be inserted so that the plunger and lip of the syringe face the inside of the frame.

3. Assemble the frame with glue and nails or screws.

4. Attach the tubing and small syringe to the large syringe, as shown in the illustration.

5. Test the frame by pushing in the small plunger. The plunger of the large syringe should extend without the syringe popping out of the retaining hole. This should work reasonably well with air (pneumatic).

6. Cut two equal-sized pieces of wood to make the two-part die. Use a series of straight cuts to make the die with a hand saw, or one continuous cut if you have a band saw, jigsaw, or coping saw. Then use glue and nails to fasten the outer piece(s) to the second piece of wood, using the single boat-shaped center die as a spacer. Allow for about 1/16" gap between the center die and the surrounding pieces of wood. Drill pilot holes for the nails to prevent splitting.

7. Bevel or chamfer the edges of the boat-shaped die, using course sand paper or a rasp, so that it fits easily into the base die.

8. Test the two-part die by placing a sheet of soft aluminum foil, like that used in disposable pie pans, between the two die parts. Press the die parts together by hand to shape a hull. If the aluminum sheet tears, then the fit between the die and mold is too tight. Chamfer the die edge further at the stress point. It also helps to use wax or soap on the die edges.

9. Your students may find that the press will not work well enough with air because the air will compress. However, water in the syringes should work quite well to put enough pressure on the die to form a hull. Try this before class to see how well it works.

10. In Task 3.8, students are expected to redesign the putt-putt boat. Some teams may want to create their own hull dies in a different shape. Curved shapes can be made with a hand coping saw.

Project 3.0

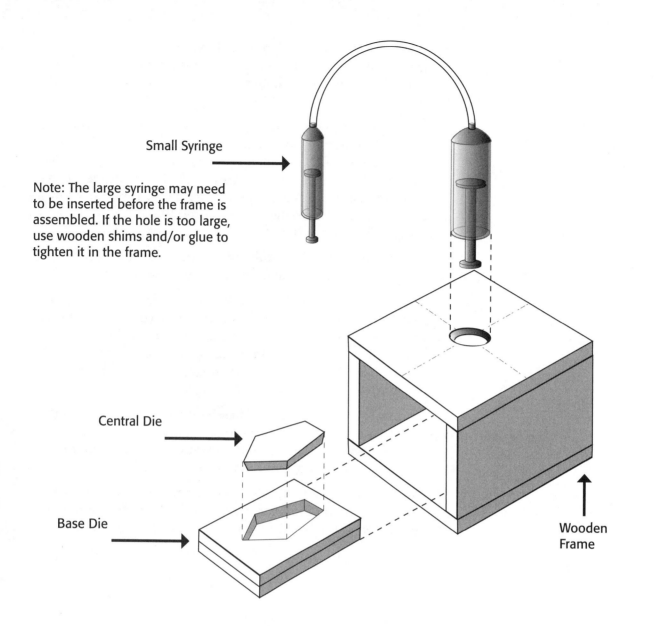

Small Syringe

Note: The large syringe may need to be inserted before the frame is assembled. If the hole is too large, use wooden shims and/or glue to tighten it in the frame.

Central Die

Base Die

Wooden Frame

Make the two-part die from two equal-sized pieces of wood. Use straight cuts to make the die out of one piece of wood. Save all pieces. Glue and nail all pieces except the central die to the second piece of wood to produce the base die. Bevel the edges of the boat-shaped central die.

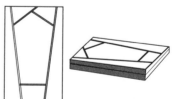

References and Resources

Deep Drawing Aluminum—Not as Hard as It Looks: http://www.thefabricator.com/Articles/Stamping_Exclusive.cfm?ID=37

Die Geometry for Embossing and Stretching: http://www.thefabricator.com/Articles/Stamping_Article.cfm?ID=683

Photos of Hand Presses at the Rattandeep Toy Factory in Delhi, India: http://www.buzzboats.com/rattandeep.htm

Task 3.1:	Putt-Putt Boats and Patents

Overview

Most students find this introduction to the putt-putt boat very engaging. They will start figuring out how it works as they go along. Encourage their interest and present the major challenge of Project 3.0: to redesign the putt-putt boat and write a patent application explaining their innovations.

Five Es

Engage students in thinking about how the putt-putt boat works; **Explore** ways that it might be modified.

Time Frame

2 class periods

Focus Questions

• What is a putt-putt boat and how does it work?
• Why are patents important and who can apply for them?

Objectives

Students will be able to:
• Use inquiry to begin to figure out how the boat works
• Identify the engineering challenge for Project 3.0
• Apply ways of thinking, learned through previous projects
• Identify the importance and requirements of patents
• Generate some initial ideas for a putt-putt boat redesign

Materials

For each student:
  1 *Engineer's Notebook*

For the class:
  1 putt-putt boat with candle, either one you build using the instructions in Task 3.1 (to familiarize yourself with them), or one that you purchase (http://buzzboats.com)
  1 test pan, basin, or channel, filled with water, for demonstrating the boat (Wallpaper trays, rain gutters, oval roaster pans, or large circular planter trays work well.)
  1 syringe
  1 long lighter or matches
  1 pair of safety glasses or goggles

Preparation

Review Slater Harrison's putt-putt boat site, http://www.sciencetoymaker.org/boat/index.htm, in advance. Notice that this site has detailed descriptions for boiler and boat hull making, explanations of propulsion, and theory of putt-putt boat operation. Then prepare a putt-putt boat demonstration for class. Before class begins, set up a boat in a tray or basin and make sure it is working.

Note: Don't forget to review your school's safety policies regarding use of tools, open flames, and adhesives in the classroom. Some schools require that teachers send home a note to parents about laboratory projects. Also, long hair should always be pulled back and away from any open flames.

1. **Demonstrate the operation of a putt-putt boat** in a basin or test channel. Model wearing protective goggles or glasses while lighting the candle. Have students gather around or approach in small groups to fully appreciate the sound effects and motion.

2. **Ask students what they saw and heard** and make a quick list of answers on the board (e.g., fire, smoke, sound, motion, wake).

3. **Ask students how they think it works,** and write these ideas on the board as well. *Do not explain how the putt-putt boat works at this early stage.* (If possible, write these ideas on butcher paper, which can remain on the wall throughout Project 3.0.) The students can return to the list as their ideas change.

4. **Introduce the challenge of Task 3.0**—to redesign the putt-putt boat and write a patent application detailing design improvements.

5. **Call attention to page 6,** which is there to remind students that they will be working in teams and using the engineering design process.

6. **Have students read page 7,** which describes the challenge in more detail.

7. **Point out Thomas Piot's patent application** on pages 8 and 9. Ask students to note the year of this first patent for a putt-putt boat (1891).

8. **Explain that patents have more than one purpose:**
   1. A patent protects the rights of an inventor to produce or license the invention for 20 years.
   2. A patent makes the details of new inventions public so that others can improve it.

You may want to provide more information about patents. For example, more than five million patents have been awarded since George Washington presented U. S. Patent No. 1 to Vermont resident Samuel Hopkins in 1790. Hopkins invented a new method of producing pot ash and pearl ash, which could be used for making lye, glass, and ceramic goods.

Preparation

2nd Class

1. **Have your students read the questions at the top of page 10** and complete the top of the page using the Think-Pair-Share method. — Demonstrate the putt-putt boat again so that they can answer the questions on their own. Have pairs of students share their ideas, then hold a brief all-class discussion about how the putt-putt boat works.— Add any additional ideas to the list on the board (or butcher paper) from the previous day.

2. **Ask students to write initial ideas at the bottom of page 10** about what they might do to improve the putt-putt boats.

3. **Conduct large-group brainstorming** for design improvement ideas. In addition to ideas that may be categorized as enhanced appearance (form) and performance (function), improvements may be proposed in product quality, purpose, method of manufacture, or materials. Mention these other categories to stimulate additional ideas.

4. **Ask students to look at the rubric on page 67,** which will be used to judge their patent applications at the end of the project. Tell them to write notes about any ideas or information they will need to learn more about in order to receive four stars in each category.

5. **Assure students that they will have opportunities to learn** much more about the scientific principles that govern the operation of the putt-putt boat before they write their patent applications.

6. **If there is time, have students read page 11,** the introduction to Task 3.2, and ask questions about building their first putt-putt boat.

7. **Assign homework.** Read Piot's 1891 patent and finish completing "Starting the Patent Process" on page 10.

Assessment

Resist all temptations to *tell* students how the putt-putt boat works. They will discover parts of the answer later, and you can gauge their progress by counting the number of key elements that they list in their answers when this same question is posed at beginning, middle, and end of the project.

Key elements, which may be expressed in various words, include:
* combustion (or burning)
* temperature difference
* conduction
* boiling/vaporization/steam production/phase change
* expansion
* pressure difference
* fluid and energy flow
* efficiency
* heat source/heat sink
* boiler metal flexing

- snap contraction (sound and motion)
- water pushed out of pipes
- speed of water through pipes
- resistance in pipes
- rocket effect (action and reaction)
- water flowing out of the boiler (jet flow)
- water flowing back into boiler (sink flow)
- water piston effect
- repeating cycle

Answers with 3–5 elements might be expected early in the project; scores tallied later on the same question can then be compared to show how much each student (and the class as a whole) has learned midway through the project and at the end.

Here is a sample answer of very good understanding (seven elements) at the first demonstration stage:

"The flame from the candle heats water in the boiler, converting to steam (water vapor). The steam expands, pushing water out of the straws. The water shooting out of the back of boat makes the boat go forward (movement). Cool water is drawn back into the boiler, and the cycle repeats.

Note each student's participation in discussions. Encourage quiet students to share their ideas in writing.

Background and Further Suggestions
Project 3.0 is more challenging than previous projects because it involves the full engineering design process, scientific inquiry, and several very important concepts about energy flow and the behavior of gases. The project also involves teamwork, innovation, manufacturing, fluid behavior, hydraulics, pneumatics, propulsion, heat engines, and resistance in pipes, as well as patents and marketing plans.

Thomas Piot's 1891 patent is just the first of several patents that have been granted for various innovations of putt-putt boats. You may want to look at the patents referenced at http://sciencetoymaker.org/boat/patents.html.

References and Resources

Fenn, John B., *Engines, Energy, and Entropy: A Thermodynamics Primer*, 1982, W.H. Freeman & Co., San Francisco.

Slater Harrison's putt-putt boat design is online at http://www.sciencetoymaker.com.

Patent information is available online at the U.S. Department of Commerce, Patent and Trademark Office, http://www.uspto.gov/.

Historical information on early U.S. patents may be found online at http://ias.okstate.edu/firstpatent.htm.

You will be able to find many more references if you use key word searches such as "pulsejet," "flash steamer," "pop-pop," "toc-toc," "putt-putt," "put-put," "steam pulse jet," "water pulse jet," "pulsating water engine," "heat engine," "Peter R. Payne," "hot-air-boats," "Rattandeep," "buzzboats," and "Miss England Steam Speed Boat."

Task 3.2:   Manufacture a Putt-Putt Boat

Overview

In this task, students work in pairs to fabricate a putt-putt boat. This task is intended for the students to 1) understand how the putt-putt boat is made, so that they are in a better position to figure out how it works; and 2) learn about manufacturing processes.

It takes care and attention to detail to make a boat that works. To increase the success rate, we have developed several quality-control steps. Call students' attention to these steps to increase the likelihood that their boats will function, and help them learn why quality control is important in manufacturing.

This task could take a week or longer for students to complete, and there are a couple of points at which you will want to leave the project overnight for the epoxy to set and silicone to dry. Consequently, we recommend that you move on to Task 3.3 during the waiting periods.

This task culminates when students test their putt-putt boats to see whether they work. You may want to allow some additional time for any students whose boats did not work at first to troubleshoot and see if they can salvage or repair them, or recycle some parts in a second attempt. However, it is not essential for the class that all boats function; students should not be penalized if their boats do not work.

Five Es

Engage students in a challenging building project; **Explore** the inside of the boat's boiler; **Explain** manufacturing methods; **Elaborate** on the value of quality control in manufacturing; **Evaluate** the result by testing the boat and observing performance factors.

Time Frame

5 class periods

Focus Questions

• What does it mean to manufacture an item to specifications?
• Why might variation from specifications be costly to a manufacturer?
• Why is quality control important?

Objectives

Students will be able to:
• Identify manufacturing equipment and processes
• Fabricate a boat from specifications
• Practice safe handling of materials and tools in a group setting
• Explain the value of quality control

Materials

For every two students:
  1 aluminum soda can or sheet of aluminum metal for boiler
  2 flex-bend straws
  1 length of tape, any kind
  2 pair of safety glasses or goggles
  2 pair polyvinyl gloves for gluing
  1 pencil
  1 marker
  1 piece of wax paper or cardboard for gluing palette
  4 toothpicks for glue application
  1 pre-washed juice or milk carton or substitute material for hull
    (plastic folder halves can substitute)
  1 ruler
  1 scissors
  1 stapler
  1 rubber band
  1 hull pattern from the *Engineer's Notebook*
  1 boiler pattern from the *Engineer's Notebook*
  1 putt-putt boat candle (tea light, birthday candles, etc.)

For every four students:
  1 utility knife
  1 pair leather gloves for cutting aluminum strips from cans
  1 package of 5-minute epoxy
  1 tube of silicone sealant
  1 small piece of fine sandpaper

For the class:
  1 container of label-recommended clean-up solvents for adhesives
    and sealants
  1 roll wax paper to protect shelf or cupboard where boats will be
    placed to dry
  1 test pan, basin, or channel, filled with water, for demonstrating
    the boat—wallpaper tray, rain gutter, or large circular planter tray
  1 small syringe for boiler priming
  1 long lighter or matches
  1 box of wet wipes for candle

Preparation

Have all materials available at the start. If you need milk cartons and aluminum cans, ask students to bring them in. Collect, rinse, and dry soda cans for boilers in advance or obtain aluminum sheets or shim stock. Either precut or leave for students to cut. For the boat hulls, teachers have also had success using plastic (polypropylene) folders instead of milk or juice containers. (Just make sure the folders can be creased, and do not tear.) Determine which adhesive/sealants students may use for their boiler fabrication and installation and have appropriate gloves and label-recommended clean-up solvents on hand.

Note that on the boat hull template (page 21), you can move the position of the hole outline for straw penetration (small center rectangle) toward the stern to accommodate wider boilers.

Follow these directions to make a putt-putt boat yourself:

1st–5th Classes

1. **Set safety rules for use of tools.** Utility knives can be dangerous. Make sure students are paying attention to the safety checks.

2. **Oversee and assist students** in measuring, cutting (separating), and clean up. You might mention the guidelines: "Measure twice, cut once, and wear gloves and safety goggles."

3. **Point out the steps with quality-control labels.** Warn students that extra care is required at those steps.

4. **Sign off.** There are places for students to ask for your approval before continuing. You should inspect and sign off on their work after they:
   1) Make their aluminum pocket for the boiler. You should make sure it is a reasonable size and that it looks as though there are no cracks or bending problems.
   2) Insert and seal the straws into the boiler, when cured and ready for leak testing. Look to see if the boiler has leaks along the edges. These can be fixed by blotting them dry and adding an overlay of epoxy or silicone. Any leaks on the end where the straws go into the boiler can be sealed at the same time the engine is mounted into the hull.
   3) Once a boiler is leak-free, make sure that there is no epoxy or silicone on the flat metal side of the boiler, which is where the flame will be applied. If there is, students must remove it by scraping very lightly, or using steel wool or sandpaper before proceeding. Failure to do so will produce noxious fumes, a clear safety hazard if boats are operated indoors.
   4) Have students test their completed boat.

TROUBLESHOOTING: If a boat doesn't function, even though it passed the previous leak test, check the following:
   1) Did students prime their boat properly? For the first attempt, have students prime their boiler twice. Be sure water comes out one straw when injected into the other. If it doesn't, one or both straws may be kinked where they penetrate the hull—or flattened, torn, melted, or plugged with epoxy inside the boiler. If possible, manipulate to open an obvious kink. To unblock a plugged pipe, straighten the straws at the bend and carefully insert a stiff wire such as coat hanger or even a paper clip. If necessary, remove one or both straws by pulling them out, and replace with new straw(s), using greater care and attention. In such cases, it may be easier to make a new boiler.

Engineering the Future Teacher Guide
©2008 Museum of Science, Boston

2) Try a "vacuum" test by gently inhaling through the ends of the straws and noting any air inflow. If any leak points are noted, apply a silicone patch and let dry 10–15 minutes. Inhale lightly again to draw some of the soft silicone into the repair. Then allow to dry fully.

3) Check for dented, flattened, or stress-cracked boilers. It might just be failed boiler metal (such light gauge aluminum does not tolerate much sanding or bending), in which case the student should build another boiler rather than patch.

4) Determine whether the heat source is sufficient, or if it has vibrated out of optimum position. Add a bit of toothpick as a wick to tea lights, or select candles of greater diameter than typical birthday size. Fix the fuel source in position with tape, silicone, wax, and so on. Also check whether the angle of the boiler is too small so that there is no room for the candle to burn, or too large so the heat bypasses the boiler.

5) See http://www.sciencetoymaker.org/boat/troubleShoot.htm for more on troubleshooting the boat.

While students are waiting for epoxy or silicone to set, you can start on Task 3.3.

5. **Assign homework.** Ask the students to read Chapter 17, "In Deep," in their textbooks and to answer the questions at the end of the chapter.

Discussion

Discuss the focus questions:
• What does it mean to manufacture an item to specifications?
• Why might variation from specifications be costly to a manufacturer?
• Why is quality control important?

Assessment

Ask students to write their answers to the benchmark questions on pages 25 and 26. Do not explain how the putt-putt boat works yet. Allow students more discovery time to apply the concepts they learn in Tasks 3.4 and 3.5 to the operation of the boat.

1) Identify at least one step in the boat construction that can be classified as the following manufacturing process:

- **Forming:** bending the boiler and boat hull into shape

- **Separating:** cutting the boiler and boat hull from their stock material

- **Conditioning:** sanding the metal so the adhesive sticks better

- **Assembling:** stapling the boat hull together

- **Finishing:** removing any extra epoxy that might have gotten onto the boat, or applying any decorative touches

2) What do you think causes the "putt-putt" sound of the boat? (It is the metal of the boiler flexing with pressure changes, moving together and apart.)

3) Write your explanation of how you think the boat works. Draw pictures and label parts if it helps you explain your ideas. You will be able to reflect back on your initial understanding later, so don't worry about being "correct" in your explanation. (Check the list of key elements in the assessment section for Task 3.1.)

Background and Further Suggestions

The design for a putt-putt boat in Task 3.2 is adapted from a design by Slater Harrison, published on his web site at http://sciencetoymaker.org/boat/. We are grateful to him for giving us permission to use the design. He invites teachers to access his web site to learn more about putt-putt boats and other educational toys.

You may want to access photos of hand presses at the Rattandeep toy factory in Delhi, India, so that your students can compare the manufacturing processes used there with the process that they use to produce their putt-putt boats. The images are available online at http://www.buzzboats.com/rattandeep.htm.

Engineering the Future Teacher Guide
©2008 Museum of Science, Boston

Task 3.3:   Investigate Fluid Systems

Overview

Many technologies are based on fluid systems. These include pneumatic systems, in which a gas is the working fluid, and hydraulic systems, in which a liquid is the working fluid. The putt-putt boat is an example of a special kind of fluid system, called an engine, in which thermal energy drives differences in pressure, which in turn produces mechanical motion.

Task 3.3 introduces students to a subset of these concepts by having them explore the properties of air and water in sealed syringes. Through these activities the students learn about the concept of pressure and how changing the pressure of gases and liquids makes it possible to transfer energy from one place to another. They also learn how pneumatic and hydraulic systems differ.

In the next task, students will apply these concepts to choose between pneumatics and hydraulics for a machine press to make boat hulls. Instructions for making a press and die out of wood are included in the "Preparing to Teach Project 3.0" section at the beginning of this project.

Five Es

Engage students in the interesting behaviors of fluids; **Explore** the differences between how gases and liquids behave; **Explain** the gas laws.

Time Frame

2–3 class periods

Focus Questions

- How do air and water behave differently when pressure is increased?
- How can energy be transferred through hydraulic and pneumatic systems?

Objectives

Students will be able to:
- Differentiate between hydraulic and pneumatic fluid systems
- Predict how fluids will behave when subjected to changing pressures

Materials

For every two students:
1 large syringe
1 small syringe
2 twist-lock end caps
1 set of colored pencils or markers (red, orange, yellow, green, and blue)
1 cup of water

1. **Review the homework.** Emphasize questions related to how energy is transmitted through fluids (driven by differences in pressure), as well as open and closed hydraulic systems.

2. **Open and closed fluid systems.** Ask students to read the top of page 27. Ask them if they can think of any other closed fluid systems. (The brake system in a car, forced hot water heating systems, and refrigerators all work with closed fluid systems. Inflatable systems like tires and blimps are also closed fluid systems, although the fluid in them does not circulate.)

3. **Have students read the bottom part of page 27**, which introduces the terms "pneumatic" and "hydraulic." Where have you heard the term "hydra"? (A hydra is a small fresh-water animal, and also a water beast in Greek mythology. The word "dehydrate" means to remove water; "hydrate" means to fill with water.) Where have you heard the term "pneum"? (Pneumonia is an infection of the lungs. The word "pneuma" is the Greek word for wind or breath.)

4. **Explore liquids and gases in syringes.** Distribute syringes, caps, cups of water, and paper towels. Allow 15–20 minutes for students to work in pairs and do the activities at the top of page 28. This is a good time for open exploration. Encourage them to experiment with pushing and pulling on the piston of the syringe with different amounts of air and water in the syringe. Students should record their observations at the top of page 28.

5. **Ask students to read the rest of page 28,** where the *Engineer's Notebook* defines "pressure" as "how hard the fluid pushes on the walls of its container." The informal descriptive term "squeezedness" indicates that it's possible to increase the pressure on a fluid by squeezing it.

6. **Introduce color coding to visualize differences in pressure.** Because it's not possible to see differences in pressure, color coding can be used to help visualize those differences. Ask your students to read page 29 and to color in the circles in the key at the top of the page. After filling a syringe with air, they should do the suggested activities so that they can feel the pressure changes while filling in the colors.

7. **Air is compressible.** Observe students while they complete this activity. They will notice that air can act as a spring; the piston moves back after it is pushed in and released.

8. **Differences drive change.** Students are asked to explain why the piston is pushed back to its starting point after it's released, using the phrase "differences drives change." Following is one possible good answer to the question: "Pushing in the piston increases

the pressure inside the syringe. When the piston is released, the *difference in pressure* from higher inside to lower (ambient) outside of the syringe *drives a change* in the position of the piston." (Note: Some students might be curious why the piston doesn't always return to its initial position for the air-filled syringe. The answer is that it loses some energy due to the friction of the piston rubbing against the syringe body, and there is a small change in temperature that occurs when gases are compressed or expanded.)

9. **Ask your students to read page 30,** and to color code the illustrations of the syringes at the bottom of the page. For liquid it's more conceptually difficult, because there is no visible or tactile change in a liquid at higher pressure (more "squeezedness"). Still, the pressure does increase when squeezed.

2nd–3rd Classes

1. **Explain how pressure "differences drives change"** for the air trapped in a syringe. Squeezing the gas increases its pressure above the "normal" air pressure. This difference in pressure will cause the piston to be pushed back out when the gas is allowed to "unsqueeze," and will stop when the difference disappears. Similarly, decreasing the pressure of the gas in the syringe below "normal" air pressure by pulling the piston out means the difference in pressure will cause the piston to be pushed back in by the higher atmospheric pressure when released.

2. **Compare the properties of liquids and gases.** Have students read page 31. You may want to lead a class discussion and fill in the chart as a class. Following are the best answers:

Answer Key

	Liquid	Gas
Name of system that uses this fluid	hydraulic	pneumatic
Mass of trapped fluid	constant	constant
Volume of fluid	constant	variable (fills container)
Density	constant	variable
Energy can be stored in fluid	no	yes

3. **Assign homework.** Have students read Chapter 18, "Shooting for the Moon," in the textbook, in which astronautical engineer Aprille Ericsson uses the properties of fluids to design rockets. Tell them to answer the questions at the end of the chapter and to bring their answers to class the next day.

Assessment
Ask students to fill out the Benchmark Questions on page 32.

1) A car has tires filled with air at up to 60 pounds per square inch (lb./in.^{2}). What characteristic of pneumatic systems makes air a good choice when considering ride comfort in a car? (Whenever the car hits a bump, the air will absorb the shock by compressing.) What would it feel like to ride in a car that had liquid-filled tires? Why? (Very bumpy! The volume of liquid-filled tires is constant. The fluid would not help absorb the shock.)

2) Explain what happens when a 4×4 vehicle drives over a big rock in terms of the pressure inside and outside the tire. (As the tire is pushed in by the big rock, the air in the tire is compressed and the pressure increases. Because it can be compressed, the air absorbs energy that would otherwise have been transferred to the car, so the road feels less bumpy. After moving past the rock, this energy is released as the tire is pushed back into shape by the internal-external pressure difference.)

3) Is the putt-putt boat a hydraulic system, a pneumatic system, or both? Explain. (Both: When the water in the boiler turns to vapor or steam, it becomes a gas. The gas pushes out a "piston" of water.)

4) When transferring energy with a syringe, you pushed on the piston. How is energy transferred to the putt-putt boat to get it moving forward? (The energy comes from the candle flame in the form of thermal energy. The thermal energy heats the fluid in the boiler, creating pressure that produces motion.)

Background and Further Suggestions

Some students might not realize that air is a gas that can be confined and transported, and that a confined gas has a definite mass. This may be due to the fact that we can't see air, nor do we normally think about "feeling" air, because it is all around us (similar to a fish constantly surrounded by water). The syringes can help students realize that a gas will expand to fill its container all by itself, and can be squeezed smaller by compressing its container, all without changing the mass of the confined gas. So a confined gas has definite mass, variable volume, and thus variable density. The energy associated with a gas increases when it is compressed, and also when it is heated. These properties make gases useful for storing and moving energy.

Liquids are incompressible; when your students push in on a piston filled with water and closed with a cap, they'll see that it's not possible to push it in very far. When they pull back on a closed syringe filled with water, they will notice that it's more difficult to pull back than a syringe filled with air. However, they may be puzzled to see that—especially with a small syringe—if they pull hard, they can pull the piston back and that a bubble, or a pocket of air, forms inside the syringe. As they pull the piston back farther, the air space gets bigger; when they release the piston, it disappears. You can ask your students what they think is in the air space, where it comes from, and where it goes when it disappears. (As the pressure on the water is reduced, dissolved air comes out of solution, forming bubbles, joining together into an air pocket at the top. As the piston is pulled back farther, the air expands. When the piston is released, the pressure returns to normal and the gas dissolves again. This is similar to carbonated beverages—when the pressure is released, gas comes out of solution.)

A note about color coding. The goal of color coding is not to get students to figure out the colors on their own, but rather to help them visualize pressure differences and how those differences drive change. You can explain to students that the colors are just a way of picturing above- and below-normal pressures. The colors do not represent pressure measurements, but rather an indication of which container of fluid is at a higher or lower pressure compared with other containers of fluid.

Color coding can also help students avoid a common problem, which is to ignore the pressure of the fluid surrounding the system in question. Coloring the air in the room yellow makes this otherwise "invisible" variable visible.

References and Resources

President and Fellows of Harvard College, 2003, Causal Patterns in Air Pressure Phenomena, Understandings of Consequence Project. www.pz.harvard.edu.

Ferguson, Joe L., 1978, "November: The Many Uses of Disposable Plastic Hypodermic Syringes—A Shot in the Arm for Small Equipment Budgets," *Am Journal of Physics*, Vol. 46, No. 11.

Boohan, Richard, and Jon Ogborn, 1996, "Energy and Change, Introducing a New Approach," A Project Sponsored by the Nuffield Foundation, University of London Institute of Education.

Project 3.0

Task 3.4:   Develop a Manufacturing Press

Overview

Students start by exploring a simple closed fluid system—two syringes connected by tubing, and filled with air or water. They find that if the syringes are different sizes, a force applied to the small syringe is amplified when transferred to the large syringe. That is the force amplification principle behind a huge number of hydraulic devices in use today.

Next the students explore the use of one-way valves in a closed pneumatic system, creating an air pump to blow up a balloon. Putting the idea of a hydraulic system and a multiple stroke pump together, students figure out how a hydraulic lift can raise a car into the air. Students apply these ideas to designing a press for manufacturing toy boat hulls.

Although these activities focus on pneumatic and hydraulic machines, the principles students learn will help them figure out how the putt-putt boat engine works in later tasks.

Five Es

Elaborate on their understanding of the differences between gases and liquids; **Explore** pneumatic and hydraulic systems and construction of a simple machine press and pneumatic pump; **Explain** how a hydraulic lift can raise a car into the air; **Evaluate** the pros and cons of hydraulics and pneumatics to build a manufacturing press for toy boat hulls.

Time Frame

3 class periods

Focus Question

• How are pneumatic and hydraulic systems used to make things move?

Objectives

Students will be able to:
   • Simulate manufacturing systems used to transmit and amplify forces
   • Identify parts of an open and closed fluid system
   • Compare advantages of pneumatics and hydraulics in manufacturing

Materials

For each group of four students, prepare a "kit" that includes:
   3 10cc syringes
   3 30cc syringes (optional)
   3 50cc syringes
   2 female quick-turn (luer) syringe caps
   6 female quick-turn (luer) 1/8" twist-lock fittings
   1 1/8" × 1/8" × 1/8" barbed tee, clear polycarbonate
   2 1/8" × 1/8" barbed check (one-way) valve, silicone/polycarbonate
   1 balloon
   1 plastic cup of water
   3–4 short length of tubing
   3 various lengths of 1/4" I.D. tubing

For the class:

    1–8 hydraulic presses, as described previously in "Preparing to Teach Project 3.0" (This activity is optional but strongly encouraged; the hydraulic press adds context and relevance to these introductory syringe activities.)

    12 6"× 6"(approximate) sheets of sturdy aluminum foil, like that used in disposable aluminum pie pans

Preparation

Be sure to work though all of the activities in Task 3.4 on your own before class, so that you can anticipate problems that students might encounter, and be ready to answer their questions. Try to find a bicycle pump to demonstrate.

1st Class

1. **Discuss homework.** Emphasize the idea that understanding how fluids work is essential for understanding and designing systems from cars to spacecraft.

2. **Ask students to read page 33.** Tell them that the work they did in Task 3.3 has prepared them to work with pneumatic and hydraulic systems that make use of fluids to do real work.

3. **Organize the class into groups of four students.** Hand out syringes and fittings to the groups, and ask them to check to be sure that they have the materials they need to make the combinations of syringes and tubes shown at the bottom of page 33. (The students do not have to make all systems at once; they can use a syringe in one system, then disconnect it to use in another system. This exercise promotes reading directions and asking questions first, though it can be time-consuming.)

4. **Have your students read and do the activities on page 34,** then record the results. They will find that for equal-sized syringes, the pistons are equally easy to push; but for systems that include syringes of different sizes, the smaller-diameter piston is easier to push.

5. **Discuss the results of the activities on page 34.** Make sure that students have all recorded the results of experiments in which syringes are the same size and very different in size. (Although it is nice to have students work with a diversity of materials, they may conduct the activities with only two syringe sizes.)

6. **Question 2 at the bottom of page 34** asks students to draw a conclusion. Students should observe that although the smaller syringe is easier to push, you have to push it farther to get a resultant movement of the piston in the larger syringe. Point this out if students do not observe it. They may also notice some delay in the movement of the other syringe due to the compressibility of air.

7. **Have students read about Boyle's Law at the top of page 35,** and then do the calculation on the bottom half of the page. The numbers have been kept as simple as possible. Invite students to work together in pairs if you wish. The calculations are as follows:

Step 1: $P_1V_1 = P_2V_2$ *or* $P_2V_2 = P_1V_1$

Step 2: $\dfrac{P_2V_2}{V_2} = \dfrac{P_1V_1}{V_2}$

Step 3: $P_2 = \dfrac{P_1V_1}{V_2} = \dfrac{14.7\ psi \times 10\ ml}{5\ ml} = 29.4\ psi$

When your students have finished, ask them, "Is your result a reasonable number?" (Most students will probably say "yes.") Tell them that being able to make such calculations is very important for engineers. They need to know whether a system they design can take the pressure it will experience. Collect the kits.

2nd Class

Build a Pneumatic Pump

1. **Pass out the syringe kits** to groups of four students, and ask them to read pages 36 and 37, which tell them how to build a pneumatic pump. Once they assemble the pump, they should test it by blowing up a balloon. (Depending on the parts used, it is possible to build a pneumatic pump with only three lengths of tubing.)

2. **Ask students to answer questions 2–6.** They should work together to discuss the questions, but each student should answer the questions in his or her *Engineer's Notebook*. Help groups as needed. Answers will vary, but following are some you may expect to find:

Answer Key

   2) What did you find out and what can you conclude about how the size of the piston affects the operation of the pump? (If all connections are air-tight, a larger piston should require fewer strokes to inflate the balloon.)
   3) In your own words, explain how the pump works. (When the piston is pushed in, air cannot escape out of the top one-way valve, so the only way it can go is into the balloon. When the piston is pulled back, air cannot come out of the balloon due to the one-way valve, but air can come in from the top valve.)
   4) Show how the pressure changes in the pneumatic pump by coloring the syringe, tubing, and balloon to show the air pressure while you are pushing the piston into the syringe (top), and when you are pulling it back out (bottom). (With the piston pushed in, the interior of the syringe, tubes, and balloon should all be colored orange or red. With the piston pulled out, the interior of the piston and tubes should be colored green or blue, and the balloon should be the same color red or orange as in the previous drawing.)

5) What can you do to release the stored energy and turn it back into mechanical energy? (Remove the balloon from the pump and let the air escape. The balloon will shoot forward as the air escapes.)

6) List some examples you can think of in the everyday world where a difference in pressure drives the flow of energy. (Real-world examples in which a difference in pressure drives the flow of energy include car engines, rocket engines, drinking from a straw, vacuum cleaner, hot air balloons, and so on.)

3. **How does a bicycle pump work?** If you have a bicycle pump, or even a picture of one, show it to your students and ask them how it works. (As the handle on the bicycle pump moves in and out, the volume and thus the pressure of the air in the pump goes above and below normal air pressure. There is a one-way valve in the pump itself, which allows air in, and a one-way valve in the bicycle tire where the pump is connected. As the pressure in the tire increases above atmospheric pressure, it is considered inflated, and cannot deflate due to the valve.)

4. **Introduce hydraulic systems.** Have students read page 38 and do the experiments involving hydraulic systems. Give each team a cup of water and paper towels to use in addition to their syringe kit. This activity is like the one on page 34, except that it is using a hydraulic system rather than a pneumatic system. (Note: Some teachers have found it helpful to admonish students not to use the syringes as squirt guns, and to wipe up any spills immediately!)

5. **Assign homework.** Ask students to read Chapter 19, "Fuel from the Fields," concerning the use of fuels made from used vegetable oil, and to answer the questions at the end.

3rd Class

1. **Discuss homework.** Specifically, ask students to explain how changes in pressure, temperature, and volume show how chemical energy from vegetable oil, such as the oil french fries are cooked in, can be used to power a car.

2. **Discuss the answers to the questions on page 38.**

Answer Key

2) If the syringes are the same size, they are equally easy to push. If they differ in size, the smaller one is easier to push, but it has to be pushed a longer distance relative to the large syringe.

3) Hydraulic systems are better for transferring energy immediately. As soon as you push on one piston, the other starts to move.

3. **Have students read page 39 on Pascal's Law,** and work on the problem at the bottom of the page. Help groups as needed, or spend 15 minutes working through an example for the entire class. Keep in mind that many students have difficulty understanding and working with ratios. The most important thing that students should remember is that, in a two-piston system, the ratio of forces needed to push the pistons to get them to move is equal to the ratio of the surface areas of the two pistons, which is the ratio of the squares of their radii. Here's an example of such a calculation:

Example

Suppose the radius of the large piston is 1.00" and the radius of the small piston is one-quarter that, 0.25". If you exert a force of 5 pounds on the small piston to move the water into the larger syringe, how much force will the large piston exert?

$$\frac{F_{large}}{F_{small}} = \frac{A_{large}}{A_{small}}$$

$$\frac{x\ lb.}{5\ lb.} = \frac{A_{large}}{A_{small}}$$

$$x\ lb. = \frac{A_{large}}{A_{small}} \times 5\ lb. = \frac{\pi(r_{large})^2}{\pi(r_{small})^2} \times 5\ lb.$$

$$x\ lb. = \frac{\pi(1\ in.)^2}{\pi(0.25\ in.)^2} \times 5\ lb. = \frac{1\ \pi\ in.^2}{0.0625\ \pi\ in.^2} \times 5\ lb. = 16 \times 5\ lb. = 80\ lb.$$

Answer: The large piston will exert 80 lb. of force (16x amplification). Also, you will need 80 lb. of force to return it to its original position.

Assessment

This task demonstrates the very important idea that, in a hydraulic system with two different-sized syringes, pushing in the smaller piston greatly amplifies the force. The amount of amplification is proportional to the ratio of the surface areas of the two syringe pistons. If the radius of one piston is ten times that of the other, the force can be amplified 100 times! That is how hydraulic machines make it possible for a person to lift an object many times his or her weight.

4. **Have students read page 40.** Tell them to spend some time on their own figuring out how the hydraulic lift at the bottom of the page works. Then have them talk with each other to discuss their ideas. Following are answers to the questions:

Step 1: When you push down on the pump, liquid (usually oil) is pushed through one-way valve 2 into the lift cylinder. It does not go into the fluid tank because of one-way valve 1.

Engineering the Future Teacher Guide
©2008 Museum of Science, Boston

Step 2: When you pull up on the pump, more liquid is drawn into the small cylinder through one-way valve 1. It does not come back out of the lift cylinder because of one-way valve 2.

Step 3: When you close valves one and two and open one-way valve 3, the fluid will drain out of the lift cylinder and go back into the fluid tank.

5. **Describe the pros and cons of pneumatic and hydraulic systems.** You may want to share the following information with your students (not in their *Engineer's Notebook*):

Pneumatics Pros
- Air is free and abundant.
- Air is easily compressed and can be stored in tanks.
- Pneumatic systems can be built easily with moderate pressure hoses, pipes, or tubing.
- Pneumatic systems can produce large linear movement.
- Air can be returned to the atmosphere; a return line is not needed.
- Compressed air is relatively environmentally friendly.

Pneumatics Cons
- Compressed air systems must be kept clean and dry.
- Using air at high pressure requires safety precautions.
- Pneumatic systems sometimes atomize small amounts of lubricating oil into the air.
- Pneumatics cannot produce as high a force as hydraulics.

Hydraulics Pros
- Hydraulics are usually simpler in design.
- Most hydraulics are closed systems, so there is no fluid exhaust.
- Flexible pipes and hoses virtually eliminate location problems.
- Hydraulic systems are smooth and quiet in operation.
- Vibration is minimized.
- Control of a wide range of speed and forces is possible.
- High efficiency occurs with minimum friction loss.
- Automatic valves guard against a breakdown from overloading.

Hydraulics Cons
- It's hard to maintain precision parts against rust, corrosion, dirt, and oil.
- Hydraulic liquids and high-pressure hoses are expensive.
- Hydraulic fluids (usually oils) can be hazardous to one's health in the event of leakage.

6. **Design a Hull Press.** Ask students to read the challenge on page 41, in which they must choose and justify use of either a pneumatic or hydraulic press system for manufacturing boat hulls. If you have built a wooden press frame, let students try it out with a pneumatic and hydraulic syringe system to see which performs better. Allow time for students to discuss this in teams, and then have the class

vote on which is better. If there is a difference of opinion, encourage students to debate the issue further, then try out the press frame configured with both systems to see which is better.

(Either answer is acceptable if it is justified. Some possible explanations: A hydraulic system would allow forces to be amplified many times, but a pneumatic system could be used if the force required is not too great. A pneumatic system could provide automatic piston repositioning for manufacturing efficiency. Hose breaks with hydraulics present more clean up.)

ERROR: The design challenge title "Design a Brake Press" on page 41 is an error. The challenge title should be "Design a Machine Press," and the word "fluid" should be substituted for "brake" in two places in the first paragraph, and again in the last paragraph. In addition, references to "die and mold" in the text and diagram should be replaced with "two-part die."

7. **Assign homework.** Ask students to read Chapter 20, "An Ingenious Engine," and to answer the questions at the end of the chapter.

Assessment

Benchmark Questions, Page 42

1) Which type of system do you think robotic arms use—pneumatic or hydraulic? Why? (Both types of systems are used commercially. Pneumatic systems are generally used for quick, light movements. Hydraulic arms are used for heavy lifting and precise positioning.)

2) Which of the listed systems are open and which are closed? (Pneumatic systems: bicycle pump [open], hot-air balloon [open], auto tire [closed]. Hydraulic Systems: city water system [open], human circulatory system [closed], auto brake system [closed].)

3) How does stepping on the brake pedal cause the brake shoes to push outward? (The brake pedal is connected to the piston, which pushes a liquid called brake fluid through high-pressure tubes to all four brake drums. This causes the brake shoe to press against the brake pad.)

4) What would happen if bubbles were not eliminated from brake lines? (The bubbles would compress, absorbing input energy, so braking would be slow and "soft.")

Background and Further Suggestions
Pneumatic and hydraulic systems are used to accomplish many tasks that people could not do alone. Also, the die-forming process, used with or without a hydraulic press, is very widely used in the industry. An excellent extension of Task 3.4 is for students to conduct research on the web to find as many different pneumatic and hydraulic devices as they can, and to look for explanations of why one system is used for a given application rather than another.

Engineering the Future Teacher Guide
©2008 Museum of Science, Boston

Manufacturing Points About the Harrison "Brake-Formed" Cardboard Hull vs. the Press-Formed Aluminum Hull

Brake-forming involves more steps (and labor) than die-pressing, but the capital costs of equipment are lower.

- The brake-formed material could be die-cut rather than hand-cut.
- There is more design flexibility (to change hull shape) in brake forming; in die-pressing, new dies and molds (expensive and time-consuming to develop) would be required for design changes.
- Brake forming as directed may provide less consistency between hulls because more steps involve the use of hand tools.

Optimum choice of hull type and manufacturing methods could be different for different improvement objectives.

Redesigning boat hulls (especially for students who finish early). Before continuing on to the next task, which discusses how engines work, all students should have completed their prototype boat from Task 3.2, and the syringe activities in Tasks 3.3–3.4.

Students can be challenged to redesign their boat hull, using sheets of scrap paper, scissors, and staples/tape. They can make many potential hulls quickly and choose one hull from which to make a pattern. Students might try to keep the hull intact from their model and draw a matching pattern on separate paper, or open up the hull, trace the outline, and draw lines over each fold. Students can then photocopy the pattern, try it out, and give copies to other students to see if they can construct it correctly. Modifications might be necessary at that point, and the cycle can repeat. Once a pattern is successful, students can test it with the final hull material (which might require further adaptation for the thicker juice carton material).

Boyle's Law is not linear. Boyle's law relates the pressure and volume of a sealed amount of ideal gas with this equation:

$$P_1 V_1 = P_2 V_2$$

It is obvious that decreasing the volume by half causes the pressure to double. But less obvious is that decreasing the volume to only 1/3 the original causes the pressure to triple, and 1/6 the volume has six times the pressure. If the pressure were to be plotted against the volume, the curve formed would not be a straight line, but a curved line. Below is a simple graph of the relationship between pressure and volume according to Boyle's Law. You can share this graph with advanced students, or to further emphasize math you can also plug in numbers to make it quantitative.

Boyle's Law

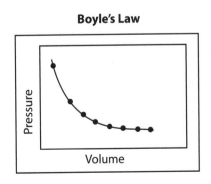

References and Resources

An online explanation of the processes and considerations for tolerances and other factors in forging metal is here: http://www.efunda.com/processes/metal_processing/forging.cfm.

Information on hydraulic machines of all sorts is available at http://science.howstuffworks.com/hydraulic.htm.

Holmes, Phil, and Dennis Marshall, "Move it Further with Air or Water," Technology Teaching Systems, Ltd., 1991.

Information, explanations, and examples of how water towers, hydropower plants, water blasters, and hydraulic systems and machinery work is available online at http://science.howstuffworks.com.

Pneumatic systems are explained at http://www.tpub.com/basae/83.htm.

A PowerPoint presentation on basic pneumatics can be downloaded at http://www.ite.edu.sg/%7Ebmsdc/eTraining/re120_ppt.htm.

University of South Florida & Robotics Educational Foundation's Team DaVinci's understanding of pneumatics as applied to BattleBot competitions is presented at http://www.teamdavinci.com/understanding_pneumatics.htm.

How paintball guns (pneumatic) work is explained at http://entertainment.howstuffworks.com/paintball.htm.

Nail guns are explained at http://home.howstuffworks.com/nail-gun.htm.

Lego Dacta's *Pneumatics Guide* (1997), which lists pneumatic system advantages, is online at http://www.eng.iastate.edu/twt/Courses/Undergrad/packet/info/pneumaticsinfo.htm.

An article on how a brake press reduced manufacturing time for a boat hull is available online at http://www.manufacturingtalk.com/news/pai/pai105.html.

Task 3.5:	Investigate Heat Engines

Overview

In Task 3.5, students learn more about how their putt-putt boat engine functions. It begins with a demonstration of a model engine. The reaction chamber is a syringe with nail polish remover (which is mostly acetone) sealed inside. Students visualize the changes in pressure inside the syringe by color coding.

Next, students learn about the gas law and apply what they learn to another kind of engine—a "drinking bird." Students learn that these two devices are "heat engines" because they are driven by differences in temperature, and that no heat engine can be 100% efficient.

Students learn about one more engine—the internal combustion engine commonly used in cars, motorcycles, boats, and lawn mowers. Finally, they apply heat-engine concepts to analyze the changes in pressure occurring in the putt-putt boat engine.

Five Es

Engage students with the interesting behavior of an "acetone engine" and a "drinking bird"; **Explore** the similarities among several heat engines; **Explain** the functions of a heat engine in general terms; **Elaborate** on these concepts by applying these ideas to their putt-putt boat engines.

Time Frame

2 class periods

Focus Questions

- What is a heat engine?
- What is an engine cycle?
- What are the pressure changes that take place in the putt-putt boat?

Objectives

Students will be able to:
- Describe the stages of an engine cycle
- Identify the importance of the relationship between temperature, volume, and pressure in a heat engine

Materials

10 ml nail polish remover (mostly acetone)
1 large syringe (50 ml) with syringe cap
1 squeeze clamp, tongs, or clothes pin to hold hot syringe
1 hot plate or immersion heater
2 beakers of water
1 cup of ice
1 drinking bird device
1 pair safety glasses or goggles

Preparation

Try out the acetone engine, as described in the guidelines for the first class, and set up at least one functioning "drinking bird." Place these where all students can easily see them.

Color the piston for the acetone engine with a marker or piece of colored paper so students can see it move easily.

If you have an extra drinking bird, remove the hat and fuzzy material so students can see what is inside its head.

1. **Discuss the homework.** Ask students for their answers to the questions after Chapter 20. Emphasize energy transfer, especially the idea that an engine must have a temperature difference to work.

2. **Introduce Task 3.5** by telling students that they will now learn about systems that combine heat and pressure to help them better understand how the putt-putt engine works.

3. **Demonstrate the acetone engine.**
   1) Boil water in a beaker using an immersion heater or hotplate.
   2) Wearing eye protection, draw about 10 ml of nail polish remover (mostly acetone) into the syringe so it is about 20% full. Tell your students that acetone evaporates very quickly.
   3) Turn the syringe nozzle up and push out any bubbles.
   4) Screw on a cap to close the syringe with the acetone inside.
   5) Turn the syringe nozzle down and grip it with tongs or a clothes pin.
   6) Call students' attention as you immerse the syringe in the hot water. Watch as the piston starts to rise.
   7) Ask students: "What is happening? Why?" (The acetone is evaporating. The gas expands and pushes the piston up.)
   8) When the piston has been pushed most of the way out of the syringe, remove the syringe from the hot water and place it into cold/ice water. The piston will start to move down.
   9) Ask the students, "What is happening? Why?" (The acetone is condensing, turning back into a liquid. The gas contracts and the higher outside atmospheric pressure pushes the piston back in.)

4. **Color code changes in temperature and pressure.** Ask students to read pages 43 and 44, which introduce Task 3.5, and ask students to color code the acetone engine. When your students get to page 44, tell them to first color code the temperature changes, then the pressure changes. They should use the same set of colors from high (red) to low (blue) for temperature and pressure. Encourage students to work together but to color their own *Engineer's Notebooks*. Circulate around the room, helping as needed.

Temperature colors:
1) syringe at room temperature (water red, everything else yellow)
2) syringe in hot water, piston moving out (water red, acetone orange)
3) syringe in hot water, piston out all the way (water red, acetone red)
4) syringe in ice water, piston just begins to move (ice water blue, acetone red)
5) syringe in ice water, piston moving in (ice water blue, acetone green)
6) syringe in ice water, piston all the way in (ice water and acetone blue)

Pressure colors:
1) syringe at room temperature (air yellow, acetone yellow)
2) syringe in hot water, piston moving out (acetone orange)
3) syringe in hot water, piston out all the way (acetone red)
4) syringe in ice water, piston just begins to move (acetone red)
5) syringe in ice water, piston moving in (acetone orange or yellow)
6) syringe in ice water, piston all the way in (acetone green or blue)

5. **Lead a discussion** and encourage participation about the colors the students chose. It is more important that students think about what happens to the pressure as the temperature changes than it is that they get the right answer.

6. **What's a heat engine?** Ask students to read page 45, and to write their answers to questions 2–4. Allow the students to discuss their answers. When everyone has finished reading and writing, lead a brief discussion about heat engines. Emphasize that a heat engine uses the difference between two temperatures to produce mechanical motion. Heat engines usually have cycles.

7. **Discuss the gas laws.** One way to do this is to show how the gas law reduces to three special laws under certain conditions, from the combined gas law:

$$\frac{P_1 V_1}{T_1} = \frac{P_2 V_2}{T_2}$$

a. If $T_1 = T_2$, the equation becomes:	$P_1 V_1 = P_2 V_2$	Boyle's Law
b. If $P_1 = P_2$, the equation becomes:	$\dfrac{V_1}{T_1} = \dfrac{V_2}{T_2}$	Charles' Law
c. If $V_1 = V_2$, the equation becomes:	$\dfrac{P_1}{T_1} = \dfrac{P_2}{T_2}$	Gay-Lussac's Law*

Project 3.0

Encourage your students to express these mathematical statements in English, such as "If the temperature is equal, then the pressure times the volume before a change equals the pressure times the volume after the change."

*Please note that there is a misprint on page 45. Gay-Lussac's Law is incorrectly labeled as Guy-Lussac's Law.

8. **Demonstrate the drinking bird.** Set up a "drinking bird" device so that it continues to "drink" automatically. You may need to adjust the pivot point and the height of the bird relative to the water container. Start by getting the fuzzy material on the head wet. Ask students to observe closely and tell you what they see. They may notice that the level of the internal fluid slowly moves up toward the head. As it does, the bird lowers its head to "drink." When the bird finally dips its bill into the water, the internal liquid flows back into the reservoir at the bottom. As it does, the bird pops upward again. Then the cycle begins again.

9. **Ask your students to write their ideas.** If you have a second device that has the fuzzy material removed from the head, pass it around the room so that students can see what is inside the head. Ask students to write their ideas on page 46 of their *Engineer's Notebook*. Allow 5–10 minutes for students to do this.

10. **Encourage students to share their ideas** about how the "drinking bird" works. Fill in gaps in their understanding as follows:

   1) The drinking bird consists of two chambers: a head and body connected by a tube. Most of the air inside is removed and is filled with methylene chloride, a fluid that evaporates easily. At room temperature, the open space inside is filled with methylene chloride vapor.
   2) Start the action by wetting the beak. When the fuzzy beak is wet, the water evaporates, cooling the head and condensing the methylene chloride vapor. That reduces the pressure in the head.
   3) When the pressure in the body becomes greater than the pressure in the head, it pushes down on the liquid, forcing it up the tube. As the liquid moves up the tube and into the head, the drinking bird becomes top heavy and tips over, wetting the beak again and spilling the liquid.
   4) When the liquid spills, the head and body chambers become connected and the pressure equalizes. As the liquid flows into the body, the bird bobs upright again.
   5) Water from the beak evaporates, so the head again becomes cooler than the body, and the cycle repeats. As long as there is a sufficient difference in temperature between the body and the head, the drinking bird will continue to function.

11. **Ask students to answer question 2** at the bottom of page 46, allowing them to work with partners, then to share their ideas with the class. (This question is challenging because there are two closed gas pockets in state 1, which combine in state 2. Consider just the volume of gas in the head. During state 1, when the bird is upright, the beak is wet and the gas inside has cooled, so T_1 and P_1 are lower than T_2 and P_2. With a reduction in pressure, the liquid rises in the tube, which reduces the volume in the head, so V_1 is greater than V_2, until the bird tips over so far that the two air pockets become one. —Similar comments can be made about the gas pocket in the body.)

12. **Tell your students that in the next class they will apply** these ideas to car engines and their putt-putt boat engine.

2nd Class

1. **Ask students to read about Sadi Carnot** and the efficiency of heat engines. There are three important ideas on this page:

   1) The working fluid in an engine must be alternately heated and cooled, so a heat engine requires both a heat source and heat sink. This cooling, "resetting" stage is one of the key ideas for heat engines.
   2) The efficiency of an engine is defined as the ratio of the useful (mechanical) energy produced divided by the total energy put into the engine. Students can feel this wasted energy as hot car exhaust.
   3) No engine is 100% efficient.

2. **Heat sources and sinks.** The idea of sinks and sources is especially important for understanding how the putt-putt boat engine works. Ask students to answer the questions at the bottom of page 47. (The heat source for the drinking bird is the room-temperature air; for the putt-putt boat it is the candle. The heat sink for the drinking bird is water evaporating from the bird's beak; for the putt-putt boat it is the cool water that comes back into the engine after each "putt.")

3. **Have your students read about the Otto Engine Cycle** on page 48. Ask them to answer the questions. Those answers are shown here:

   1) Students should use Chapter 20 in their textbooks to fill in the names of the four steps of the Otto Engine Cycle (intake, compression, combustion, and exhaust). However, the information can also be found on the Internet.
   2) The spark plug should be inserted where it can ignite the mixture. Please note the spark plug would need to be turned around to be inserted into the drawing.
   3) Students learn about the difference between a diesel and gasoline engine. (In a gasoline engine the air and gasoline vapor are mixed, then compressed and ignited. In a diesel engine only the air is compressed, and it is compressed much more than in a gasoline engine. The gasoline vapor is then injected and ignition occurs as a result of the very high compression, which raises the temperature of the air. There are no spark plugs in a diesel engine.)

4. **Assign homework.** Ask students to read Chapter 21, "Energy from the Earth," in their textbooks and to answer the questions at the end of the chapter.

5. **Lead a "think-pair-share" discussion about how the putt-putt boat works.** Have your students turn to page 49. Ask them to write what they think is happening in the boxes to the right of each drawing. They should do this on their own first, then share their ideas with another classmate. They may not have it all figured out just yet.

ERROR: The arrows showing the water flow out of and in to the straw are drawn incorrectly. The arrows showing water coming out of the straw should be drawn in line with the straw hole to demonstrate jet flow. The arrows showing water coming back in to the straw should be drawn coming in from all directions to demonstrate sink flow.

Following is a summary of what's actually happening:

Step 1: The boiler is filled with water and the candle is lit.
Step 2: The water boils. Vapor expands and pushes water out of the straw. The boat moves forward when the water is pushed out the back.
Step 3: Outside pressure pushes water back into the straws. The boat moves backward a small amount.
Step 4: The fresh, cool water is heated, and the cycle starts again. The water boils. Vapor expands and pushes water out of the straw. The boat moves forward.
Step 5: Outside pressure pushes water back into the straws. The boat moves backward a small amount.

Answer Key

EN Page 50: Benchmark Questions
Acetone Engine
1) Why is acetone, not water, used in the syringe? (Acetone vaporizes very quickly, and condenses when it's cooler.)
2) If you keep the syringe in hot water, is it possible that the piston will be pushed completely out of the syringe? Why or why not? (Yes, it is possible. As long as there is greater pressure inside the syringe, there will be pressure on the piston to move up.)
3) What if you took the piston out of the hot water but did not put it in the ice bath? Would it still cool down? What would happen to the position of the piston? Why? (Yes, but it won't cool as quickly. The piston would eventually move to its starting position as it reached room temperature.)

Drinking Bird Engine
4) Explain why the liquid moves up the tube in terms of the combined gas law. (Cooling in the head of the bird causes the gas to condense, so the pressure of the methylene chloride vapor in the head decreases, allowing the liquid to be pushed up from the body.)

Engineering the Future Teacher Guide
©2008 Museum of Science, Boston

5) Where do conduction, convection, and radiation come into play in the drinking bird engine? (The bird as a whole reaches room temperature through **conduction**, **convection**, and **radiation**. When the beak is wet, thermal energy leaves the head by **conduction** and **radiation**. Heat is distributed throughout the interior of the bird through **convection** when it tips and the liquid flows back down to the body.)

6) What are the main thermal transfers occurring in the drinking bird engine? (Heat energy into the bird from the room, and heat energy out of the head when the beak is wet.)

Otto Engine

7) The Otto engine is an internal combustion engine because it burns fuel inside the engine. In the Stirling engine heat is provided by a source outside the engine, so it's called an (external combustion) engine.

Piot (Putt-Putt Boat) Engine

8) At what point in the Piot engine cycle does cooling occur? (Initially, when the water vapor expands and pushes out a plug of water; cooling continues when cool water is drawn back into the engine.)

9) What would happen if the Piot engine cycle didn't include a cooling cycle? (Without a cooling cycle, the water would never be drawn back into the putt-putt boat for the engine cycle to complete. The boat would stop.)

10) What are the sources of inefficiency for the Piot engine cycle? (Some energy is expended, making the boiler metal expand and contract. Thermal and sound energy is lost to the surrounding air and water. Some mechanical energy is lost when water is drawn into the engine and the boat moves backward. Efficiency is limited by the difference in temperature between the hot boiler and the temperature of the water that is drawn into the engine [cooling and reheating losses].)

All Engines

11) What do all these engines have in common? (They all involve conversion of thermal energy to energy of motion. The engines in this task all have a cycle.)

12) What are some ways that engine efficiency can be improved? (Increase the difference between the temperature of the boiler or cylinder and the exhaust. Insulate all surfaces where thermal energy is lost. Design the engine so that as much energy as possible goes into mechanical motion of the vehicle in the forward direction.)

Assessment   There are many opportunities for in-class assessment in this task. As your students provide their explanations for each type of energy, listen for the assumptions that they are making, such as the relationship between temperature, pressure, and volume, or the causes of mechanical motion. Take notes about any misconceptions so that you can correct them later.

The extensive benchmark questions provide a further opportunity to check student understanding. Collect these papers and see if you can find patterns indicating that the class as a whole has missed key ideas. Plan to discuss these in class on another day so that students have an opportunity to correct their misconceptions.

Background and Further Suggestions

Heat Engines. A heat engine uses a difference in temperature to create a change in pressure, which in turn creates mechanical motion. In most heat engines, thermal energy is transferred by the agency of a working fluid. But a heat engine need not just use an expanding gas; even solids can be used for a heat engine because they expand and contract with heating and cooling, allowing a temperature difference to be turned into motion. The "rubber band heat engine" is a particularly neat demonstration of this concept. A description of it can be found online at http://lecturedemo. ph.unimelb.edu.au/heat_thermodynamics/heat_engines/the_rubber_band_heat_engine.

Carnot Efficiency. Carnot introduced the key theory of heat engines, which is that there must be a cooling cycle that limits the amount of energy an engine can use. It is the difference in temperature between the heat source (often a fire) and a heat sink (often the atmosphere) that determines the maximum efficiency of an ideal engine:

$$\textit{Carnot Efficieny} = \frac{(T_{source} - T_{sink})}{T_{source}}$$

This is the maximum possible efficiency, which no real engine can ever achieve. The most important idea is that there has to be a way to cool an engine, which limits how much energy the engine can use.

References and Resources

A nice animation of Newcomen's historic atmospheric engine is provided online at http://keveney.com/newcommen.html.

A similar animation of Watt's Beam Engine is online at http://keveney.com/watt.html.

An explanation of heat engines, including Hero's, is available online at http://www.engineering. com/Library/ArticlesPage/tabid/85/articleType/ArticleView/articleId/193/Heat-Engine.aspx.

The howstuffworks.com web site has explanations for how car engines, Stirling engines, diesel, biodiesel, two-stroke engines, rotary engines, and gas turbine engines work at http://science. howstuffworks.com/engine10.htm.

R. Driver, E. Guesnes, and A. Tiberghien (Editors), *Children's Ideas in Science, Milton Keynes*, Séré, Marie, Chapter 6: "The Gaseous State," Open University Press, pages 105–123. This chapter provides an excellent overview of children's misconceptions about gases.

Task 3.6:	The Rocket Effect

Overview

Understanding the putt-putt boat as a heat engine is only part of the story. The other major concept concerns the rocket effect, which drives the boat forward.

Rockets move by ejecting a fluid backward and moving forward according to the Law of Conservation of Momentum (often noted with Newton's Third Law of Motion called the Law of Action-Reaction or Reciprocal Action). As the mass of the propellant goes one way, the rocket goes the opposite direction. A popular misconception about rockets is that they move by ejecting hot gases that push on the air. In fact, the ejecting mass doesn't have to "push" on anything (which is why rockets work in the vacuum of space).

In this task students compare the propulsion system of the putt-putt boat to a demonstration water rocket. They find that air is a much poorer propellant than water, because it has far less density (mass per unit volume). Students further investigate the rocket effect with tubing and syringes, and use this apparatus to test different pipe diameters and pressure differences. They can also use this apparatus to test boat hulls of different shapes.

Five Es

Engage students' interest in how their putt-putt boat works by demonstrating a water rocket; **Explore** the difference between using water and air to propel the rocket; **Explain** the difference using Newton's laws; **Elaborate** students' understanding of the putt-putt boat engine in light of this new information.

Time Frame

2 class periods

Focus Questions

• Which travels faster, a water rocket or an air rocket? How would Newton explain this difference?
• How do rockets work in space? How does this relate to the putt-putt boat?

Objectives

Students will be able to:
- Explain how a "reaction engine" works
- Identify the "amount of motion" (momentum) as the product of mass (m) times velocity (v)
- Relate the "amount of motion" of expelled fluid backward to the amount of motion forward
- Be able to explain Bernoulli's principle in terms of the relationship between fluid velocity and pressure

Materials

For the class:
1 water rocket
1 10-foot length of fishing line or string
1 plastic drinking straw
1 6" piece of masking tape
1 source of water
1 roll of paper towels
1 bottle of liquid soap with suspended particles
1 candle
1 long lighter
3 straws
6–12 sets of a large and small syringe connected by varied lengths of tubing

For each team of three or four students:
2 syringes of different sizes
2 varied lengths of tubing of different diameters with connectors
2 boat hulls of different shapes
1 tape
1 yard stick
Basin for testing

Preparation

Prepare the water rocket demonstration for the first class. Decide where to launch the rocket so that students do not get wet. Tape a 2-inch length of straight drinking straw to a commercial water rocket toy. Thread a fishing line or string through the straw. Secure the two ends of the fishing line. You might use two chairs, or a chair and a table, so that you can slacken and tighten the line.

Prepare materials for "Exploring the Rocket Effect" and for the "Trade Off of Mass vs. Acceleration." Pour soap solution (with suspended particles) into pairs of syringes joined by a tube. Don't fill them too much or one will pop out if the other is pushed too far. The syringe pairs should be different sizes, and different pairs should be connected by different-sized tubes.

1st Class

1. **Discuss the homework.** Emphasize the role that fluids play in both traditional and geothermal power plants.

2. **Demonstrate the water rocket as follows:**
   1) Fill the water rocket up to the line on the tank with water. There needs to be an air space at the top so that you can pressurize the air.
   2) Pump up the rocket.
   3) Release the pump; the rocket should shoot along the fishing line, spraying water out the back. You may repeat the demonstration, asking, "What was the spray like? What sounds did you hear? What did you see happening to the rocket?"

Engineering the Future Teacher Guide
©2008 Museum of Science, Boston

4) Discuss why students think the rocket moved. Ask what they think will happen if you repeat the experiment without any water in the rocket—just air.

5) Repeat the experiment with only air in the rocket. It will move neither very fast nor very far.

6) Discuss the effect of mass on the motion of the rocket. Water has more mass than air, so it moved the rocket farther and faster.

7) Ask students whether they would rather you throw a one-inch cube of wood at them at a slow speed or fast speed (slow will cause less damage). Discuss how mass is one aspect of the effect, but speed is another aspect of the rocket effect.

3. **Introduce the rocket effect.** Ask your students to read page 51, and to answer the questions at the bottom of the page. Invite students to compare answers, then discuss the questions with the class.

   1) How do you think the rocket engine is different from the heat engines you observed in the previous task? (There is just one cycle; the rocket goes until all of the fluid is gone; it works by creating a difference in pressure directly rather than heating with a fuel; the energy is stored in a pocket of compressed air.)

   2) Observe the rocket as it is propelled with air, and then with water. What does this tell you about the rocket effect? (The strength of the effect depends, at least in part, on how much mass escapes from the rocket engine, as well as how much pressure is built up.)

4. **Ask the students to read the top of page 52,** and then lead a discussion about what the optimum amount of air and water in the rocket should be. If there is time, try three of four experiments with different amounts of air and water. It's important that the students realize that if the rocket is completely filled with water, it will not be possible to store any energy when it's pumped up because water is incompressible. On the other hand, if it is completely full of air it won't go far either because air provides so little mass. There is an optimum combination of air (for storing the energy) and water (to shoot out the back and propel it forward).

5. **Explain the Rocket Effect.** Ask students to read the second half of page 52 and see if they can explain the rocket effect to you in their own words. They may need help. The main idea is summarized in the illustration at the bottom of the page: The mass of the exhaust fluid times its acceleration (rate at which it speeds up) is equal to the mass of the whole rocket times the rate at which it speeds up in the opposite direction.

6. **The rocket effect and Thomas Piot's engine.** Ask students to work in pairs or small teams on the questions on page 53. Then lead a large-class discussion about the best answers.

1) What happens to the water:
   A. In the rocket engine? (It is pushed out the back at high speed.)
   B. In the Piot engine? (It is pushed out the back at high speed.)
2) Some people think that bubbles drive the putt-putt boat forward; others think that it is water pushed by the bubbles that drive the putt-putt boat forward. Who do you think is right, and why? (Water. Most boats emit no bubbles. The bubbles do not have enough mass to push the boat through the water.)
3) Is the water rocket a pneumatic system, a hydraulic system or both? (It is a combined system; it requires a pressurized pocket of air to store the energy and a water jet to push the rocket forward.)
4) Is the Piot engine a pneumatic system, a hydraulic system, or both? (It is a combined system; it requires a heated and pressurized pocket of water vapor to push the rocket forward.)
5) Is the water rocket an open system or a closed system? (Open system; water leaves the rocket in order for it to work.)
6) Is the Piot engine an open system or a closed system? (Open system; water enters and leaves the engine in order for it to work.)
7) How is the Piot engine similar to a rocket engine? (Both engines push a vehicle forward by forcing water backward at high speed.)

2nd Class

1. **Explore the rocket effect on the putt-putt boat.** Ask the students to turn to page 54, which describes how to conduct experiments with different hull shapes and different diameters of tubing. Explain that activities will help them better understand how the putt-putt boat works, and provide ideas for redesigning the putt-putt boat at the end of the project.

2. **Demonstrate to the students how they can use the equipment.** Point out that the syringe is the model for the boiler in their boats, and the tubing is the model for the pipes. Students can move water in and out and feel the motion of the water by putting their fingers near the end of the tubing. They can compare water and air coming out of the tubing (just like for the water rocket filled with water and air). They can feel the difference in velocity that comes with different diameter tubing. They can also feel the difference between in flow (sink flow) and out flow (jet flow).

3. **During the experiments,** point out how they can make the boat go forward and back a little by moving the syringe in and out. This models the action of the putt-putt boat very nicely.

4. **Lead a discussion** about the results when teams finish their experiments.

5. **Why does the putt-putt boat move forward more than it moves backward?** Ask this question right after the discussion. Students will probably be aware that the water flowing back into the engine causes it to go backward, but they may not know why the boat moves forward more than it moves backward. Have them read about the distinction between a jet flow and a sink flow at the top of page 55.

6. **Demonstrate jet flow and sink flow** by blowing through a straw at a candle. Notice how quickly it goes out. Now relight the candle and try to extinguish it by sucking in the air through a straw. It is much more difficult to extinguish the candle flame because the air comes in from all directions around the end of the straw, whereas in a jet flow nearly all the air is directed out the end in a strong narrow stream.

7. **Have your students read the bottom of page 55,** which is about the trade-off of mass and acceleration when designing rockets of any sort. Provide students with pairs of syringes linked by tubing. These should be prepared in advance so that pairs have a large and small syringe, and are linked by tubes of different sizes. Students can trade to see how the differently sized tubes affect the trade-off of mass versus acceleration. Using soap with suspended particles as the fluid will help the students to see the difference in acceleration.

8. **Discuss the results.** Expect that students will observe that fluid flows faster in smaller-diameter tubing and fastest in the smallest-diameter tubing. The main point of this activity is that larger tubes in the putt-putt boat engine will allow more water to flow, but the speed will be slower. A smaller tube, on the other hand, will make the water flow fast, but the mass of water ejected by the engine will be less. There are many choices for optimizing design, many interrelated factors, and no simple answers for how to optimize a given design parameter, which is why building prototypes is so valuable.

9. **Ask students to complete the benchmark questions,** incorporating all that they learned about jet flow in explaining how their putt-putt boat works. Answers are provided below.

10. **Assign Chapter 22, "Good Chemistry," in the textbook.** Have students answer the questions at the end of the chapter.

Answer Key

EN Page 56: Benchmark Questions

At this point, your students should have a thorough understanding of how the putt-putt boat engine works.

ERROR: The arrows showing the water flow out of and in to the straw are drawn incorrectly. The arrows showing water coming out of the straw should be drawn in line with the straw hole to demonstrate jet flow. The arrows showing water coming back in to the straw should be drawn coming in from all directions to demonstrate sink flow.

Following is a step-by-step summary:

Step 1: The boiler is filled with water and the candle is lit.

Step 2: The water boils. Vapor expands and pushes water out of the straw. The boat moves forward when the water is pushed out the back. This is a jet flow.

Step 3: Outside pressure pushes water back into the straws. The boat moves backward, but not much, because it's a sink flow, not a jet flow.

Step 4: The cycle starts to repeat. The water in the boiler is heated by the candle and boils. Vapor expands and pushes water out of the straw. The boat moves forward when the water is pushed out the back. This is a jet flow.

Step 5: Outside pressure pushes water back into the straws. The boat moves backward, but not much, because it's a sink flow, not a jet flow.

Assessment

During class, circulate to small groups while they are working so that you can find out what individual students are thinking about the project. Look for understanding of the basic concepts: jet flow and sink flow, how jet flow pushes the boat forward, and the trade-off between velocity and mass when the size of the pipes is changed.

Your students' explanations for how the putt-putt boat engine works are the best measure of understanding at the end of this task. Look to see whether they explain that the jet flow moves the boat forward, and the sink flow moves the boat back just a little bit on every cycle.

Background and Further Suggestions
Another way to view the motion of the putt-putt boat. You may want to share with your students this idea from Jeff Bindon, explained by Slater Harrison, and slightly edited for brevity. http://www.sciencetoymaker.org/boat/howBoatWorksl.html.

Imagine a man standing at the front of a small boat. He runs across the deck toward the back and, as he accelerates, he exerts a force on the deck, which propels the boat forward. He continues to accelerate and exert a force until he comes to the end of the deck and leaps into the water. The boat is now moving and, as it does so, it passes another man in the water who grabs hold of the ladder at the back of the boat. The boat jerks him into motion and is slowed slightly. He climbs onto the deck and slowly walks to the front of the boat. He then turns around and runs to the back of the boat, pushing off with his feet and accelerating the boat forward again. He leaps off the back of the boat, and another man grabs the ladder. So a series of men floating in the water, climbing on board, and running and jumping back into the water can propel a boat!

There are several advanced topics that could be related to this task if there is time and interest.

Parabolic Fluid Flow: Students may wonder what a "piston" or "plug" of water looks like as it is pushed out of the straws at the back of the putt-putt boat. Engineers who have studied this phenomenon find that the fluid flows faster in the center than along the edges near the pipe. This forms a parabolic shape for the cross-sectional flow. The phenomenon of liquid flowing more slowly along the walls and faster near the middle of the tube can be observed using the liquid soap–filled syringe system. The suspended particles near the walls can be seen to move very slowly, while most of the fluid flows through the center of the connecting tubing and syringes.

Bernoulli's Principle: A second advanced topic that could be introduced in this lesson is Bernoulli's principle, which states that pressure decreases as the rate of fluid flow increases. So when a fluid travels through a series of connected pipes of different diameters, like the syringes and tubes that students use in Task 3.6, where the pipe narrows the fluid speeds up. According to Bernoulli's principle, the pressure in the more rapidly moving fluid is less than in the wider sections, where the fluid slows down.

There are a couple of quick demonstrations that students can do in class to help them see the concepts in Bernoulli's Principle. Have students hold strips to paper at an end and blow across the top long side. Since the fluid flow rate is increasing across the top, the pressure is less, and the paper will rise. This same idea can be viewed using a spoon and a water faucet. If a spoon is held down so that water stream runs over the rounded part, the spoon will actually be pulled toward the water flow instead of being pushed away. The increased fluid flow from the faucet causes a decrease in pressure on the rounded side of the spoon. The same principle can also be seen if you hold two balloons so they dangle from strings a couple of inches apart. Blowing between the balloons causes them to be drawn together.

Have your students use Bernoulli's Principle to explain why a roof of a house might come off during a hurricane. (The fluid flow from the wind increases to move over the slanted roof of a building. An increase in the fluid flow causes a decrease in the pressure on the roof of the house. If the pressure difference is great enough between the area on the roof and under the roof the roof will lift. Remember: Difference drives change.)

Textbooks typically use Bernoulli's Principle to explain why airplane wings provide lift. While that is at least partly true, other factors, such as the "angle of attack" of an airplane wing, are also at work. (Bernoulli's Principle alone cannot explain how some airplanes are able to fly upside-down.)

Momentum: A lesson on the rocket effect can include a reference to momentum, which is defined as mass times velocity, and can be interpreted loosely as "quantity of motion." It's a useful quantity for calculating how fast a given quantity of reaction mass (the material ejected from a jet engine) will propel the vehicle forward, as the momentum of the vehicle equals the momentum of the reaction mass. It may be possible to measure the speed and mass of the putt-putt boat and make a rough calculation of the speed and mass of the water pushed out the back.

References and Resources

Rocket engines. The explanation of how rocket engines work on the www.howstuffworks.com web site is helpful. Students interested in applications of their learning to events around them may also want to read the linked explanation of how the Space Shuttle works.

Newton's Laws. The Law of Action-Reaction (Reciprocal Action) or Newton's Third Law of Motion is explained online at many sites, one of which that discusses all three of Newton's laws of motion: http://www.physicsclassroom.com/Class/newtlaws/newtltoc.html.

Explanations for The Law of Conservation Momentum can be found at http://www.physicsclassroom.com/Class/momentum/U4L2b.html.

Task 3.7:	Investigate Resistance in Pipes

Overview

In order to prepare for redesigning the putt-putt boat, students research fluid flow through pipes to determine how the number, diameter, length, and shape of pipes affect resistance to fluid flow. The activities involve students blowing through straws of different diameters and lengths in series and parallel combinations. They compare the resistance in various straight straws and straws with elbows. Students consider the relationship of resistance to pressure difference and volume flow rate.

Five Es

Engage students' interest with new ideas for improving the performance of their putt-putt boats; **Explore** resistance in pipes by blowing through straws; **Explain** resistance of pipes in a way that relates the fluid flow through the pipe to the flow of thermal energy in Project 2.0; **Elaborate** on their understanding by thinking of ways to use this information to improve the performance of their putt-putt boats.

Time Frame

1 class period

Focus Questions

- What factors increase resistance to fluid flow through pipes?
- What is the relationship between volume flow rate, pressure difference, and resistance?

Objectives

Students will be able to:
- Compare fluid flow through pipes and combinations of pipes of different resistance
- Explain the difference in resistance between series and parallel pipes
- Explain that pressure difference (ΔP) is the driving force for the rate of fluid flow (I) through a resistance (R) ($\Delta P = I \times R$)
- Identify energy loss as a result of any flow through a resistance

Materials

For teams of two students:
    6 each of stirrer, straight drinking, bendy, and large straws (juice box straws—optional)
    12" piece of masking tape
    1 scissors
    1 clock or watch

Preparation

Collect an assortment of different kinds of straws: stirrer straws, straight drinking straws, bendy drinking straws, bendy juice box straws (if available), and jumbo straws.

Consider sanitation and safety issues involved in students blowing through straws and plan your rules of conduct.

Provide work areas for teams of two students.

1. **Discuss the homework,** Chapter 22, "Good Chemistry." Point out that the major difference between nuclear, fossil-fuel, and geothermal power plants is the source of thermal energy. All thermal power plants work by using thermal energy to create differences in pressure, which result in movements that generate electricity. All involve large systems of fluid flow through pipes.

2. **Have students read page 57.** Explain that the purpose of this next task is to find out how changes to the straws might affect the performance of the putt-putt boat.

3. **Discuss rules for safety and sanitation** while avoiding unnecessary waste. For example:

   • Do not blow through a straw that someone else has blown through.
   • Direct the stream of air downward, away from people's faces.
   • Each person should do the activity separately and record his or her data, then compare notes.

4. **Effect of straw diameter.** Have students read the bottom half of page 57 and ask them to summarize what they are expected to do. (Compare how long it takes to exhale a deep breath through straws of different diameters.)

5. **Distribute materials to pairs of students.** Allow 10 or 15 minutes for them to finish the activity and record their results. Observe and assist groups as needed.

6. **Discuss and record the results** of all groups on the board. Students will most likely agree that they can exhale most quickly through a larger-diameter straw. Continue discussion with other questions, such as:

   • Why is this section called "Trade Off of Mass vs. Acceleration" rather than "Compare Straw Diameters"? (Bigger diameters allow for a much faster volume flow rate, but the speed of the air will be faster in the smaller diameter straws.)
   • Why do you think it's easier to blow through a straw with a greater diameter? (The walls of a smaller tube provide greater resistance to the flow of air.)

7. **Discuss energy in fluid systems.** Communicate how blowing through a straw transfers energy from your lungs to the surroundings by asking a series of questions:

   • What causes fluid to flow? (Differences in pressure.)
   • Is the fluid energy? Or does it carry energy? (Fluid carries energy from one place to another.)
   • What is the source of energy in this activity? (Us!)

- Where do you want the energy to go? (Out the other end of the straw.)
- Is any energy lost? And, if so, where? (The resistance of the pipes causes energy loss. It goes to heating the pipes and surrounding air.)
- How is the flow of air through a pipe like the flow of thermal energy through a wall? (A difference in pressure pushes fluid through a pipe, while a difference in temperature pushes thermal energy through a wall. The wall resists and slows the flow of thermal energy, while the pipes resist and slow the flow of air.)

8. **Ask students to do the activities on pages 58 and 59,** and to record the results of all their tests. When they finish these activities, they should read about "Direct and Inverse Relationships" at the top of page 59. Be sure to use the terms "series" and "parallel"; these terms become especially important in Project 4.0.

9. **Discuss the results of the tests** and record them on the board. After summarizing the findings for each test, ask students about the implications for the putt-putt boat. You may need to remind students that some resistance is needed, or the boiler could not build up enough pressure to force water out of the straws rapidly.

10. **Discuss "Direct and Inverse Relationships"** at the top of page 59. Explain that the curved symbol means "is proportional to" just as an equals sign means "is equal to." If an *increase* in the quantity on one side of the symbol causes an *increase* on the other side, it's a **direct** relationship. If an increase in the quantity on one side of the symbol causes a *decrease* on the other side, it's an **inverse** relationship.

11. **Using the "proportional to" symbol.** If students have had time to compare the flow rate through two drinking straws in series with two stirrer straws in parallel, ask for the results, and write these on the board. Ask students how they would represent the results with the "proportional to" symbol. (It's okay if teams disagree. Some would write the result as a direct proportionality, others as an inverse proportionality.)

12. **Assign Homework.** Ask students to read Chapter 23, "Down the Pipes," in the textbook and to answer the questions at the end of the chapter.

13. **Benchmark Questions.** Have students answer the benchmark questions on page 60.

EN page 60: Benchmark Questions

1A) What if the pipes (straws) gave no resistance? How well would the engine work? (It would not work at all because the boiler would not be able to build up any pressure.)

1B) What if the pipes (straws) gave too much resistance? (The boiler would probably spring a leak as pressure increased but could not escape; and, of course, the boat would not work at all.)

2) Describe the changes in the pipes that you think might improve the putt-putt boat's performance. (Many answers are possible.)

3) Which of these pipes and combinations of pipes has the least resistance? Which has the most resistance? Explain your choices. (Several answers are possible. Here are some reasonable responses.

- Least resistance: two drinking straws in parallel will have the biggest area and thus the least resistance.
- Most resistance: either three drinking straws in series [long], one bendy straw at 90-degree angle [bendy], or a single stirrer straw [narrow].)

4) How is fluid flow similar to the flow of thermal energy? How is it different? (In both cases, energy goes from one place to another. There is always a source and a destination. Resistance is involved. In the case of thermal flow through a wall, resistance is due to the type and thickness of material and the area of the wall. In the case of fluid flow, the resistance is due to the pipe through which the fluid flows, which depends on the pipe's diameter, length, and shape [number and degree of bends].)

Assessment

Students' answers to the benchmark questions will provide one measure of their understanding of the concepts introduced in Task 3.7. Students' responses to the tasks and class discussions will also provide evidence of their understanding.

In assessing how well your students understand the key ideas in Task 3.7, and deciding whether or not to go on or spend a day reviewing the ideas, consider the concepts at two levels:

- **Basic.** At a basic level, students learn how the rate of flow depends on the number of tubes, as well as their diameter, length, and shape. They also learn that too little or too much resistance will cause the boat to malfunction. Choosing just the right combination of straws will involve some intuition and creativity; it is not possible to determine this from the activities in this task alone.

- **Advanced.** There are two more subtle and powerful sets of ideas presented in Task 3.7. The first is the mathematical idea that quantities may be directly or inversely related. Most students are familiar with direct relationships—if A gets bigger, B gets bigger too. They are probably also familiar with inverse relationships—if A gets bigger, B gets smaller—but they may not have thought about these ideas as classes of relationships.

The second big idea concerns energy. Students are asked to think not only of the flow of fluids, but also the energy carried by those fluids. The following table compares various aspects of thermal and fluid energy:

	Fluid Energy	Thermal Energy
Energy flow is driven by changes in...	Pressure	Temperature
To maintain a constant flow of energy...	Maintain a constant pressure difference	Maintain a constant temperature difference
Energy flow can be measured by...	Volume flow rate	Thermal/heat flow rate
Resistance to energy flow increases with...	• Longer pipes • Narrower pipes • Bent pipes	• Thicker walls • Less wall area • Materials with high R-value

Background and Further Suggestions

Internet research. Students can learn about how doctors have contributed to an understanding of fluid flow by conducting Internet research on French physician Jean Poiseuille, who lived in the 19th century. His primary interest was how blood flows in the human body, but the relationship he discovered concerning pressure differences, volume flow rate, and the resistance of pipes could be applied to any liquid flowing through narrow tubes. Advanced students may want to learn more about Poiseuille's law, in which the resistance in pipes is defined as:

$$R = (8nL) / (\pi r^4)$$

L is the length of the pipe, r is the radius of the pipe, and n is a compound variable dependent on the pipe material and the viscosity of the fluid flowing through it.

From Poiseuille's law you can see that resistance increases with an increase in length and decreases with an increase in radius. This helps explain how resistance changes with series (longer) and parallel (more area) straws. This key idea will be used again for understanding series and parallel resistances in electrical circuits.

Energy and fluid resistance. There is "friction" as a fluid flows through a pipe. As with all friction, some of the energy goes toward making the temperature of the objects that are rubbing slightly higher. Seen in this way, the fluid flowing into a pipe has more energy than the fluid flowing out, because some of the energy is used to overcome friction.

In redesigning the putt-putt boat, and for engines in general, students should be aware that although energy is needed to overcome friction, the energy losses to resistance are less than the energy "wasted" in cooling the engine so it can repeat its cycle. In other words, the friction of the fluid flow is a loss, but it is not the primary loss.

Task 3.8:   Redesign the Putt-Putt Boat

Overview

Tasks 3.8 and 3.9 are the culminating activities of Project 3.0. In Task 3.8 students meet in teams and discuss how to modify the putt-putt boat design in some way. The goal is not for students necessarily to make the boat go faster, though that is one possible improvement. The goal is for students to redesign some aspect of the boat, be it performance, appearance, or the manufacturability. The assessment of their understanding comes when they have to write a patent application and present their understanding of how the boat works, as well as what they chose to modify and their justification for why they chose it.

This task should be done in parallel with the next task regarding the communication of results. When students are waiting for adhesives to set or for materials, they should be working on preparing their patent write-up and whatever presentation you will expect from them at the end.

Five Es

Engage students' creativity by challenging them to decide how to modify the basic putt-putt boat design; **Explore** several different ideas; **Explain** how the idea they select will be unique; **Elaborate** their idea by developing a plan and actually building a prototype; **Evaluate** by testing it.

Time Frame

2–5 class periods

Focus Question

• What would you like to change about the putt-putt boat design and why?

Objectives

Students will be able to:
- Integrate their knowledge in redesigning the putt-putt boat
- Prepare a patent-style write-up of design and implementation results
- Assess which changes work and why

Materials

1 set of all materials needed to build and test another set of putt-putt boats

Preparation

Although students should build a prototype of their redesign of the putt-putt boat, if time is short you can shave several days off by having students just draw their ideas and describe them in their patent applications (Task 3.9). Shortening the unit this way will not impair the students' understanding of the concepts too much.

Provide space for team meetings to brainstorm and decide on improvement ideas. If your students will be making prototypes, arrange for places to construct them and store them.

Decide in advance if you want to require your students to include an innovation that affects the boat's performance, or if it's okay for teams to make only cosmetic changes. The former instruction will require that the students recall and apply what they learned in the previous tasks.

Prepare to review homework by researching the local source of water and information about your community's sewer system.

1st Class

1. **Review the homework:** Chapter 23, "Down the Pipes." Emphasize the idea that many different kinds of engineers, including environmental engineers, need to understand fluid flow in pipes. This topic is tremendously important in maintaining the many systems people depend on every day.

2. **Ask students to read page 61,** which provides the challenge for this task—to decide how to redesign the putt-putt boat and, if there is time, to build a prototype to test their ideas for improvement. If you want to require all teams to make at least one modification that will affect the performance of the boat, now is the time to tell them.

3. **Review with students the Teamwork Guidelines,** at the beginning of Project 3.0, for individual contributions to the team, team behaviors, and team tools for creativity and decision-making. Observe team interaction, paying special attention to the decision-making process and delegation process.

4. **Ask students to read the rubric on page 67** carefully, which describes how their final project—a patent application—will be evaluated. Because the ideas that they develop in Task 3.8 will determine what they can say on their patent application, they should be aware, before they begin the redesign process, how they will be evaluated. Answer any questions they may have about it.

5. **Start the engineering design process.** Have the teams read pages 62 and 63. They should discuss the ideas in each section first, and each person should record the ideas discussed and/or decided on by the entire team. Teams should complete all steps during this class except for the last step—"Create a Prototype."

6. **Circulate and help teams as necessary.** If teams will be building prototypes, have them read the rest of Task 3.8; if they will not build prototypes, students should go ahead and read the "Communicate" and "Redesign" sections on page 64.

2nd–5th Classes
Build Prototypes

1. **If teams will be building a prototype,** give ground rules to the class as a whole. (For example, you may require students to have a detailed plan before being given materials to build a prototype.) Tell students where they can work, what precautions to take, and where their prototypes will be stored between class sessions.

2. **Help individual teams** with planning and building their prototypes. If they want special materials, encourage them to bring the materials from home. If necessary, remind teams that there should be some difference in their boats' performance, if possible.

Test Prototypes

1. **Set up test equipment.** If speed is the goal, a team could test different prototypes against each other in two 4-foot rain gutters placed side by side. If duration is the goal, an oval roasting pan might be the perfect test basin. If going the distance is important, a 10-foot rain gutter may be the most satisfying test apparatus. Provide as much freedom for student creativity as possible within the constraints of materials, space, and time.

2. **Oversee, advise, and evaluate team testing programs.** When all teams are ready to test their prototypes, organize a class to test and discuss each one.

3. **Marketing.** As described on the bottom of page 63, while some students build the prototype, others may develop advertisements or posters to describe their product and/or interview potential customers and write a brief report.

4. **As described on page 64, communication is a very important part of the engineering design process.** In Task 3.9, the students will communicate their ideas through a patent application.

5. **Have students read about redesign** at the bottom of page 64, and encourage them to redesign if they have ideas during the building process, and even as they write their patent application.

6. **Hold a brief concluding discussion** when all groups appear to be finished. Ask each team to report briefly an answer to the question, "What would you like to change about the putt-putt boat design and why?"

Assessment

The two major skills in this section are teamwork and the engineering design process. Assess teamwork using the guidelines on the front page of the *Engineer's Notebook*. Assess students' understanding of the engineering design process by reading their *Engineer's Notebooks* on pages 62–64, and by carefully listening to their discussions as they plan and carry out the steps of Task 3.8. If necessary, call the entire class together to emphasize the importance of teamwork and the engineering design process.

At the end of Task 3.8, you will need to assess whether or not each team is ready to develop a patent application. This will mean staying in close touch with the teams throughout this series of lessons. The class discussion at the conclusion of Task 3.8 will also help in determining whether all teams are ready to proceed.

Background and Further Suggestions

This task is the culmination of the research and development phase, when students are responsible as team members for the quality of their own product. This is an opportunity to assist and reinforce the various concepts presented throughout Project 3.0. However, it is also a time when the students should have freedom to be creative and make their own decisions, so it's best not to be too "heavy" with regard to concepts and techniques.

Boat performance improvements. The efficiency of the putt-putt boat is considered to be quite low, perhaps under 1%. We do not know what changes will definitely improve the engine performance. There is an optimum resistance of the pipes; too low a resistance will reduce the velocity of the fluid coming out too much, and too high a resistance will reduce the mass of the fluid coming out. Students could try to increase the loudness of the boiler. They could also see what happens if they only use a single straw instead of two (will it still work?), straightening the bend in the boiler (will the resistance drop too much?), and adding a second boiler (what if the boilers are "out of phase," with one filling with water as the other pushes water out?).

Students are free to think about which changes will have an effect on engine performance. They should consider why they think the changes will make a difference. They are also free to think about waste and speed of manufacturing, or what the boat looks like. On Slater Harrison's site, www.sciencetoymaker.org/boat, he has instructions for adding an aesthetic boat top to his design. Students might even want to investigate and build an alternative Piot engine design by coiling a metal tube, as first patented by William Purcell in 1923, http://sciencetoymaker.org/boat/joelPDFs/PurcellPatent1923.pdf, and shown at http://sci-toys.com/scitoys/scitoys/thermo/thermo.html.

References and Resources

The following articles about the performance of the putt-putt boat are available for download from an Indian journal *Resonance:*

V Sharadha and Jaywant H Arakeri. "Propulsion of the Putt-Putt Boat–I." *Resonance*, June 2004. http://www.iisc.ernet.in/academy/resonance/June2004/pdf/June2004p66-73.pdf.

V Sharadha. "Propulsion of the Putt-Putt Boat–II." *Resonance*, August 2004. http://www.iisc.ernet.in/academy/resonance/Aug2004/Aug2004p64-69.html.

Task 3.9:   Present Your Patent

Overview

In this final task of Project 3.0, each student writes a patent application that explains how the putt-putt boat works, and describes the way that their team decided to improve it. Team members will be encouraged to discuss their ideas and share information, but each student will be expected to make his or her own drawings and write the application in his or her own words. Teachers may decide to have students self-evaluate their own application, using the rubric in addition to the teacher evaluation.

(An optional conclusion for this project is for teams to present their ideas for improving the putt-putt boat design, and why they think it will be a successful invention.)

Five Es

In the final session students **Explain** why their innovation is worth a new patent; **Elaborate** on the idea by writing a patent application; **Evaluate** their own work on the project by applying a rubric.

Time Frame

2–5 class periods

Focus Questions

- What changes most affect boat performance?
- What changes most affect boat marketability?

Objectives

Students will be able to:
- Describe their design improvement process and solution
- Identify, sketch, and name boat hull and heat engine system components
- Fulfill the requirements for a patent application
- Demonstrate presentation skills

Preparation

Decide whether students will create their patent applications as homework or in school. If you have other requirements—such as writing them on a computer, or with a particular format—then prepare these in advance.

Determine whether you would like teams to present their inventions to their classmates, or perhaps to other students and teachers in the school. If so, create guidelines for the teams to prepare their presentations. For example:

"Prepare a 10-minute presentation about your team's invention. Your presentation should include answers to at least some of these questions:

- How did you improve the putt-putt boat design?
- In what ways does this improve on the old product?
- How well did your product match your expectations?
- What was the inspiration for your design improvements?
- How will you market this product?
- If you had more time and materials, what would you do different?"

Engineering the Future Teacher Guide
©2008 Museum of Science, Boston

1st Class

1. **Have students read page 65**, which provides an overview of what they will be doing in this last task.

   ERROR: The title of the second part of the page, "Drawing Exercise," is an error. It should be titled "Preparing a Patent Application."

2. **If you intend to have students write their patent applications as homework**, let them know now. Also tell them if you have any other rules about the length, style, format, and so on, of the patent application.

3. **If you plan to have teams make presentations** about their inventions, tell them the ground rules so that they can begin to prepare.

4. **Have the students read page 66**, which describes how to write a patent application. This is not a form to be filled in, but rather a list of elements to include. There are no guidelines for length, so you may want to provide an estimate. (For example, no fewer than two, nor more than five pages plus drawings.) Discuss each step with the students and ask if they have any questions.

5. **Teams may spend remainder of the class to meet** and discuss the ideas they'd like to include in their patent applications. Students should be encouraged to continue to help each other when one has a question or needs some assistance, but each student should compose his or her own patent application.

2nd–5th Classes

1. **It can be a very good experience for students to evaluate their own work** before receiving input from the teacher. If you choose to do this, have your students turn to the rubric on page 67 and give themselves a rating (one, two, three, or four stars) on each of the three dimensions (Communication, Knowledge and Understanding, and Application and Reasoning). For each rating they should provide a sentence or two to justify their self-evaluation.

2. **Collect patent applications (if done as homework).** Add your ratings and comments to the students' self-evaluations.

3. **If teams will be presenting their inventions**, create a schedule and have the first team stand in front of the room and describe their invention. If they have a prototype, they should display it and describe how well it worked. Follow up each presentation with questions and constructive feedback from the other students.

Assessment

- Assess individual patent applications using the rubric.
- Assess each student's participation in discussions, question asking, and teamwork.
- Administer the end-of-project test (shown later in the Teacher Guide).
- Lead a discussion about how students enjoyed Project 3.0. Make notes for the future.

Background and Further Suggestions

Scientists, engineers, technologists, and virtually everyone striving for success in a technological world must be able to communicate their ideas, actions, and proposals to others. Working as a team to produce ideas, products, written reports, and presentations will broaden your students' communication skills as well as their abilities to work as effective team members. It will also help them realize that, by working as a team, they will be able to develop far better solutions and products than they could by working alone—and have a better time doing it.

However, communication and teamwork are just part of what people need to succeed in the 21st century. Developing solutions to practical problems involves an understanding of the engineering design process, as well as how to conduct research, improve existing solutions, and invent new ones, and the ability to design, draw, build, test, and redesign. Developing these skills is a lifetime challenge; you are giving your students a very good start through this course.

Project 3.0 also has laid the groundwork for the next challenge—Project 4.0, which is concerned with communication technology and electricity. These subjects have been saved for last because they are more abstract. Electricity cannot be seen, although its effects can be observed, and generating electricity is essential to modern civilization. Additionally, communication is more than a set of skills for making oneself understood—it is a collection of concepts and technologies that can help people better understand the way devices such as computers, radios, and all forms of information transmission and processing work.

Energy transfers in gases and liquids. The focus so far has been mostly on fluid flow, though energy was mentioned regarding how gases can both store and transfer energy due to their compressibility, whereas liquids can only transfer energy through themselves. Seen in this way, energy stored by compressing a gas can be released to make something move, just as energy transferred through a liquid can make something move. The equation for energy transferred by pushing, often called "working," is

Energy transferred by working (W) = Force applied (F) × Distance moved (d)

$$W = F \times d$$

As a force is applied to move a gas-filled piston, the gas is compressed, and a certain amount of energy is transferred to the gas. This is stored energy.

As a force is applied to move a liquid-filled piston, the liquid is moved and energy is transferred through the liquid. When a secondary piston gets this energy, it can either move a large area a small distance using a large force, or a small area a large distance using a small force. The energy (W) is constant, so F and d are inversely proportional (increase force, distance decreases, and vice versa).

This is no different than the way simple machines work, trading off force and distance. Think of a lever where a long arm moves a big distance using a small force, and the short arm moves a small distance using a big force. The energy transferred by working can be the same. It can be understood in terms of conservation of energy, though it is often not presented that way in introductory teaching. If students have seen simple machines, you can present a hydraulic press as a simple machine that works based on the conservation of energy, trading force for distance. Pascal first realized that fluids could be used the same way as simple machines, though he didn't use energy to explain it.

Project 4.0: Electricity and Communication Systems:
Electrical Systems and Communication Technologies
Project Guide

Electricity is perhaps the most important and widespread technological system on our planet today. A vast network of electrical systems powers our cities and enables global communications, yet few people understand electricity well enough to design even the simplest circuits. Project 4.0 intends to change that. By completing this series of tasks, students will learn how to build and design simple circuits and to develop a functional mental model of what is going on inside the wires and components of any electrical circuit. At the end of each major topic, the students apply what they learned to a creative engineering design project.

The traditional approach to teaching electricity is to start with the basics of electrical circuits, then graduate to applications. However, we have found that students are much more interested in starting with the practical field of communications. So, we have developed the following unconventional sequence to maximize student interest while ensuring that they also learn fundamental concepts. In Tasks 4.1–4.3, students learn to use electricity for communications. Tasks 4.4–4.6 focus on the use of ammeters and voltmeters to explore series and parallel circuits, as well as resistance and control. Task 4.7 relates how electricity is generated, and, in Task 4.8, students apply what they've learned to analyze everyday electrical devices such as televisions and flashlights.

This course combines elements of the way electricity is taught in physics with how it's taught in technology, in a format that leads students to a scientific model of current flowing through an electrical circuit. The scientific model is built over time in a cycle of learn/apply activities. Students use a kit of Snap Circuits™ parts from Elenco Electronics Inc. to design basic circuits and see how they work. Components are soldered to snaps and mounted on plastic with the schematic symbol visible. Circuit construction just requires snapping parts together, and the finished arrangement also forms the schematic diagram. This helps students visualize what is happening in circuits and also makes it easier for them to design. Students are not required to know how to read resistors, how to identify an LED's orientation, how to use a breadboard, or how to solder. These are important skills, but they can be obstacles to understanding and to creative design.

Project 4.0

In the following Gantt chart, each column represents five 45-minute classes and each bar is an estimated number of classes per task. This chart also lists the corresponding text chapters to the tasks in the last column.

Project 4.0: 45-Minute Class Periods	5	10	15	20	25	30	35	40	Text Chapter
Task 4.1: Create a Scoreboard Code Students learn about conductors, insulators, and basic circuits, then build a scoreboard display and develop binary code sequences for using it.	▓								24
Task 4.2: Design a Mouse Detector Students learn about all of the Snap Circuits™ parts and what they do, then design a circuit to detect a mouse.		▓							
Task 4.3: Design a Communications System Students learn about the fundamentals of communications systems by using an amplifier to build a radio, a voice amplifier, and to communicate with light.			▓						25 26 27
Task 4.4: Explore Circuits with an Ammeter Students are introduced to series and parallel circuits and how ammeters work.				▓					28
Task 4.5: Explore Circuits with a Voltmeter Students learn how to make and use a voltmeter and how to work with Ohm's law.				▓					29
Task 4.6: Design a Fan Control System Students put their understanding of electrical systems to work in designing and building a system to control two electric fans.					▓				30
Task 4.7: Provide Energy to a Lighthouse Students explore different energy sources while learning about electric power.						▓			31 32
Task 4.8: Analyze Consumer Electronics Students learn how electricity is used in home electrical systems by building a version of the one-pixel color display and learning how to use a multimeter.							▓		

Preparing to Teach Project 4.0

Introduction

You will need to purchase kits for your students that have been specially designed for this course. Kit packages are available for every four students. Each kit package contains two basic Snap Circuits™ kits, for when students are working in pairs, and a few additional components for when students are working in groups of four. (See the Materials List section after the Introduction for ordering instructions.)

You should use one of the kits to go through the activities ahead of the students so that you can better help them troubleshoot problems in class. The first task of the project will be to introduce the students to the parts in the Snap Circuits™ kits and to set up a system for retrieving, using, and storing the kits while they work on their projects. You may want to designate a person in each group to be responsible for the pieces. Additionally, you may find it helpful to identify where the kits should be stored each night before students begin using them. Project 4.0 introduces students to the components in various circuits by having them work with the easily manipulated parts in the Snap Circuits™ kit; the reading gives them an overview of how analogies are used to better understand how charge flows in a circuit.

It is not uncommon that teaching a unit takes longer than expected so that the last parts are skipped or covered too quickly. In this project, the last two tasks—involving power, energy, and communications—are two of the most enjoyable activities for students (allowing creativity in pursuit of individual interests) and directly address important technology/engineering standards. Use the Gantt chart to plan ahead, track your progress, and adjust to avoid rushing at the end.

Some teachers have asked why we use the simple ammeter in the Snap Circuits™ kit rather than a much more versatile and accurate multimeter. Field trials showed that very few students were able to read the complex scales on multimeters. While digital multimeters were easier to read than the analog versions, they were not as engaging as a simple meter with a needle that clearly moves in response to a current or voltage. However, because it is a valuable skill for students to learn to use a multimeter, we introduce these during the final activities in Task 4.8, after the students have a good grasp of the fundamental concepts.

Prior to beginning the project, watch the video "Minds of Our Own: Can We Believe Our Eyes?" to find out how challenging it can be for students to learn about the concept of a circuit, and to realize how important it is that students understand this simple yet important concept before they go to college or enter the work world. The video shows classroom teachers allowing their students ample time to discover the continuous conducting path arrangements that allow a battery to light a bulb. You may also want to have your students view the video after they have finished Task 4.1 (they will see that they already have a better understanding of electricity than many college students). The video is available free on DVD from www.aprivateuniverse.com/order, and free online (after registration) at http://www.learner.org/resources/series26.html.

Rechargeable batteries. If you want to buy rechargeable batteries, we recommend Nickel Metal Hydride (NiMH) over Nickel Cadmium (NiCd) cells. NiMH batteries have a higher capacity than NiCds, and do not contain toxic cadmium.

Note that both NiMH and NiCd batteries have a typical voltage of 1.2V, while disposable alkaline batteries have a typical voltage of 1.5V. This will affect the results in many of the measurements made later in this project. Additionally, certain battery packs also allow users the option of recharging their batteries using solar power. These battery packs may include a solar power–charging component or allow for the addition of a separately purchased solar power–charging accessory.

References and Resources

Arnold, Michael and Robin Millar. "Being Constructive: An Alternative Approach to the Teaching of Introductory Ideas in Electricity." *International Journal of Science Education.* October 1, 1987. Volume 9, Issue 5, 553–563.

Arnold, Michael and Robin Millar. "Teaching About Electric Circuits: A Constructivist Approach." *School Science Review.* December 1988. Volume 70, Issue 251, 14–16.

Arons, Arnold B. "Chapter 9: Batteries and Bulbs." *The Various Language.* New York, NY: Oxford University Press, 1977.

Berger, Carl; Coffman, Joan; Davis, Jr., Joseph; Mayer, Barbara; Young, Hugh. *Models for Electric and Magnetic Interaction.* Science Curriculum Improvement Study, 1968.

Clement, John J. and Melvin S. Steinberg. "Step-Wise Evolution of Mental Models of Electric Circuits: A 'Learning-Aloud' Case Study." *The Journal of the Learning Sciences.* Volume 11, Issue 4, 389–452.

Cosgrove, Mark and Roger Osborne. "A Teaching Sequence on Electric Current." In R. Osborne and P.S. Freyberg (Eds.), *Learning in Science,* Chapter 10, 112–113. Auckland, N.Z.: Heinemann.

Dupin, J.J. and S. Joshua. "Analogies and 'Modeling Analogies' in Teaching: Some Examples in Basic Electricity." *Science Education.* 1987. Volume 73, Issue 2, 207–224.

Dupin, J.J. and S. Joshua. "Teaching Electricity: Interactive Evolution of Representations, Models, and Experiments in a Class Situation." In R. Duit, W. Jung, C. von Roneck (Eds), *Aspects of Understanding Electricity: Proceedings of an International Workshop,* Verlag Schmidt & Klaunig, 1985. 331–341.

Dupin, J.J. and S. Joshua. "Taking Into Account Student Conceptions in Instructional Strategy: An Example in Physics." *Cognition and Instruction.* 1987. Volume 4, Issue 2, 117–135.

Elenco Electronics. *Student Guide for Electronic Snap Circuits, Model SC-300R and Model SC-500R.* Illinois: Elenco Electronics, 2004.

Evans, James. "Teaching Electricity with Batteries and Bulbs." *The Physics Teacher.* January 1978. Volume 16, Issue 1, 15–22.

Grayson, Diane. "Concept Substitution: A Teaching Strategy for Helping Students Disentangle Related Physics Concepts." *American Journal of Physics*. August 2004. Volume 72, Issue 8, 1126–1133.

Grotzer, Tina and Margot Sudbury. *Causal Patterns in Simple Circuits: Lessons to Infuse into Electricity Units to Enable Deeper Understanding*. Understandings of Consequence Project, Project Zero, Harvard University. Also available online at http://www.pz.harvard.edu/ucp/curriculum/circuits/.

Grotzer, Tina A. *How Conceptual Leaps in Understanding the Nature of Causality Can Limit Learning: An Example from Electrical Circuits*. April 2000. Paper presented at the annual conference of the American Educational Research Association, New Orleans, LA.

Gunstone, Richard and David Shipstone. "Teaching Children to Discriminate between Current and Energy." In R. Duit et al. (Eds.), *Aspects of Understanding Electricity*, 287–297. Kiel, Germany: IPN, 1985.

Herrmann, Friedrich and Georg Job. *Der Karlsruher Physikkurs (The Karlsruhe Physics Curriculum), Volumes I and II*. Translated by Robin Fuchs on December 2006. Also available online at http://www.physikdidaktik.uni-karlsruhe.de/kpk/english/KPK_Teacher.pdf.

Kariotoglou, P., P. Koumaras, and D. Psillos. "Causal structures and counter-intuitive experiments in electricity." *International Journal of Science Education*. 1997. Volume 19, Issue 6, 617–730.

Koumaras, Panagiotis and Dimitris Psillos. "Multiple Causal Modeling of Electrical Circuits for Enhancing Knowledge Intelligibility." In Michel Caillot (Ed.), *Learning Electricity and Electronics with Advanced Educational Technology*, 57-75. Berlin: Springer-Verlag, 57–75.

Koumaras, Panagiotis, Dimitris Psillos, and Andree Tiberghien. "Voltage Presented as a Primary Concept in an Introductory Teaching Sequence on DC Circuits." *International Journal of Science Education*. January–March 1998. Volume 20, Issue 10, 29–43.

Koumaras, Panagiotis, Dimitris Psillos, and Andree Tiberghien. "Physics Instruction from Epistemological and Didactical Bases." *Instructional Science*. November 1994. Volume 22, Issue 6, 423–444.

Koumaras, Panagiotis, Dimitris Psillos, and Odysseas Valassiades. "Pupils' Representations of Electric Current Before, During and After Instruction on DC Circuits." *Research in Science & Technological Education*. 1987. Volume 5, Issue 2, 185–199.

Kruger, Colin, Jenny Mant, and Mike Summers. "Electricity for Primary School Teacher Education." IDATER 96, Loughborough University.

Kruger, Colin, Jenny Mant, and Mike Summers. *Teaching Electricity Effectively*. London: Association for Science Education, 1997.

Kruger, Colin, Jenny Mant, and Mike Summers. *Current Understanding*. London: Oxford University Department of Educational Studies, 1995.

Licht, Pieter. "Teaching Electrical Energy, Voltage and Current: An Alternative Approach." *Physics Education*. September 1991. Volume 26, Issue 5, 272–277.

McDermott, Lillian. *Physics by Inquiry, Volumes I and II*. USA: John Wiley & Sons, Inc., 1996.

Project 4.0

McDermott, Lillian and Peter Shaffer. "Research as a Guide for Curriculum Development: An Example from Introductory Electricity. Park II: Design of Instructional Strategies." *American Journal of Physics.* November 1992. Volume, 60, Issue 11, 1003–1013.

McIldowie, Eric. "Teaching Voltage-Current Relationships without Ohm's law." *Physics Education.* 1998. Volume 33, Issue 5, 292–295.

Modeling Project. *Modeling-Modified CASTLE.* For more information, see http://modeling.asu.edu/Curriculum.html.

Psillos, Dimitris. "Teaching Introductory Electricity." In Andree Tiberghien et al (Eds.), *Connecting Research in Physics Education with Teacher Education.* International Commission on Physics Education, 1997. Also available online at http://www.physics.ohio-state.edu/~jossem/ICPE/E4.html.

Rogers, Eric M. *Physics for the Inquiring Mind: The Methods, Nature, and Philosophy of Physical Science.* Princeton, NJ: Princeton University Press, 1960.

Steinberg, Melvin, et. al. "Capacitor-Aided System for Teaching and Learning Electricity (CASTLE)." Also available online at http://store.pasco.com/pascostore/showdetl.cfm?&DID=9&Product_ID=1478&Detail=1.

Task 4.1:	Create a Scoreboard Code

Overview
Task 4.1 introduces students to a few of the parts in their Snap Circuits™ kit and challenges them to light a bulb with a battery and a single wire. They then use a simple circuit that they have built to test various objects to see whether they are insulators or conductors, and learn about what is happening inside a light bulb. Next, they apply what they learned about simple circuits to build and analyze a "seven-segment display" for a scoreboard. Building on this activity, the students develop binary code sequences that can be used to light the seven-segment display. Finally, they reflect on how scoreboards communicate information from sports officials to fans, using these communication terms: *encode, transmit, signal, receive,* and *decode.*

Five Es
Engage students in snapping together functional circuits; **Explore** using materials that are insulators and conductors; **Explain** the concept of an electric circuit; **Elaborate** by building a complex circuit for communication; **Evaluate** the result by testing the circuit to see if it works.

Time Frame
4 class periods

Focus Questions
- What do the parts in the Snap Circuits™ kit do?
- What is needed to make an electrical circuit?
- What are insulators? What are conductors?
- How can circuits be combined to build complex electrical systems?
- What is a binary code? And how can it be useful?
- How is information transmitted from one place to another?

Objectives
Students will be able to:
- Identify components of a circuit, including input devices, output devices, energy sources, and controllers (e.g., switches)
- Identify the function of some of the parts in their kit
- Differentiate between conductors and insulators
- Identify a continuous conducting path through circuit components
- Draw and interpret schematic diagrams

Materials
For each student:
  1 *Engineer's Notebook*

For the class:
  Electrical cord to split apart (or just extension cord to show)
  Materials to test for conductivity (coins, pencil lead, keys, density cubes, straws, toothpicks, aluminum foil, chalk, and so on)

For every two students:
  1 basic Snap Circuits™ kit for ETF curriculum
  4 AA batteries (which should become part of their kit from now on)
  2 paper clips (to use as test probes)
  1 fine-point permanent marker

Preparation

Do the activities described in the *Engineer's Notebook* before the first class so you will be better able to assist students.

1st Class

1. **Hand out the *Engineer's Notebook* for Project 4.0.** Have students read the first page, which introduces Project 4.0. Ask them what experiences they have had with electricity, and how they feel about starting a unit about it. Allow some time for discussion.

2. **Call attention to page 6,** which is there to remind students that they will be working in teams and using the engineering design process.

3. **Have students read the top of page 7,** which describes the challenge of Task 4.1, while you distribute the student kits.

4. **Distribute the basic Snap Circuits™ kits for the ETF curriculum.** Every two students should share a kit. If there are an odd number of students, one group can have three students.

5. **Number kit parts.** If this is your first time distributing the kits, assign each kit a number, and have students mark every part in their kit with that number using a permanent marker to keep track of the parts. Remind students that they are responsible for all the parts in their kit. If more than one class of students shares the kits, you may want to start each class by having the students take inventory to be sure all the parts are there.

6. **Demonstrate how to use the Snap Circuits™ components.** Lay down the clear plastic grid and show the students how to snap the battery holder in place. Even simple circuits will be easier for the students to assemble if they use the plastic grid.

7. **Hand out batteries** and ask the students to note the positive (bump) and negative (flat) sides of the batteries and to observe the symbols inside the battery holder when inserting their batteries.

8. **Ask the students to read the bottom of page 7** and assemble their first circuit. Help students to get the bulb to light if they need to troubleshoot their circuit.

   Note: Students do not need to understand how the circuit works at this point, but they should have some success in building their first circuit.

9. **Have the students read page 8 and fill in the boxes** with their understanding of the function of the circuit's components. Check on students and look at what they have written as an indication of whether or not they understand the functions of simple circuits. Here is what you may expect to see if the students have a simple functional understanding of electricity versus a more sophisticated understanding of electrical circuits:

Engineering the Future Teacher Guide
©2008 Museum of Science, Boston

	Functional	Sophisticated
Batteries	Provides electricity	Source of energy
Switch	Turns bulb on and off	Opens and closes circuit
3-snap wire	Carries electricity	Carries charge
Light bulb	Lights up	Resistance or load

Use this activity for insight into their understanding at this point, rather than attempting to teach these ideas now.

10. **Ask the students to read the box at the bottom of the page** and to try and identify the various parts in their kit that serve as input and output devices, controllers, energy sources, and connectors.

11. **Discuss the functions of circuit elements.** Select two or three electrical devices and ask the students to identify their inputs, outputs, controllers, and energy sources. For example:

> **Fan:** switches are input devices and controllers; motor is output device; wall outlet or batteries are energy sources

> **Radio:** antenna is input device; speaker is output device; wall outlet or batteries provide the energy source

> **Flashlight:** on/off is input device/controller; bulb is output device; batteries provide the energy source

Note: If students tend to move quickly, you can continue on to the next activity. However, be sure to reserve five minutes at the end of class for the students to put away their materials. If some small groups move faster than others, they can continue to the next step—there will be suggestions for early finishers at the end of Task 4.1.

2nd Class

1. **Light a bulb with a battery and wire.** Ask the students to do the activities on page 9. Students should make a single bulb light using only a single AA cell and an alligator wire. They should not use a lamp socket or a battery holder. While this might seem simple, it is not intuitive, and you should not rush students.

2. **If students have difficulty drawing schematics,** call their attention to the box with "Schematic Drawing Hints," or draw an example on the board.

3. **Note the students' answers** to the questions at the bottom of the page. Students should note that successful arrangements show that the two contacts on the bulb (tip and side of the base) are connected to the plus and minus sides of the battery. Keep in mind that this is intended to be an exploration. The concept of a circuit will be introduced later in Task 4.1. The following are examples of successful arrangements:

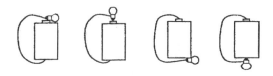

These four sketches can be represented by the following two equivalent schematics:

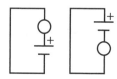

4. **Light a bulb with a battery and** *two* **wires.** Ask the students to do the activities at the top of page 10. Encourage them to see the similarities between the diagrams they drew using two wires with those in which they used just one wire. The only difference should be a line representing the wire. Or they may express the deeper insight that there is really *no difference* between the diagrams because the second line (wire) can be eliminated and the bulb will still light.

5. **Have the students read the box at the bottom of page 10** and fill in the boxes with their best guesses for insulators and conductors. Students will probably have a good idea about common conductors and insulators.

6. **Have the students build the simple testing circuit** at the top of page 11. Ask each team to set up their test circuit using the black-and-red snap wires or their alligator clips. Have students demonstrate how they tested a conductor to ensure they are doing so correctly. Then have them test a variety of materials, and fill in their answers to the questions at the bottom of the page.

Answer Key

Students' answers to the questions at the bottom of page 11 likely will show that, in general, metals are conductors and nonmetals are insulators.

Note: If students are moving quickly, go on to the next activities.

3rd Class

1. **Demonstrate how to use paper clips as probes** with the snap wires (or just alligator wires) as the test circuit. This is necessary in order to test the various parts of the tiny light bulb to see which parts are insulators and which are conductors.

2. **Have the students fill in the blanks on page 12,** indicating which parts of the bulb are insulators and which are conductors.

3. **Introduce the concept of a circuit.** Have the students read the box at the bottom of page 12. Invite and answer questions, then test their understanding by asking them to draw a circuit to show how to light

Engineering the Future Teacher Guide
©2008 Museum of Science, Boston

Preparation

a bulb at the top of page 13. Students do not need to use a colored pencil, but the color does help to see where they've drawn lines. Walk around the room and look at their drawings.

4. **The important thing for students to realize** is that they should always think about where the continuous conducting path is through components. If necessary, lead a large-class discussion about how the electricity is flowing through the entire circuit.

5. **Demonstrate that an electrical cord has two wires.** Students might not realize that a single electrical cord is really two separate wires with their insulation often fused together. This might explain why many students fail to realize that there are two contacts on a bulb to connect to the two ends of a battery. Split an electrical cord in two—if you have a scrap available—to show that lamps and other electrical appliances are also components of circuits with wires going to both poles of an energy source.

6. **Have the students answer the benchmark questions** at the bottom of page 13.

7. **Prepare for the Scoreboard Design Challenge.** The next activity may take more than a full class period, so if there is time, get it started during the previous session. Do the following:

   • Using the student kits, have student pairs examine the seven-segment display module and then read the activity on page 14.
   • Answer any questions the students may have about what they are supposed to do. Explain that they will make the circuit shown at the bottom of page 14 the next day. Collect the materials. Or, if there is time, have the students go on and do the entire activity. (If students are struggling, explain to them that the snap parts will not all be at the same level. Students must "build up" at certain connections.)

4th Class

1. **Have students do the Scoreboard Challenge on page 14.** You may need to help students troubleshoot their circuits. (Note: This activity can be completed with one student kit, but it requires the most parts of any activity.) Explain to students that they will be using all of their snap wire connectors (1, 2, 3, 4, 5, and 7). To ease in building the circuit, the diagram was labeled with numbers to specify the snap wire connector used. Explain to students that at certain connections they will need to "build up" using the snap parts. Besides the grid, there are three levels to this build.

2. **Have students answer questions 1–4** on the lower-left side of the page by disconnecting the snap wires as indicated. They should put the snap wires back before answering the next question. For part 4, students can use the red-and-black snap wires in their kit.

1) 8
2) 0
3) +
4) No

3. **Encourage the students to go further** and disconnect the other snap conductors, one at a time, to see what happens. They will be able to form any number by disconnecting the right connector(s).

4. **If students are puzzled** about why the display does not work when the poles of the battery holder are reversed, explain that these lights are not ordinary light bulbs. They are LEDs—Light-Emitting Diodes—which will only work when electricity passes through them in one direction, but not the other direction.

5. **Ask the students to read page 15** and to create a binary code sequence for each combination of circuits that is required to display any digit from 0 to 9.

6. **Discuss the significance of the binary code** with your students. Ask them if they know of other uses for binary codes. Explain that all computers function with binary codes, using just two digits—0 and 1—which means that a circuit is either open (0), or closed (1). Because a string of ones and zeros can represent all letters and numbers, *any information can be represented by a binary code.* Although it may be difficult to read binary information without a lot of work, it is a "natural language" for communicating with computers.

6) 11111100 (no decimal point)
7) 0: 11111100 1: 01100000 2: 11011010 3: 11110010
   4: 01100110 5: 10110110 6: 00111110* 7: 11100000
   8: 11111110 9: 11100110

*Please note that the digital number 6 is generally presented with the top, A, LED on. The binary code sequence for that is 10111110.

7. **Introduce communications systems.** Have the students read page 16. Encourage them to work together in pairs. This page introduces terms that will be used later in the course to take a closer look at communications systems. The important thing here is for the students to recognize that the process of communicating a message can be viewed as a system in which information is encoded, transmitted as a signal, then received and decoded.

8. **Have the students demonstrate their understanding** of communications systems by filling in the boxes at the bottom of page 16. They will revisit these important ideas in later tasks.

9. **Assign Homework.** Ask the students to read Chapter 24, "A Highway for Ideas," in their textbooks and to answer the questions

at the end of the chapter. (Note: You may want to collect the seven-segment display module from the kits because students will no longer specifically need this part.)

Assessment   Look at students' responses in their *Engineer's Notebooks* to see how well they were able to explore insulators and conductors, observe how a light bulb includes both types of materials, and demonstrate their understanding of a circuit. Check their codes on page 15 to determine whether they are able to construct binary code sequences in response to the major challenge of Task 4.1.

It is just as important for your students to know why certain circuits do not work as it is for them to know why others do work. Draw some simple circuits on the board and ask students to explain whether or not the bulb will light, and, if not, to explain why.

At the conclusion of the last class, ask students to write their ideas to the focus questions, then discuss them in class:

- What do the parts in the Snap Circuits™ kit do?
- What is needed to make an electrical circuit?
- What are insulators? What are conductors?
- How can circuits be combined to build complex electrical systems?
- What is a binary code? How can it be useful?
- How is information transmitted from one place to another?

If students have difficulty with one or more of these questions, spend additional time on that part of Task 4.1 before going on.

Background and Further Suggestions

Students who finish early can use their Snap Circuits™ kit to meet additional challenges, such as:

- Light two bulbs with the same circuit, so that they are both just as bright as a single bulb.
- Connect a red or green LED to a test circuit and determine whether it is a conductor or insulator. Remove it from the circuit and reconnect it so that the direction is reversed. Then test it again. (The current will only conduct in one direction.) If students look carefully at the LEDs, they will notice that there is a flat side and a rounded side. The rounded side connects to the positive side of the battery. Remember, LEDs should only be used in conjunction with a 100-ohm resistor in series.

Students' mental models for circuit behavior. Most people know how to flip a switch or plug a cord in a socket and use electricity, but few understand what is going on in the wires. Educational research has revealed four main ideas that students hold about electrical flow in circuits, in some cases even after they have been told how circuits work. If there is time and interest, invite your students to discuss how they think the electricity is flowing in a simple circuit like the one shown below, but do not pronounce them "right" or "wrong" at this point. In Task 4.4 the students will use an ammeter to find out that evidence only supports the last model.

"Source-Sink" or "Single Wire" model: Electric current flows from battery to bulb and gets used up. Only one wire is needed. The second wire acts as a "safety" wire, or is "just required to get the bulb to light," like a catalyst in chemistry.	*No current* *Current* *No current*
"Clashing currents" model: Electric current comes from each end of battery to the bulb, and there may be two different types of electricity ("plus" and "minus"). Some students say these two types of current produce a "spark" to make the bulb light.	*Opposite current*
"Consumption" model: There is more electric current in the "outgoing" wire than in the "return" wire. The bulb "uses up" or "wears out" the current, and eventually the batteries "run out." Current and energy might be considered the same thing.	*Less current* *More current* *Less or no current*
"Scientist" model: The current is the same everywhere in the circuit, and continues in one direction as long as the circuit is not broken. Electric current is not "used up."	*Same current* *Same current* *Same current*

Systems approach to electronics. The "Systems Approach" to electronics was developed in the United Kingdom. Its aim is to get students designing circuits quickly, using a functional understanding of the parts without worrying about how they're going together in a circuit. The kits that are used with the Systems Approach have circuit boards with a component to be connected with other circuit boards. The emphasis is on inputs, outputs, and any "processing" (like amplification) that occurs in between. It is a problem-solving, design-based approach and seems to be effective in helping students think analytically about circuits and avoid some misconceptions.

Engineering the Future adapts some of this functional approach, but also uses a more traditional approach that emphasizes the concept of a circuit. This perspective will be especially important when students are asked to analyze parallel and series circuits in subsequent tasks.

References and Resorces
General

Barclay, J.A. and D.R. Hutton. "Systems Approach for Teaching Electronics to Scientists." *American Journal of Physics*. April 1977. Volume 45, Issue 4, 367–370.

Cosgrove, Mark and Roger Osborne. "A Teaching Sequence on Electric Current." In Roger Osborne (Ed.), *Learning in science: The implications in children's science*. 1985. 112–123.

Electronic Systems with Control Studio. Available on the Control Studio 2 software CD-Rom, New Wave Concepts Limited, 2003.

Geddes, Mike. *Electronics through Systems*. London: Peter Peregrinus Ltd., IEE Educational Series, 1983.

Geddes, Mike. "The Systems Approach in Electronics Teaching." *Physics Education*. 1984. Volume 19, 268–271.

Misconceptions About Electricity

Bano, Yasmeen and Harcharan Pardhan. "Science Teachers' Alternate Conceptions about Direct Currents." *International Journal of Science Education*. Volume 23, Issue 3, 301–318. 2001.

Beh, Kian Lim and Robin Millar. "Students' Understanding of Voltage in Simple Parallel Electric Circuits." *International Journal of Science Education*. 1993. Volume 15, Issue 4, 351–361.

Borges, A.T. and J.K. Gilbert. "Mental Models of Electricity." *International Journal of Science Education*. 1999. Volume 21, Issue 1, 95–117.

Carr, Malcolm, Mark Cosgrove, and Roger Osborne. "Using practical and technological problems to promote conceptual change." In Duit et al (Eds.), *Aspects of Understanding Electricity*. 1985. 247–256.

Dupin, Jean-Jacques and Samuel Joshua. "Conceptions of French Pupils Concerning Electric Circuits: Structure and Evolution." *Journal of Research in Science Teaching*. 1987. Volume 24, Issue 9, 791–806.

Dupin, Jean-Jacues and Samuel Joshua. "Using 'Modeling Analogies' to Teach Basic Electricity: A Critical Analysis." In Michel Calliot (Ed.), *Learning Electricity and Electronics with Advanced Educational Technology*, 39–55. Berlin: Springer-Verlag, 1993.

Gentner, Dedre and Donald Getner. "Flowing Waters or Teeming Crowds: Mental Models of Electricity." In D. Gentner and A. L. Stevens (Eds.), *Mental Models*, 99–129. Hillsdale, NJ: Lawrence Erlbaum Associates, 1983.

Gentner, Dedre and Yvette Tenney. "What Makes Analogies Accessible: Experiments on the Water-Flow Analogy for Electricity." In. Duit et. Al (Eds.), *Aspects of Understanding Electricity*, 311–318. 1985.

Finley, Fred and Patricia Heller. "Variable Uses of Alternative Conceptions: A Case Study in Current Electricity." *Journal of Research in Science Teaching*. 1992. Volume 29, Issue 3, 259–275.

Hartel, Hermann. "The Electric Circuit as a System." In Duit et. Al (Eds.), *Aspects of Understanding Electricity*, 352. 1985.

Hartel, Hermann. "The Electric Voltage." In Duit et. Al (Eds.), *Aspects of Understanding Electricity,* 353–362. 1985.

Iona, Mario. "Teaching Electrical Resistance." *The Physics Teacher.* May 1979. 299–305.

Iona, Mario. "In My Opinion: We Ought to Use the Conventional Current Direction." *The Physics Teacher.* May 1983. 334.

King, Tom and Robin Millar. "Students' Understanding of Voltage in Simple Series Electric Circuits." *International Journal of Science Education.* 1993. Volume 15, Issue 3, 339–349.

Kruger, Colin, Jenny Mant, and Mike Summers. *Current Understanding.* London, England: Oxford University Department of Educational Studies, 1995.

McDermott, Lillian and Peter Shaffer. "Research as a Guide for Curriculum Development: An Example from Introductory Electricity. Part I: Investigation of Student Understanding." *American Journal of Physics.* November 1992. Volume 60, Issue 11, 994–1003.

Osborne, Roger. "Towards Modifying Children's Ideas about Electric Current." *Research in Science & Technological Education.* 1983. Volume 1, Issue 1, 73–82.

Osborne, Roger and Ross Tasker. "2: Science Teaching and Science Learning." In Osborne, Roger; Freyberg, Peter, Heinemann (Eds.), *Learning in Science,* 15–27. 1985.

Shipstone, David. "Electricity in Simple Circuits." In Driver et al (Eds.), *Children's Ideas in Science,* 33–51. Open University Press, 1985.

Shipstone, David. "Pupils' Understanding of Simple Electrical Circuits." *Physics Education.* 1988. Volume, 2, 92–96.

Shipstone; von Rhoneck; Jung; Karrqvist; Dupin; Joshua; Licht. "A Study of Students' Understanding of Electricity in Five European Countries." *International Journal of Science Education.* 1988. Volume 10, Issue 3, 303–316.

Stocklmayer, Susan and David Treagust. "Images of Electricity: How do Novices and Experts Model Electric Current?" *International Journal of Science Education.* 1996. Volume 18, Issue 2, 163–178.

Storey, Neil. *Electronics: A Systems Approach.* Second Edition. Harlow: Addison-Wesley, 1998.

Task 4.2:	**Design a Mouse Detector**
Overview	Task 4.2 introduces students to the rest of the parts in their Snap Circuits™ kit and challenges them to create a "mouse detector" that sends an electronic signal when it senses the presence of a mouse. The primary purpose of this activity is for the students to realize that they can be creative in designing circuits to carry out a given task. Encourage students to use as many of the different components as possible in designing their mouse detector.
Five Es	**Explore** the various components in their Snap Circuits™ kits; **Elaborate** their understanding by designing a circuit; **Explain** how they think it will work; **Evaluate** their understanding by testing the circuit to see if it works.
Time Frame	4 class periods
Focus Questions	• What does it mean to design an electrical circuit? • How is information transmitted electrically from one place to another?
Objectives	Students will be able to: • Identify components of a circuit, including input devices, output devices, energy sources, and controllers (e.g., switches) • Identify the function of all of the parts in their kit • Design a simple circuit and explain its functional operation
Materials	For every two students: 1 basic Snap Circuits™ kit for ETF curriculum
Preparation	Do the activities described in the *Engineer's Notebook* before the first class so you will be better able to assist students. Following are some possible mouse detector circuits:

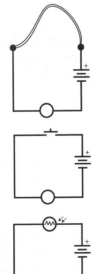

Top: This circuit uses a trip wire as a controller and bulb as an output device. When the mouse trips on the wire, one end will disconnect and the bulb will go out. Disadvantage: the bulb must be on all the time until a mouse trips the wire, which drains the batteries.

Middle: This circuit uses a press switch as the input and a bulb as the output. A board is placed on top of the switch. When the mouse steps on it, the added weight closes the circuit and the light goes on. Disadvantage: You need to monitor the light. Also, because students do not have a press switch in their kit, they can only draw a schematic.

Bottom: Another option is to use a photoresistor as the input device. Place cheese on top of the photoresistor. When the mouse eats the cheese, the light turns on. Students may find that this circuit works better with an LED and resistor than with the light bulb.

Engineering the Future Teacher Guide
©2008 Museum of Science, Boston

Project 4.0

1st Class

1. **Discuss the homework.** Lead a whole-group discussion. Have students share their answers.

2. **Have the students read page 17,** which presents the challenge (to design a mouse detector) and which gives some guidelines for using the electrical components, including batteries. Answer any questions the students may have.

3. **Have the students read and complete the activity on pages 18 and 19.** The purpose of this activity is for the students to learn about the function of each component in their kit by building the circuit they used previously to test conductors and insulators. They may also want to put the meter into the circuit in place of the bulb to test components that are not easily tested with the bulb alone. The students fill in the boxes on page 19 as they learn more.

4. **The students are not asked to investigate all components** at this time. They are not asked to explore the capacitor, which is used in the amplifier and radio activities, but whose function is not explicitly addressed in the course. They are also not asked to explore the resistors at this time (except for the photoresistor), which they will explore later, in Task 4.5. Nor are they asked to explore the plastic grid, snap wires, fan, or two-spring socket device whose functions are obvious.

Note: If students do not finish with this activity, continue during the second class.

2nd Class

1. **Complete the activities on pages 18 and 19.** When students have questions, help them by suggesting that they try different test circuits. Or feel free to give straight answers, as the main goal of this activity is for the students to become aware of how the various components function.

2. **Meet the challenge.** When students have finished filling in the grid on page 19, have them read page 20 and start their design challenge: to design a circuit that would detect the presence of a mouse and send a signal.

3. **Discuss the steps of the engineering design process** on page 20, and ask for questions about what they are expected to do. Point out that the investigations they did to find out the function of the components in their kits was one form of research.

4. **Students should work in groups of two,** using the materials in their basic student kit, although you may want to provide other materials if the students have specific requests. Allow teams to work on their designs for the rest of the period. They should use the materials to test possible ideas before deciding on a solution.

Engineering the Future Teacher Guide
©2008 Museum of Science, Boston

3rd Class

1. **Have the students read the rubric** for judging their designs at the bottom of page 20. Tell them that although they are working in teams, they will each be expected to prepare a written description of their mouse detector, including a schematic diagram.

2. **Answer any questions** they may have, and then allow them to spend some time finishing their designs.

3. **Have students form groups and exchange ideas.** At the end of class, take 15 minutes to have students exchange their drawings with another team and brainstorm the pros and cons of each solution. For homework, have teams finish up their reports and any ideas for redesign.

4th Class

1. **Have each team of two present their ideas** to the class and demonstrate how their circuit works. After each presentation, ask, "What are the advantages of this design? What are the disadvantages?"

2. **Focus questions.** Conclude the class by discussing the focus questions:

   - What does it mean to design an electrical circuit?
   - How is information transmitted electrically from one place to another?

Assessment

Assess the students' designs and explanations, using the rubric on the bottom of page 20. Note common difficulties that you can address in class the next day.

Look for evidence in their reports and discussions that your students may hold the various mental models about circuits, described in the "Background and Further Suggestions" section of Task 4.1. You do not need to address these yet, but it will be helpful to be aware of them early on.

Background and Further Suggestions

You may want to ask students who finish early to experiment with the materials. Or they can write a supplement to their assignment concerning different input devices that could be used, and different output devices so that a person who cannot hear or see receives the signal.

Why do light bulbs glow? Students can rub their hands together and feel them getting warmer as a result of the rubbing. This is used as an analogy for what happens when charge flows through a conductor that provides some resistance—some energy goes toward making the conductor warmer. Bulb filaments are heated when the charge flows through and "rubs against fixed matter," kind of like water flowing past rocks. The light is caused by the glowing of the heated filament inside the bulb.

Task 4.3:   Design a Communications System

Overview

The purpose of any communications system is to transmit a message from one place to another. As the students learned in previous tasks, all communications systems involve encoding a message, transmitting a signal, then receiving and decoding the signal to get the message. This task focuses on the signal itself. Students learn about analog and digital signals; the difference between AM and FM signals; how signals can travel as patterns in electricity, light, and radio waves; and how these different types of waves are related through the electromagnetic spectrum.

Students expand their understanding of these systems by building an amplifier, AM and FM radio, and communicating with light. Finally, they collaborate in teams to use the engineering design process and their knowledge of communications to recommend a communications system that NASA could use to support a future moon colony.

Five Es

Engage students in building and using communications devices; **Explore** the various ways that messages can be encoded as signals; **Explain** how many of these signals are related through the electromagnetic spectrum; **Elaborate** on what they have learned by designing a series of communications systems for a moon colony.

Time Frame

6 class periods

Focus Questions

• How do communications systems work?
• How do telephones work?
• What are analog and digital signals?
• How can one signal be transmitted as sound, electricity, and light?
• What are fiber optics?

Objectives

Students will be able to:
- Identify the components of a communications system
- Describe what amplifiers do
- Explain what radios and telephones do as communications systems
- Differentiate between a message and its signal
- Differentiate between digital and analog signals
- Explain how fiber-optic cables carry a signal in the form of light

Materials

For the class:
   3 or 4 functioning remote-control devices (such as for a TV)
   Optional: fiber optics demonstration materials

For every four students:
   1 Snap Circuits™ kit package for ETF curriculum
   2 20-foot lengths of speaker wire (optional)
   2 copies of the following page on the U4 amplifier circuit (optional)

What's Inside the Amplifier?

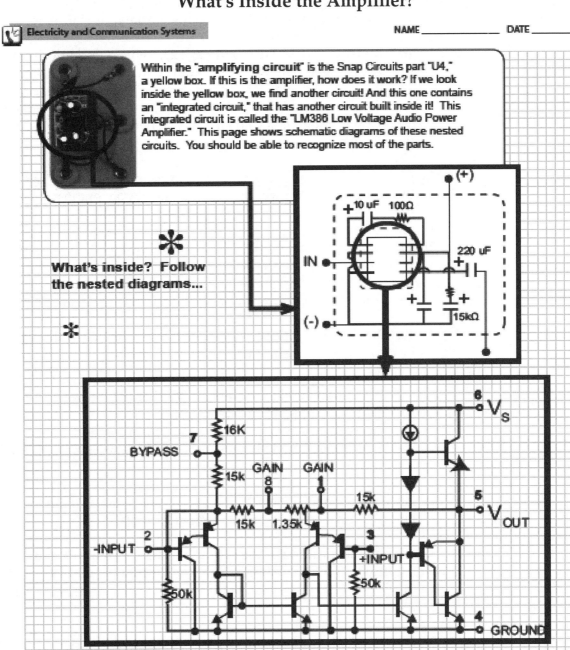

Within the "amplifying circuit" is the Snap Circuits part "U4," a yellow box. If this is the amplifier, how does it work? If we look inside the yellow box, we find another circuit! And this one contains an "integrated circuit," that has another circuit built inside it! This integrated circuit is called the "LM386 Low Voltage Audio Power Amplifier." This page shows schematic diagrams of these nested circuits. You should be able to recognize most of the parts.

What's inside? Follow the nested diagrams...

Even though you may not know how the "amplifier circuit" works, you can still use it. Knowing how to use something without understanding how it works is not uncommon in engineering. The "amplifier circuit" takes in a signal and outputs a bigger signal. That's good enough for now.

| Preparation | Do all the activities in this task before class. Notice that not all circuits are built from scratch; some are slightly modified from those built previously. |

1st Class

1. **Ask students to read the top of page 21.** Invite questions. Explain that in this task the students will build communications systems, and, by the end, they will be familiar enough with communications to advise NASA on what kinds of systems they will need for the first Moon Base—though, of course, they will not actually be building those systems.

2. **Have students read the bottom half of page 21.** Ask them to write their answers to the three questions at the bottom of the page.

Answer Key

1) The scoreboard signal is in the form of binary (on-off) code.
2) Answer will depend on what the students designed.
3) When two people are standing a few feet from each other, and one person says something, a signal is then sent to the other person in the form of sound, sound waves, or vibrations in the air.

3. **Test the students' ability to separate the message from the signal** by asking questions such as:

   - "When you watch the news on TV, what's the message?" (The news stories.) "What's the signal?" (Either radio waves in the air or electrical patterns in a cable.)
   - "When you answer a question, what's the message?" (Whatever you want to tell me.) "What's the signal?" (Vibrations in the air between your mouth and my ear.)

4. **Have students read page 22** and ask for questions. Explain that binary codes are just one form of digital signals.

5. **Discuss the meaning of the section on changes in pitch and amplitude.** You can demonstrate the distinction by humming a note in which pitch is sustained, but the volume (amplitude) gets louder and softer.

6. **Have students read the top of page 23,** concerning AM and FM radio signals. The idea that radio signals are not the carrier waveform itself, but rather how it is changed in amplitude (AM) or frequency (FM), is very difficult for most students to grasp. Ask them to look carefully at the images of both types of waveforms and notice how in each case the top two waveforms add together to produce the waveform at the bottom.

7. **Assign Chapter 25, "Teaching a Machine to Listen," as homework.** Have students answer the questions at the end of the chapter.

Engineering the Future Teacher Guide
©2008 Museum of Science, Boston

8. **Build an FM radio receiver.** If there is time, organize the class in groups of four and give each group one Snap Circuits™ kit package. Have the students study the FM radio receiver design at the bottom of page 23, and identify the parts they will need in their kits. This will allow the groups to work faster during the next session—they will be expected to work fairly quickly. If other students will be using these kits before the next class, have the students put the parts back carefully.

2nd Class

1. **Discuss the homework.** Emphasize the distinction between the message and the signal that carries the message. Have students consider the following: What does it mean to be "intelligent"? Is the ability to decode spoken language a sign of intelligence? If so, can machines be intelligent? Spend whatever time students need to discuss this important idea.

2. **Have students finish assembling the FM radio receiver.** Tell them to examine the controls on their receiver and to answer the four questions to the left of the drawing on page 23. If students are having trouble creating this circuit, tell them that there is more than one way to set up the snap wire connectors to build the circuit.

Answer Key

1) Slide the slider on the variable resistor (triangular component).
2) Push the button on the FM module.
3) It's an antenna. Move the wire around and you can show how the stations come in stronger or weaker.
4) Because it receives messages transmitted by an FM radio transmission somewhere.

3. **Build a voice amplifier.** Have students read page 24, and follow the directions to build a voice amplifier by removing the FM module and inserting a microphone as shown in the illustration on page 24. (Note: They do not have to rebuild the entire circuit.) Students may have to adjust the slider on the variable resistor to get the best output.

4. **Have the students answer the questions on page 24.**

Answer Key

1) You hear your voice a little louder and possibly distorted.
2) Slide the slider on the variable resistor (triangular component).
3) Your voice.
4) Whoever may be listening.
5) Possible answers: Listening to radio, TV, DVDs, or any electronic music. Listening to speeches in the school auditorium. Listening to a live rock band in which the guitar or piano is connected to an amplifier.

Project 4.0

5. **Have the students read the top of page 25,** and fill in their answers to the questions in the two boxes.

6. **Optional: Discuss the idea of "black boxes."** Hand out copies of the sheet "What's Inside the U4 Amplifier Circuit?" This shows the complicated circuitry inside the plastic box labeled "U4." It also shows that inside the circuit is another even smaller circuit on a silicon chip (called an "integrated circuit"). Ask the students if they can identify any of the parts. (They will notice resistors, diodes, and inputs.) Explain that even electrical engineers sometimes use components for a specific function, even though they don't know the details of how the circuit works. They call such mechanisms "black boxes," because they don't know what's inside.

7. **Explain how an amplifier works.** This is a good opportunity to introduce the idea of energy in electrical systems. The purpose of the circuit is to use some of the energy from the batteries to increase the amplitude (volume) of the sound of your voice. The sound is poor quality because the parts being used are inexpensive. Additional electronics are added to commercial amplifiers to improve sound quality, but the principle is the same—electrical energy from batteries or wall current is used to increase the volume of the sound.

8. **Make a telephone.** Conclude the class by having two teams of four students form a group of eight to combine their amplifier circuits to make a telephone. Either give each team two 20-foot lengths of speaker wire or have teams use the snap wires and alligator clips to lengthen the wires attached to the microphone (~3 ft.). Have them use the wires to attach the microphones to their amplifier circuits. Tell the students to set up the two circuits as shown on page 25 and use the two circuits to talk back and forth as through a telephone. Tell them to answer the questions at the bottom of the page.

Answer Key

1) The microphone is the part that you speak into; the speaker is the part you'd put to your ear. The amplifier is somewhere in the body of the phone.
2) The microphone encodes the sound—vibrations in the air—from the mouth as an electrical signal. The electrical signal travels through a wire to an amplifier, and the amplified signal is decoded back into sound by a speaker on the other end.
3) The person on the other end inputs a message that is encoded and travels as an electrical signal. This signal is received and decoded as sound waves, which are interpeted by the destination.

Note: When the last class for the day has completed their work, put the finished amplifier circuits aside for use the next day, rather than having the students disassemble them.

3rd Class

1. **Have the students read page 26,** and then work in groups of four to do the activity at the top of the page. First, have one of the groups replace the speaker in the amplifier circuit with a Light-Emitting Diode (LED) and resistor. Remind students that the diode will work in one direction but not the other, so if it doesn't work at first, they might try reversing the diode. Additionally, students should adjust their variable resistor to the optimal position by speaking into the microphone and watching the Light-Emitting Diode to see if it is responding.

   They should then fill in answers to the questions, as follows:

Answer Key

1) The light changes brightness, getting louder when you speak louder, and going out completely when there is no sound.
2) Just as sound changed before, the light brightness can also be changed as resistance is changed on the variable resistor. There is an optimum resistance range that the LED will really light up in.

2. **Transmitting light signals.** Have the other team in the group build the amplifier circuit with a solar panel (or photoresistor) instead of a microphone. Ask the students to read the second half of page 26 and combine their circuits as described. Holding the solar cell about one inch above the LED from the other system, the students will be able to speak into the microphone in one circuit and hear the sound come out of the speaker in the other circuit. That means that sound travels at a distance of about one inch in the form of light. (Note: It may take a few minutes to adjust the variable resistor to the optimal position in both circuits.)

Answer Key

3) You can hear the sound come out of the speaker of the other circuit.
4) The sound vibrations are turned into a changing electrical signal, amplified, and encoded into a changing light signal by the LED. This signal is received by the solar panel and changed back into an electrical signal. The signal is again amplified and decoded into a sound signal, which is output by the speaker. This signal is finally received as sound by the person listening.

3. **Have the students read page 27,** and draw the path for the beam of light for 1). If you have a piece of fiber optics, now is a good time to lower the lights in the classroom and demonstrate how the glass or plastic fibers conduct light through curves and out the end as a bright light.

4. **For homework, have the students read Chapter 26,** "Shedding Light on Communications," by an engineer from Cisco Systems who works with fiber optics. Tell the students to answer the questions at the end of the chapter.

Project 4.0

4th Class

1. **Discuss homework.** Ask the students to share the answers to the questions at the end of the textbook chapter. Focus on the advantages of fiber optics compared to all-copper wires.

2. **Ask students to read page 28.** It is not intuitive that light, the "stuff" you see with your eyes, is the same "stuff" as radio waves or x-rays. The difference lies in how frequently it oscillates back and forth (called the frequency, measured in the number of cycles per second). Higher frequency means more energy, so higher-frequency carrier waves allow for bigger messages to be transmitted. That is why signals for TV (pictures) use a higher-frequency carrier wave than FM (music), which, in turn, uses a higher-frequency carrier wave than AM (mostly talk).

3. **Demonstrate the sound of a remote control.** As a class or with groups of two teams, have students examine a circuit with a Snap Circuits™ solar cell module connected to an amplifier circuit with a speaker. Point a remote-control device at the solar cell and press the button so that the speaker outputs clicking or beeping sounds. The solar panel picks up the infrared signal from the remote-control device, amplifies it, and turns it into sound. Have your students answer the questions on page 28. They will find that infrared light can be "bounced" off of surfaces, just as light bounces off a mirror—even though you can't see it.

4. **Discuss digital vs. analog signals.** Have students read page 29. Remind them that they have experienced the "digital" nature of the remote-control device with its distinct output. Remind them of other digital and analog signals that they've seen so far in this unit. Have them answer the questions at the bottom of the page.

Answer Key

1) These two devices provide the same information, but one communicates with analog signals and the other with digital signals. What are the advantages and disadvantages of each?

	Advantages	Disadvantages
Analog	Reflects natural sounds and images directly Cheaper technology	Signal can be noisy due to interference
Digital	Less noisy Easier to read More information can be sent in same signal than analog	Requires special electronics Loses some of the detail of analog signals

Engineering the Future Teacher Guide
©2008 Museum of Science, Boston

2) Answers will vary but should include something about digital representation of commands.

5. **Discuss the challenge.** Divide the class into groups of four to tackle the major challenge of Task 4.3. Have the students read the challenge on the top of page 30. Specifically, point out the engineering design process that each team should go through in developing their solution to the challenge.

6. **As a homework assignment, have the students read** Chapter 27, "Riding the Waves," in which Alex Hills describes a communications system he set up for people who live in remote regions of Alaska. Tell them that this chapter will be especially helpful in formulating ideas in response to the challenge of Task 4.3.

5th Class

1. **Review the homework.** Emphasize the way Alex Hills defined the problem, the constraints he had to work with, and how he eventually solved it. This discussion should provide some very good ideas for the students in meeting their own design challenge.

2. **Have teams meet to discuss the challenge.** Remind teams to follow the engineering design process on page 30 and to look at the rubric at the bottom of the page to see how they will be judged. Tell the students that each team will make a short oral report, and that each person should turn in his or her own written report of how his or her team went through the entire engineering design process to find a good solution (or series of solutions) for NASA.

3. **Teams prepare their oral presentations.** Before the end of the period, remind teams that they'll have to make a short oral presentation, decide who will speak, and what they want to share.

6th Class

Allow teams to make oral presentations on how they would advise NASA to solve its communications problem. You might limit each team to a ten-minute presentation, including pictures. After each presentation, invite comments and questions.

Assessment

Conclude Task 4.3 by briefly discussing the focus questions:
• How do communications systems work?
• How do telephones work?
• What are analog and digital signals?
• How can one signal be transmitted as sound, electricity, and light?
• What are fiber optics?

Answers to the above questions will provide some evidence of whether you should revisit the key ideas before going on. The project reports will also indicate whether students can properly identify the main components of a communications system.

Background and Further Suggestions

AM and FM radio signals. Here are Java applets that will allow your students to manipulate AM and FM signals and really get a feel for how they work:

http://contact.tm.agilent.com/Agilent/tmo/an-150-1/classes/liveAM_popup.html
http://contact.tm.agilent.com/Agilent/tmo/an-150-1/classes/liveFM_popup.html

Computer oscilloscope. It can be very helpful for students to see different sounds displayed on an oscilloscope. The Snap Circuits™ 750-in-1 kit comes with a CD that has WinScope software for Windows, authored by Konstantin Zeldovich, and a PC-interface cable, with a mini-headphone plug on one end and alligator clips on the other. A PC version of the software can be found at http://www.mitedu.freeserve.co.uk/Downloads/download.htm. For Macintosh OS X.2 or later, you can download a demo version of SignalScope at http://faberacoustical.com/SignalScope/index.php.

Connect the PC-interface cable to the line-in input jack on a computer. Using the software, display the input signal from the line-in input jack. You can also adjust the horizontal time divisions for the x-axis, with longer times allowing more of the signal to appear on the screen at one time.

A good place to introduce the oscilloscope is with the microphone input and speaker output. If you connect the oscilloscope probes (the alligator clips) across the microphone, you will measure the varying voltage difference (+/- 30mV) being generated by the microphone. If you connect the probes across the output speaker, you'll see the varying voltage difference (+/- 300mV) driving the speaker. This lets students see the analog signal caused by voice sound waves and the amplification effect of the amplifier circuit.

You can also use the oscilloscope for the solar cell and speaker alone to allow the remote-control signal to be heard and seen at the same time, and then to show the amplified signal.

Naming the parts of a communications system. It's a good practice for students to identify the parts of a system using the proper jargon—source, encoder, transmitter, receiver, decoder, and destination. However, it is sometimes difficult to assign a single name to a subsystem. Does a microphone "encode" a sound signal? Does it "transmit" the signal to the amplifier circuit? Does it do both? And does a TV receive, decode, and interpret an "off" signal, thus also functioning as the destination? It's useful to talk about the names, but they are somewhat arbitrary and should be interpreted relative to the rest of the system.

More on analog and digital signals. For the 7-segment display, it's easy to see the relationship between the 8-digit binary number sequence containing 1s and 0s, and the letter or number that appears on the display. This system is known as binary because, just as a bicycle has only two wheels, there are only two numbers used: 1 and 0. A binary signal is a special digital signal; it needs only two levels to represent everything, and these can be represented by a switch that is either on or off. Just like an 8-binary-digit (or bit for short) number can represent a code for displaying a letter or number on the 7-segment display, an 8-bit number could also represent the intensity of a color, or part of an email address used for Internet routing. Thinking of binary numbers can get abstract quickly, but it is at the heart of computing.

Digital signals can also represent analog signals. The sampling rate is the number of measurements made on an analog signal in a second (in Hz). You might also allow students to connect their own devices into the circuits. A CD player can be connected as an input to an amplifier circuit and speaker using a PC-interface cable.

Gelatin fiber-optic cables. You can make a fiber-optic channel from gelatin. You will need the following:

>   4 packages unflavored, clear gelatin
>   1.5 cups very hot water (could come from a water cooler)
>   1 medium-sized container or pan lined with aluminum foil
>   1 sharp knife
>   1 laser point

Mix the gelatin into the hot water and stir for a few minutes until the gelatin dissolves completely. Pour the mixture into the mold until it's about ½-inch deep. Put it in the refrigerator for at least three hours. When it is solidified, remove the aluminum foil and gelatin from the container, then carefully peel off the aluminum foil. Cut some straight ½ in.-wide strips of gelatin, and square off the ends of these strips to make long, rectangular boxes to be used as fiber-optic cables. Students shine a light bulb, LED, and laser (if available) down the cable, with a solar cell or a photoresistor at the other end. (From Graber, Cynthia. "Making Edible Fiber Optics." Scientific America Explorations Magazine, Spring 2001, p. 10–11.)

A more detailed web site reference can be found at http://eosweb.larc.nasa.gov/EDDOCS/RadiationBudget/fiber_optics.html.

Laser modulator. If you have a small laser pointer, you can set it up to be modulated. The laser point can be inserted into the amplifier circuit in place of the LED. The laser pointer normally runs on three 1.5V coin cell batteries, so connecting it between the positive end of the battery and the amplifier output provides a high enough voltage and allows the current through the laser pointer to be modulated. To connect the laser pointer in the circuit, use alligator clips to connect the inner spring to negative (the output of the amplifier), and the outer case to positive (the positive end of the battery).

References and Resources
General

Graf, Calvin. *Exploring Light, Radio, & Sound Energy With Projects.* Blue Ridge Summit, PA: Tab Books, 1985.

Lewis, Edwin and Johnston, John. "A Pie Plate Radio." *The Physics Teacher,* Volume 16, Issue 5, May 1978, p. 302–303.

Manos, Harry. "Hearing Infrared." *The Physics Teacher,* Volume 35, December 1997, p. 552.

Mak, Se-yuen and Din-yan Yip. "The measurement of the speed of light using a laser pointer." Physics Education, Volume 38, Issue 2, March 2000, 95–100.

O'Connell, James. "Decoding the TV Remote Control." *The Physics Teacher,* Volume 38, January 2000, p. 6.

Peterson, John. "Hearing by Bone Conduction." *The Physics Teacher,* Volume 38, Issue 4, 2003, p. 281

Rathjen, Don. "Modulated Coil." *The Physics Teacher,* Volume 36, October 1998, p. 416.

Spradley, Joseph. "Hertz and the Discovery of Radio Waves and the Photoelectric Effect." *The Physics Teacher,* Volume 26, Number 8, November 1988, 492–497.

Taylor, Bernard. "The Amazing String Radio." *Physics Education.* Volume 38, Number 4, July 2003, 281.

Project 4.0

Task 4.4:   Explore Circuits with an Ammeter

Overview

Starting with Task 4.4, the focus shifts from communications to helping students develop a mental model of electricity. This task begins with the discovery that an electric current affects the needle of a nearby magnet. That discovery led to the development of the *ammeter*, a device for measuring the strength and direction of electric current. Students use their ammeters to explore the direction and magnitude of current at various points in a circuit to test alternative ideas for how electric charge is moving in the circuit. Next, students learn the formal definitions for electric current and charge and observe the "Hula-Hoop Model" to reinforce their evolving mental model of electric current and the battery's role. Finally, students use their ammeters to explore the differences between series and parallel circuits.

Five Es

Engage students in measuring current at different points in a circuit; **Explain** the strength and direction of current in a simple circuit; **Elaborate** their understanding of current flow by observing the differences between series and parallel circuits.

Time Frame

3 class periods

Focus Questions

• How does an ammeter measure the strength and direction of an electric current?
• What direction does current flow in different parts of a circuit?
• Do lights connected in a circuit light up one by one or all at once?
• What is the difference in current on both sides of a light bulb?
• What happens to the current at a branch point in a parallel circuit?

Objectives

Students will be able to:
  • Explain how an ammeter works
  • Use an ammeter to measure strength and direction of an electric current
  • Describe electric current as the movement of electric charges through a conductor
  • Predict the brightness of bulbs in series and parallel circuits

Materials

For the class:
  1 Hula Hoop®
  Optional: 1 compass
  Optional: 1 magnet, 1 coil of insulated wire, and large 6-volt battery

For every two students:
  1 basic Snap Circuits™ kit for ETF curriculum

Preparation

Do the various activities on your own before the class so you can help students as needed.

1st Class

1. **Have students read page 31,** about the discovery that led to the invention of the ammeter. Use the compass and coil of wire attached to a battery to demonstrate Oersted's discovery that an electric current affects the needle of a magnet.

2. **Explain how the ammeter works.** Rather than use a compass, which has a magnetic needle, Ampere decided to connect the needle to a coil of wire that was suspended near a permanent magnet. The principle is the same, but this arrangement makes it possible to measure the electric current accurately.

3. **Demonstrate how to use the ammeter.** Show students how to connect an ammeter by making it one component in a series circuit. Discuss the three rules for using ammeters at the bottom of page 31.

4. **Ask students to work individually** to read and answer the questions on page 32. Look at their papers while they are working, or have them tear out the page from the *Engineer's Notebook* carefully for you to look at more systematically later. Compare their ideas with the common concepts of circuits summarized in the "Background" section of Task 4.1. (You may want to code each of their papers according to one of these conceptions, and create a bar graph, or profile, of your students' ideas at this point in the course.)

5. **Hand out Snap Circuits™ kits** and have the students work in pairs to do the activities, and fill in answers to the questions on page 33. Ask students not to change their answers on page 32. They should put their own predictions in the spaces on page 33 before closing (turning on) the switch.

6. **Ask the student teams to see if they can agree** on the answers to the two questions at the bottom of the page.

Answer Key

5) The current moves from the positive side of the battery in a circle, toward the negative side. It moves in the same direction and magnitude before and after the bulb.

6) Answers will vary.

2nd Class

1. **Ask your students to read page 34,** which explains Ben Franklin's idea that electric current consists of a fluid that flows through wires from the positive to the negative side of the battery. He was right that something flows inside the wires. Today you know that the flowing electrical charges are tiny particles called *electrons*, which flow through metals. Even though Ben Franklin was wrong about the direction of charge flow, engineering books and diagrams still use his idea of current flow from positive to negative. Like engineers, this course uses the conventional flow direction.

Project 4.0

2. **Discuss the Hula Hoop model for electrical energy, charge, and current.** These three terms are defined at the bottom of page 34, but it is not easy for students to separate these three distinct but interrelated ideas. One approach to communicate these ideas is to demonstrate the Hula Hoop model as described on the top of page 35. The teacher holds the Hula Hoop firmly while two or three students, who represent lights, hold it lightly with one hand.

Key ideas to demonstrate are that:
- **Charge is everywhere.** It is a basic constituent of all matter. Charge is in the wires, in the battery, and in the light bulb. Charge by itself cannot do anything except carry energy. In the Hula Hoop model students can imagine that charge is embedded throughout the plastic of the Hula Hoop.
- **Electrical energy is stored inside the battery in the form of chemicals.** When the two ends of the battery are connected, a chemical reaction occurs that pulls charge (electrons) toward one side of the battery and pushes it away from the other. Demonstrate this idea by pushing the Hula Hoop in a circle, through the students' hands. The students raise their free hand, indicating that they are lit up, the second they feel the Hula Hoop move.
- **Current is represented by the moving Hula Hoop.** There is current as long as you, the battery, put energy into the system by pushing the charge through the circuit, represented by pushing the hoop around.

Another good analogy is water waves. The water is like the charge. It is there whether or not there are waves. An energy source is needed to get the waves moving, and once it is moving there is a current of energy that moves along with the waves.

The Hula Hoop model is demonstrated in the ETF "Teacher Tips" DVD.

3. **As a homework assignment,** have the students answer the questions at the bottom of page 35.

Answer Key

1) The correct answer is yes, because charge moves everywhere in the circuit at once. Students may have difficulty grasping this idea.
2) The direction and magnitude of the moving charge—that is, the current—must be the same everywhere in the circuit.
3) True or false:
   A. False.
   B. True.
   C. False. Charge is always present.
   D. True.
   E. True.

Engineering the Future Teacher Guide
©2008 Museum of Science, Boston

3rd Class

1. **Hand out basic student kits to pairs of students.**

2. **Ask the students to read page 36,** which describes how to use the tic marks on the meter to measure electric current.

3. **Measure the current flow through a light bulb** connected to two AA batteries. Make sure your students connect the ammeter in series with the bulb and battery. 1) *0.3 amps.*

4. **Measure current in series and parallel circuits.** Have the students read about types of circuits at the bottom of page 36, then assemble the circuits shown on page 37. Tell them to be sure to predict what current they'll read and how bright the bulbs will be before they actually build the circuit. Bulb brightness can be indicated on a scale of 0 (no light) to 5 (very bright).

Answer Key

1) How does the current change when you add another bulb in a series circuit? Current goes down.
2) What happens to the current at the branch point in a parallel circuit? The current splits into two branches. Current in the parallel circuit is greater than when the same number of bulbs is used in a series circuit.

5. **Assign homework.** Ask students to read Chapter 28 "Designed Learning," in which Joel Rosenberg describes his mental models of the universe. They should also answer questions at the end of the chapter.

Assessment

Ask the students to answer the Benchmark Questions on page 38.

Answer Key

1) Only A and B should be circled.
2) Correct answer is E. All of the Above.
3) Which statements are true, which are false, and why?
   A. Bulb 1 is brighter than all the others. False: Bulb 1 is equally as bright as bulbs 4 and 5 because bulbs 4 and 5 are in parallel.
   B. Bulb 2 is brighter than bulb 3. False: They are equally bright; because they are in the same series circuit, there must be the same current running through both.
   C. Bulb 4 is brighter than bulb 5. False: Both are wired in parallel, so both are equally as bright.
   D. Bulbs 2 and 3 are brighter than bulbs 4 and 5. False: Bulbs 2 and 3 are wired in series, while bulbs 4 and 5 are wired in parallel. Bulbs 4 and 5 are brighter.
4) Explain how the stream idea represents what happens to the flow of charge in these two (series and parallel) kinds of circuits. In a parallel circuit the water splits at a branch point, with some going one way and some going another. Each stream then provides energy. In a series circuit the water stays in one stream, so the energy must be shared all along its length.

Background and Further Suggestions

Students may struggle to acquire a scientific view of electricity. Many students start with the idea that something flows and is used up in the circuit, but they don't realize that there are two flows (charge and energy) rather than just one (electricity).

The next obstacle is when students think that the battery provides the charge for the circuit, instead of considering that the charge is everywhere to begin with and the battery simply moves it.

The third obstacle is realizing that energy is transferred from a battery to a bulb (or motor or other load), where it leaves the circuit, and eventually depletes the energy in the battery. In contrast, charge does not leave the circuit, but continues to move around and around, as long as there is energy to drive it.

The purpose of the Hula Hoop demonstration is to help students visualize these ideas so that they become part of the students' mental model of what is going on in a circuit. It may help them to revisit the Hula Hoop demonstration a few days later to see how well they recall and understand these ideas.

Conventional charge flow vs. electron flow. One argument for sticking with conventional charge flow is that electrical engineers draw schematics using the conventional direction. Also, students invent the idea of charge, instead of simply accepting the teacher's idea of electrons without evidence of their existence. This is more like what researchers did for hundreds of years before the discovery of the electron (by J.J. Thompson in 1897). It also makes the model more personal and imaginative for students. Revising the conventional charge flow model to account for electron flow in the opposite direction is a revision that can occur later.

References and Resources
Historical

Nielsen, Rud. "Hans Christian Oersted—Scientist, Humanist and Teacher." *American Physics Teacher,* 7, 10–22, 1939.

Water Circuits

Bauman, Robert. "Hydraulic Models For Electrical Circuit Elements." *The Physics Teacher,* Volume 18, May 1980, 378–380.

Greenslade, Thomas B. "The Hydraulic Analogy for Electric Current." *The Physics Teacher,* Volume 48, November 2003 464–466.

Koumaras, Panagiotis. "A New Hydraulic Model For The Electric Circuit." *School Science Review,* September 2003, 85(310), 19–23.

Krishnan, Sudha and Monoranjan Rao. "Hydrostatic Analogy For The Two-Capacitor Problem." *American Journal of Physics,* Volume 50, Issue 7, July 1982, p. 662.

Madsen, Ernest. "A Water Flow Analogy To Capacitor Discharge." *The Physics Teacher,* Volume 14, Issue 4, April 1976, p. 236–239.

Mayer, Raymond and John Jeffires. "Capacitor-Hydraulic Analogy." *The Physics Teacher,* Volume 31, May 1993, 260.

Newburgh, R.G. "Capacitors, Water Bottles, and Kirchoff's Loop Rule." *The Physics Teacher*, Volume 31, January 1993, 16–17.

Pfister, Hans. "Illustrating Electric Circuit Concepts with the Glitter Circuit." *The Physics Teacher (42)*, September 2004, p. 359–363.

Schwedes, Hannelore, and Wolff-Gerhard Dudeck. "Teaching Electricity by Help of a Water Analogy (How to Cope with the Need for Conceptual Change)." 50–63.

Schwedes, Hannelore. "The Importance of Water Circuits in Teaching Electric Circuits." *Aspects of Understanding Electricity*, ed. Duit et al, 1985, 319–329.

Smith, Frederick, and Jerry Wilson. "Electrical Circuits and Water Analogies." *The Physics Teacher*, Volume 12, Issue 396, October 1974, p. 396–399.

Task 4.5:   Explore Circuits with a Voltmeter

Overview

In Task 4.5 students are introduced to the idea of "voltage difference." To demystify the inside of a battery, students make a lemon battery. They also make a voltmeter, using an ammeter and a variable resistor—in fact, commercial voltmeters are just ammeters with a resistor in series. The combined ammeter-resistor component that makes up the voltmeter is connected in parallel to measure the change in voltage across that part of the circuit. (By including a switch so users can choose among different resistors, commercial voltmeters are able to measure different voltage ranges.) The key concept that makes this possible is Ohm's law—the relationship of voltage, current, and resistance ($V = IR$). Students learn about resistors before they are introduced to Ohm's law. They then use their built voltmeter to explore voltage differences in series and parallel circuits. Finally, the students use Ohm's law to measure resistance.

Five Es

Engage students in making a lemon battery, a voltmeter, and ohmmeter; **Explore** circuits using their built voltmeter and ohmmeter knowledge; **Explain** how Ohm's law makes it possible to construct a voltmeter using an ammeter and resistors; **Elaborate** students' understanding by building and measuring various series and parallel circuits.

Time Frame

3 class periods

Focus Questions

- What is electrical resistance?
- How does total resistance change when resistors are combined in series and parallel?
- What is voltage and how is it different from current?
- How is voltage related to current and resistance?
- How does voltage change when additional components are added?

Objectives

Students will be able to:
- Describe how to make an electric cell
- Explain how to make a voltmeter and ohmmeter
- Use a voltmeter to measure voltage in parallel and series circuits
- Calculate resistance of two or more resistors
- Use Ohm's law to find voltage, current, or resistance
- Predict how the addition of components will change the voltage

Materials

For every two students:
  1 basic Snap Circuits™ kit for ETF Curriculum
  1 lemon
  2 nails or screws of two different metals (e.g., copper and zinc)
  5–6 straws of at least two different diameters
  1 plastic cup for water

For the class:
  ½ cup of salt

Engineering the Future Teacher Guide
©2008 Museum of Science, Boston

Preparation	Try all activities yourself before presenting them to the students.

1st Class

1. **Students make electric cells.** Have the students read page 39, which introduces the task and describes how to make an electric cell. Hand out Snap Circuits™ kits, lemons, and nails of two different metals to teams of two students, and ask students to follow directions on page 39 to make an electric cell. They should also fill in the answers to the three questions on page 39. (It requires a large number of lemons to light a light bulb, but with enough lemons students may be able to light an LED.)

2. **Ask students to share their answers** to the three questions and to share their results. Then have students read about the invention of the battery by Alessandro Volta on page 40.

Answer Key

1) Answers will vary.
2) The current flows from the copper side to the zinc side.
3) The copper is the positive side; the zinc is the negative side.

3. **Collect the lemons and nails** and hand out several straws of at least two different diameters to the teams of students. Caution the students that for health reasons they should not blow through a straw that someone else blew through. Ask them to try the three activities shown on page 40 and to write their answers to the questions about resistance.

4. **Ask the students to summarize** the results of their experiments.

   1. Which combination of straws was easiest to blow through?
   2. Which straws were hardest to blow through?

5. **Have the students read** about resistance in electrical circuits at the bottom of pages 40 and 41. Ask, "How is resistance in straws similar to resistance in wires?" (Resistance increases when electricity has to flow through a thinner or longer wire.)

6. **Invite the students to try the activity** at the top of page 41, in which they create a circuit using two bulbs, a battery, and a jump wire. The students will notice that when the jump wire is connected, one of the bulbs will go out and the other becomes brighter. Ask, "In terms of resistance, why do you think that one bulb goes out?" (The current will flow through the jump wire rather than through the filament because it has less resistance.) "How can you explain why the other bulb glows brighter?" (With one of the two bulbs out of the circuit, the total resistance has decreased, so the current is greater.)

7. **Ask the students to read the bottom of page 41,** and to find the various resistors in their kits.

8. **Have students read about loads at the top of page 42.** Answer any questions they may have. Emphasize that any device that uses energy in an electrical circuit is a load.

9. **Ask the students to read the questions about voltage** at the bottom of page 42, and to answer the questions.

   1) What is the voltage difference measured in volts? (1.5 V)
   2) If you connect two cells in series, what will be the difference in voltage from the open end of one battery to the open end of the other? (3.0 V)
   3) Indicate the voltage next to each diagram. (1.5 V [top] and 3.0 V [bottom])

10. **Introduce Ohm's law.** Have the students read the top of page 43 and then apply what they learned about Ohm's law beneath that. Do not skip this page or go over it too quickly. Emphasize that Ohm's law is very important in many different situations, and they will soon find out why.

2nd Class

1. **Review Ohm's law,** which was discussed the previous day. Hand out basic Snap Circuits™ kits to pairs of students. Ask the students to set up the circuits as shown on pages 43 and 44 and to answer the questions by making measurements and calculating answers using Ohm's law. Following are the answers to the questions on pages 43 and 44.

Answer Key

1) In this circuit:
   What is the value of ΔV? 3.0V
   What is the value of I? Measured with ammeter, between 0.3 and 0.4 amps
   What is the value of R? $R = V/I = 3.0V/0.35 \approx 8.6 \ \Omega$

2) In this circuit:
   What is the value of ΔV? 3.0V
   What is the value of I? Measured with ammeter, between 0.2 and 0.3 amps
   What is the value of R? $R = V/I = 3.0V/0.25 \approx 12 \ \Omega$

3) In this circuit:
   What is the value of ΔV? 3.0V
   What is the value of I? Measured with ammeter, between 0.2 and 0.3 amps
   What is the value of R? $R = V/I = 3.0V/0.25 \approx 12 \ \Omega$

4) In this circuit:
   What is the value of ΔV? 3.0V
   What is the value of I? Measured with ammeter, between 0.9 and 1.0 amps
   What is the value of R? $R = V/I = 3.0V/0.95 \approx 3.2 \ \Omega$

How did the fan blade change the circuit? It increased the current.

Why do you think that happened? Adding the fan blade caused the motor to work harder, so it drew more current from the battery. This is like screwing in a higher-wattage light bulb. Higher current means lower resistance. (Do not confuse electrical resistance with physical resistance. Yes, the motor meets more resistance from the air with the fan in place, but its electrical resistance is less than without the fan.)

5) Add a light bulb in series with the motor. Compare the current with the fan blade and without the fan blade....Describe and explain what you observed in terms of Ohm's law. As before, adding the fan blade increases the current, which makes the light bulb glow brighter. Odd as it may sound, adding the fan blade *reduces* the electrical resistance of the circuit.

2. **Ask the students to read page 45,** and build a voltmeter. Help students by checking that they are connecting the ammeter to the correct branch of the variable resistor. Tell them to be careful not to change the position of the slider after it is set. Remind students that the ammeter should be set on low.

3. **Have the students use their voltmeter** to measure the voltage difference between the sets of two points in the circuit shown at the bottom of the page. Remind students that, unlike an ammeter connected in series, a voltmeter is connected in parallel with the component it is measuring voltage across. They should measure the following approximate values:

Answer Key

1) Points A and C: 3.0 V
2) Points A and B: 1.5 V
3) Points B and C: 1.5 V

4. **Use the voltmeter to explore series and parallel circuits** on page 46. Notice that the students need only build two circuits. For each circuit they are asked to predict the voltage between two different points, and then to measure the difference in voltage between those points. They should measure the following approximate values:

A to B: 3 V
C to D: 3 V
E to F: 2 V
G to H: 1 V

5. **Ask the students to answer the questions** at the bottom of page 46.

Answer Key

1) How does voltage change when you add another bulb in a parallel circuit? It does not change at all.

Project 4.0

2) What happens to the voltage at a branch point in a complex circuit? Unlike current, voltage does not split at a branch point. Voltage is the same before and after the branch.

6. **If there is still time at the end of class,** have students compare a circuit with one light bulb, a circuit with two light bulbs in series, and a circuit with three lights bulbs in series. Ask students what they find when they add another of the same light bulb in series. (Students should find the voltage is the same across each light bulb in the circuit and that the sum of the voltages is the value of the total voltage provided by the batteries.)

3rd Class

1. **Review the previous day's lesson** on voltage and brightness in parallel and complex circuits. Hand out basic Snap Circuits™ kits to teams of two students. If students need more time, give them a few minutes to finish the activity, and then discuss observations.

   Ask students, "Have you noticed a difference between the way a voltmeter is connected in a circuit, compared to the way an ammeter is connected." (A voltmeter is connected in parallel with the component that it is measuring the voltage across. An ammeter is connected in series in the circuit to determine the current for the whole circuit.)

2. **Use Ohm's law to determine resistance** with a 1) fixed resistor. Have the students read and do the activities on page 47. In the first activity, they use Ohm's law to predict the current given a known voltage and resistance. They then check this value against the reading of the ammeter to determine the accuracy of their ammeter. Record students' findings on the board to see how much variation there is from meter to meter. The value should be about 0.3 amps. ($I = V/R = 3V / 10\ \Omega = 0.3A$.)

3. **Measure the resistance of the 2) photoresistor.** In the second activity, students use their ammeter to measure the resistance of the photoresistor, using Ohm's law. They will find that the current ranges from zero with no light to over 1 amp, depending on the room light. At 300 microamps (full scale on the low setting), the photoresistor has more resistance than a 10 Ω resistor. ($R = V/I = 3V / 0.0003A = 10,000\ \Omega$).

4. **Measure the resistance of the 3) variable resistor.** In the third activity, students use their ammeter to measure the resistance of the variable resistor, using Ohm's law. By sliding the slider from one end to the other and using both scales on their ammeter, they will find that the current ranges from 30 microamps on low to over 1 amp on high. This means that the electrical resistance ranges from less than 1 Ω to more than 100,000 Ω.

Engineering the Future Teacher Guide
©2008 Museum of Science, Boston

5. **Measure the resistance of 4) water.** In the last activity on page 47, students use their ammeter to measure the resistance of a glass of water. The resistance of water varies greatly depending on the type and amount of impurities. If the current is too high for the low setting and too low for the high setting, you can change the sensitivity of the ammeter for a middle range by connecting a 10Ω resistor in parallel. If that happens, students will not be able to make a quantitative measurement, but they will be able to see how the resistance changes if they add salt to the water. Resistance will decrease as the salt improves the conductivity of the water and the current increases.

6. **As a homework assignment,** ask students to read Chapter 29, "On the Grid," and to answer the questions at the end of the chapter.

Assessment

Ask students to answer the benchmark questions on their own.

Answer Key

1) The first part requires that students use Ohm's law to calculate resistance.

The students are told that $I = 0.1$ A.
The value of ΔV is 3 V.
According to Ohm's law, for the circuit, $R = 30\ \Omega$.
The value of R for each bulb is $R = 10\ \Omega$.

2) Educational research shows that the misconceptions students have about circuits are widespread and difficult to change. By now students should have enough experience with circuits to know that current is the same throughout a series circuit and flows in the same direction around the circuit. This question will help you determine whether they understand this concept, and, if not, what their misconceptions are at this point.

Student A: Only the wire from the positive side is needed: Disagree. Both wires are essential parts of the circuit.
Student B: The electricity is worn out by the time it gets through all three bulbs: Disagree. The electric current will be the same before and after the bulbs.
Student C: Electric current moves away from the battery in both directions, meeting at a lamp or other device. Disagree. Current moves from one side of the battery toward the other side.
Student D: The ammeter will show that the current continues to go in the same direction with the same magnitude all around the circuit. Agree.

Background and Further Suggestions

Thinking of a circuit as a system. In Task 4.4 we differentiated between current and charge. We established that initially charge is everywhere in a circuit and is not provided by the battery. And we reasoned that energy is transferred from the battery to the bulb or other load when the charge is flowing. In Task 4.5 students learn that both the number and the arrangement of bulbs in a circuit affect the current through each bulb, and thus its brightness. The difficulty here is in thinking beyond either the battery or the bulbs as the cause, but instead considering them together as a system.

For example, once students learn that a cell always produces 1.5 volts, it seems natural to think that it always produces the same electric current. In fact, that is not the case; as more light bulbs or motors in parallel are added, they will draw more current. So, although the battery provides the energy to the circuit, it is the entire system of loads and sources and how they are arranged that determine the current in any part of the circuit.

A good analogy for the systems view of circuits is to think of two sisters. Neither girl alone is the "cause" of being sisters. It is the relationship between the two that "causes" them to be sisters. Like sisters, the batteries and bulbs combine together to determine what the current in the circuit will be. The relationship between them is what's important. Neither the battery nor the bulbs alone is the cause of the behavior. That relationship can be expressed mathematically as $\Delta V = I \times R$.

Students still might have a hard time understanding that a change in the bulb or motor in a circuit that is "downstream" from a battery can cause the battery to push more or less charge through a wire. You may be able to help students overcome that difficulty by saying that the battery doesn't just *push* charge through a wire; it also *pulls* charge from the other side of the circuit. This idea can be reinforced with the Hula Hoop analogy.

The variable resistor. Students might be unsure how to connect the variable resistor or how it works. If the two snaps farthest apart are used, it's like a single large resistor, and moving or adjusting the slider will have no effect. If the middle snap is used instead of one of the far snaps, the value of the resistor can be changed, anywhere from no resistance to maximum resistance.

You can demonstrate a model for how the variable resistor works using pencil lead. Put the pencil lead in a circuit with batteries, a bulb, and alligator wires by placing the wire ends along different lengths of the pencil lead. The brightness of the bulb will change accordingly to the distance between the wires ends. The longer the length of the pencil lead between the wire ends, the greater the resistance.

When does Ohm's law apply? Ohm's law is the name given to the equation $\Delta V = IR$, because Ohm discovered that for metallic conductors at constant temperature, the resistance is constant. Physics textbooks usually state that Ohm's law applies only when the resistance, R, is a constant. Most engineering textbooks say that Ohm's law always applies, but that R is not necessarily a constant. To be clear, *resistance* is a measure of an object's ability to hold back or partially block charge flow in circuits. The devices we call "resistors" retain the same measure of resistance across a wide range of electrical currents. For light bulbs, on the other hand, resistance increases as it gets warmer, and for diodes, the resistance decreases as the voltage difference increases.

Engineering the Future Teacher Guide
©2008 Museum of Science, Boston

Students' mental models. The activities in this and the next task are specifically designed to encourage students to reveal their mental models in a way that you can see easily, by looking at their *Engineer's Notebooks* and by listening carefully to their discussions. They should be encouraged to discuss the solutions to problems, as students sometimes learn more from wrestling with problems and arguing with classmates than they do when listening to a teacher explain the right answer. Of course, you'll want to have a mixture of both student discussions and teacher lectures, provided the lectures follow the students' own efforts, so they will be attuned to what you are saying.

It also helps to know what to expect. Educational researchers have questioned students about their understanding of circuits and found a number of common misconceptions. The most common ideas about series and parallel circuits with several bulbs are summarized on the following two pages, including the scientific models that we want students to learn by the time they finish this course.

Students' Mental Models for Two Bulbs in Series

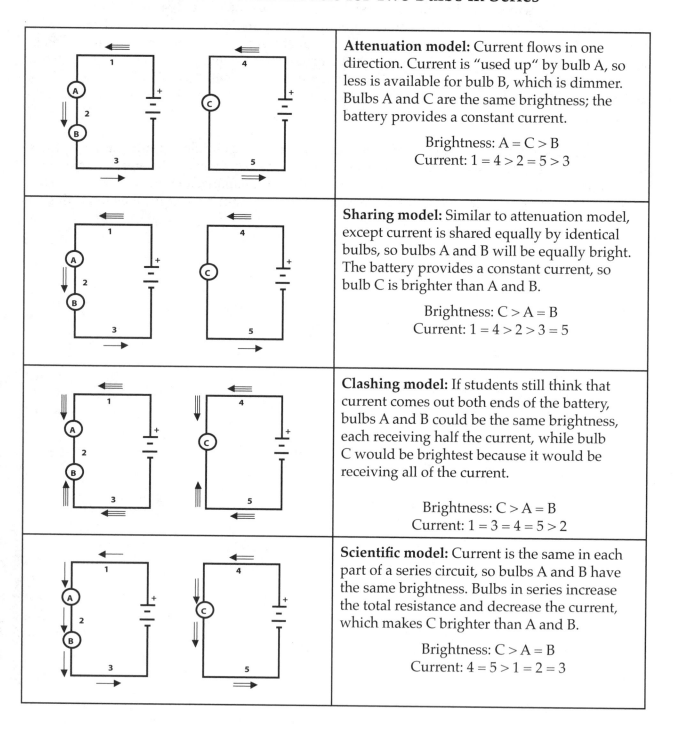

Attenuation model: Current flows in one direction. Current is "used up" by bulb A, so less is available for bulb B, which is dimmer. Bulbs A and C are the same brightness; the battery provides a constant current.

Brightness: A = C > B
Current: 1 = 4 > 2 = 5 > 3

Sharing model: Similar to attenuation model, except current is shared equally by identical bulbs, so bulbs A and B will be equally bright. The battery provides a constant current, so bulb C is brighter than A and B.

Brightness: C > A = B
Current: 1 = 4 > 2 > 3 = 5

Clashing model: If students still think that current comes out both ends of the battery, bulbs A and B could be the same brightness, each receiving half the current, while bulb C would be brightest because it would be receiving all of the current.

Brightness: C > A = B
Current: 1 = 3 = 4 = 5 > 2

Scientific model: Current is the same in each part of a series circuit, so bulbs A and B have the same brightness. Bulbs in series increase the total resistance and decrease the current, which makes C brighter than A and B.

Brightness: C > A = B
Current: 4 = 5 > 1 = 2 = 3

Engineering the Future Teacher Guide
©2008 Museum of Science, Boston

Students' Mental Models for Two Bulbs in Parallel

	Ignore junction: Current is the same at all three points because the current has not yet reached the bulbs. All three bulbs are equal brightness. (Correct prediction, wrong reasoning.) Brightness: A = B = C Current: 1 = 2 = 3 = 4 = 5
	Sharing (equal split) model: Current divides evenly at every junction. Battery provides constant current, so bulb C is brighter than A or B. Because constant current is shared, A is as bright as B. Brightness: C > A = B Current: 1 = 4 = 5 > 2 = 3
	More current goes straight: The current doesn't make "the turn" as easily as it goes straight, so most of the current goes through bulb B, which is as bright as bulb C, and bulb A is dimmer. Brightness: B = C > A Current: 4 = 1 = 3 = 5 > 2
	Current stays closer: More current goes down the closer path, so bulb A is as bright as bulb C, and bulb B is dimmer. Brightness: A = C > B Current: 4 = 1 = 2 = 5 > 3
	Scientific model: The current divides at the junction in proportion to the resistance of the bulbs in each branch. For equal resistances, the current splits evenly. But all bulbs are the same brightness because the overall resistance of the bulbs in parallel allows a bigger current to flow. Brightness: A = B = C Current: 1 > 2 = 3 = 4 = 5

Project 4.0

How to Read the Color Code on a Resistor

The colored bands printed on resistors can be "decoded" using a chart. You can see the resistors mounted on top of the Snap Circuits™ parts. You can check the resistors in the kits to be sure they are labeled correctly.

Color	1st Band first digit	2nd Band second digit	3rd Band* multiplier	4th Band accuracy
Black	0	0	1	
Brown	1	1	10	
Red	2	2	10^2	
Orange	3	3	10^3	
Yellow	4	4	10^4	
Green	5	5	10^5	
Blue	6	6	10^6	
Violet	7	7	10^7	
Gray	8	8	10^8	
White	9	9	10^9	
Gold				5%
Silver				10%
None				20%

* $10^2 = 100$ $10^3 = 1,000$ $10^4 = 10,000$ $10^5 = 100,000$ $10^6 = 1,000,000$ etc.

References and Resources
Ohm's law

Hubin, W. N. "Light on LED's." *The Physics Teacher.* May 1993. Volume 31, Issue 5, 262–263.

Lehman, Thomas A. and Steven A. Waltner. "When Is Ohm's law Valid?" *The Physics Teacher.* February 32, 1993. 102–103.

Monk, Martin. "Introducing Electricity 2: Electricity, Laws, Theories and Physics." *Physics Education.* September 2002. Issue 5, 427–429.

McKnight, John. "Laboratory Notebooks of G.S. Ohm: A Case Study in Experimental Method." *American Journal of Physics.* February 1967. Volume 35, Issue 2, 110–114.

O'Sullivan, Colm T. "Ohm's law and the Definition of Resistance." *Physics Education.* July 1980. Volume 15, Issue 4, 237–239.

Rehfuss, Donald E. "Current Concepts Consolidated." *The Physics Teacher.* February 2004. Volume 42, Issue 2, 103–107.

Schagrin, Morton L. "Resistance to Ohm's law." *American Journal of Physics.* July 1963. Volume 31, Issue 7, 536–547.

Teaching About Electricity

Asami N., King J. and Monk M. "Tuition and Memory: Mental Models and Cognitive Processing in Japanese Children's Work on D.C. Electrical Circuits." *Research in Science & Technological Education.* November 1, 2000. Volume 18, Number 2, 141–154.

Finley, Fred N. and Patricia M. Heller. "Variable Uses of Alternative Conceptions: A Case Study in Current Electricity." *Journal of Research in Science Training.* August 18, 2006. Volume 29, Issue 3, 259–275.

Kariotoglou, P., P. Koumaras, P. and D. Psillos. "Causal Structures and Counter-Intuitive Experiments in Electricity." *International Journal of Science Education.* September 1997. Volume 19, Issue 6, 617–630.

Shipstone, David. "Electricity in Simple Electrical Circuits." *Children's Ideas in Science.* Open University Press. 1985. 33–51.

Trumper, Ricardo. "Applying Conceptual Conflict Strategies in the Learning of the Energy Concept." *Research in Science and Technological Education.* May 1997. Volume 15, Issue 1, 5–18.

Task 4.6:	**Design a Fan Control System**

Overview	In Task 4.6 students are challenged to design a circuit to solve a complex electrical control problem—to control two fans independently, to allow them to be turned on and off, and for their direction to be reversed. As an extra challenge, students can also build in controls for the fans to run at different speeds. To prepare them for this challenge, students are introduced to color coding as a way of analyzing circuits, and several ways to control circuits, as well as the use of LEDs to indicate circuit direction.
Five Es	**Explore** circuits using color coding; **Explain** how to control circuits with the placement of switches, jump wires, and bulbs; **Elaborate** on their understanding of series and parallel circuits to design a fan control system; **Evaluate** their ideas by building the circuits and trying them out.
Time Frame	5 class periods
Focus Questions	• How can you change the direction of a motor? • How can you change the rate at which a motor spins? • How can color coding help you predict what will happen in a circuit? • What do electrical engineers do?
Objectives	Students will be able to: • Analyze an electrical problem and design a circuit to solve it • Turn a motor on and off, reverse its direction, and change its speed • Use parallel and series circuits in a creative design process
Materials	For every four students: 1 Snap Circuits™ kit package for ETF curriculum 1 set of colored pencils or fine-tip markers for every pair of students (yellow, orange, red, green, and blue)
Preparation	Design at least one solution to the challenge before presenting it to your students.
1st Class	1. **Discuss homework.** Soung-Sik Kim's chapter in the textbook, Chapter 29, is about efforts to reduce the environmental impact of burning coal to produce electricity. It also includes a very good overview of how most electricity is produced and distributed through a huge network of circuits called the "North American Grid." Ask students how the distribution of electrical energy relates to the activities they have been doing with circuits. You might ask, for example, if an entire street of houses would be wired in parallel or series. (Parallel, so that the voltage difference for each house would be the same.)

2. **Have the students read the challenge** at the top of page 49. Ask them for any ideas they have about how to solve the challenge. Then tell them that in this task they will learn several things that will help them come up with the best answer they can for the challenge. The first is how to use colors and symbols to analyze complex circuits.

3. **Call attention to the bottom of page 49,** which introduces color coding in circuits. Hand out a set of colored pencils or markers to each pair of students and ask them to color the key at the bottom of page 49.

4. **Have the students turn to page 50** to see other symbols they can use in analyzing circuits.

5. **Hand out basic Snap Circuits™ kits** to pairs of students. Ask them to read the bottom of page 50, color the diagram, and then build this simple circuit and answer the question at the bottom of the page.

6. **Have the students color code the circuits on page 51,** then build them and answer the question "How did the results differ from your prediction?"

   Note: Students should use color-coding and predict what will happen *before* building the circuits. The prediction process encourages the students to construct and modify their mental models. There will be more of these activities on subsequent pages.

7. **Have your students continue on page 52** with the process of color coding, predicting, and then building circuits to see whether their predictions are correct. These circuits will help them understand how to reverse motors (and fans) and to change the motor's speed.

2nd Class

1. **Color code parallel circuits.** By continuing the activity of color coding, predicting, and then building and testing circuits as shown on page 53, your students will build further skills and knowledge to help them meet the challenge for this task. When the motor is added, the three lights in parallel splitting the current do not light. When two of the light bulbs are unscrewed, the third light bulb will start to glow dimly and the motor will slow down.

2. **Have the students color code,** predict, and build the circuits on page 54.

3. **Students may be surprised** to find that closing a switch can actually turn off lights. Usually switches turn on lights, but in this case that doesn't happen. Color coding the circuits at the bottom of the page with the switch open and closed will reveal why that happens.

Project 4.0

When the switch is open, bulb C has one color on one side and another color on the other side—so there is a voltage difference, which drives current through the bulb. But when the switch is closed, bulb C has the same color on both sides, so there is no voltage difference and therefore no current.

4. **Ask students to read page 55 and answer the questions.**

5. **After students have had a chance** to try answering the questions on page 55, ask them for their answers and lead a large-group discussion about how to add resistances in series and parallel. Students need to understand why resistors in series increase the total resistance, while resistors in parallel reduce overall resistance. You may want to reinforce these ideas by recalling the experience of blowing through straws from Project 3.0.

ERROR: There is an error in the *Engineer's Notebook* on the bottom half of page 55. In the diagrams the two bulbs wired in parallel should be labeled "A" and "B" and the bulb at the bottom, wired in series, should be labeled "C." The text should read:

> **5)** When the switch was closed (on), the current ran directly trough bulbs A and B alone, as shown at right. Use the current values found previously to answer these questions. A. What is the resistance of bulbs A and B in parallel?

Answer Key

4) A) ~0.3 amps B) ~0.65 amps C) The current now goes through the two light bulbs in parallel and then through the switch. It does not go though C.

5) A) ~4.6 ohms (resistance of two bulbs in parallel)
   B) ~10 ohms (resistance with the three light bulbs)
   C) When the switch is turned on, the current runs through the single bulb and the parallel combination. Since the current must split at the parallel part and run through the single bulb, it is not strong enough to light the light bulbs in parallel.

3rd Class

1. **Have two student teams work together.** The circuits on page 56 include both parallel and series components. It also offers suggestions about how to use the jump wire as a switch, which will be very helpful in solving the double fan problem. 1) B and C are brighter than A and D. 2) B and C do not even turn on. A is slightly brighter than D. 3) A is bright and both B and D are equally dim.

2. **Color code circuits with diodes.** You do not need Light-Emitting Diodes (LEDs) for meeting the design challenge in this task, but LEDs can also be used as direction indicators in a fan control system. Have the students color code, predict, and build the circuits that use LEDs on page 57.

3. **As homework,** ask the students to read Chapter 30, "Electrifying!," in their textbooks, and to answer the questions at the end of the chapter.

4th Class	1. **Discuss the homework.** Have the students share their answers to the questions. Ken McAuliffe is not an engineer, but as an electrician he needs to solve electrical problems every day, many of which call for circuit design.
	2. **Have the students read the challenge on the top of page 58** and the rubric at the bottom of the page. Group the students in teams of four and provide each team with one Snap Circuits™ kit package. Tell them to be sure to follow the instructions in the middle of page 58. Have them try their best to come up with the best design that they can in the time allotted. As long as teams put in a good effort, they should not be penalized. **Note:** It will be easiest for students to try different design ideas, rather than to draw a schematic of what worked. Do not insist that they draw a design first unless they are very advanced.
5th Class	1. **Have each team present their design.** After each presentation, ask the class, "What are the advantages of this design? What are its disadvantages?"
Assessment	**Look for misconceptions.** Look for evidence of the misconceptions about series and parallel circuits identified at the end of the previous task. If you observe these, plan on a large-group discussion aimed at correcting those specific misconceptions. Use the rubric on page 58 to evaluate the students' designs.

Project 4.0

Background and Further Suggestions

Three possible designs are shown below; many different approaches are feasible.

Schematic	Analysis
	Advantages: Fan motor has two speeds, accomplished by shorting out the light bulb with a switch. Each fan is controlled independently. *Disadvantages:* Two separate power sources are needed. Cannot reverse direction.
	Advantages: Two fan motors are controlled by the same power source. Both can be switched on or off independently. *Disadvantages:* Cannot change direction or speed.
	Advantages: Two fan motors are controlled by same power source. Both can be switched on or off independently. Can change the speed of either motor independently. Can reverse direction of both motors at once. *Disadvantages:* Cannot control the direction of each fan independently.

Calculating total resistance. Students will find it obvious that the resistances of several resistors in series can be summed to find the total resistance. However, calculating total resistance of resistors in parallel is not so obvious. After blowing through straws in parallel, students should realize that resistors in parallel *decrease* the total resistance, so that two straws in parallel have one-half the resistance of one. Students must develop this intuitive understanding before learning the formula for calculating the total resistance of resistors in parallel presented in this chapter.

For the case of identical resistors in parallel, the calculation is very simple. Two 100Ω resistors in parallel have a combined resistance of $(100\Omega/2) = 50\Omega$. Three 100Ω resistors in parallel have an equivalent resistance of $100\Omega/3 = 33.3\Omega$, and so on.

For non-identical resistors in parallel—say, a 200Ω and 300Ω resistor—the 300Ω resistor is equivalent to two 600Ω resistors in parallel, and the 200Ω is equivalent to three 600Ω resistors in parallel. So the two resistors in parallel are equivalent to five 600Ω resistors in parallel, or $600\Omega/5 = 120\Omega$. As James Evans (1978) writes in his article describing this approach, "Students are usually delighted when they discover the correspondence between this scheme and the familiar mathematical problem of finding a common denominator for the addition of fractions."

References and Resources
General

Page, Chester. "Electromotive Force, Potential Difference, and Voltage." *American Journal of Physics,* 45(10), 1977, 978–980.

Evans, James. "Teaching Electricity with Batteries and Bulbs." *The Physics Teacher,* January 1978, 15–22.

Task 4.7: Provide Energy to a Lighthouse

Overview

Up to this point, the only source of energy that has been considered in the *Engineer's Notebook* activities has been batteries. In Task 4.7, students learn about other sources of electrical energy, including electrical generators and photovoltaic cells. The context for studying different energy sources is the need to choose an electrical energy source to power a lighthouse. The lighthouse is on an island, so you can't just "plug it in." In this task students also learn about the concept of power and its relationship to energy.

Five Es

Engage students with the challenge of finding a source of electrical energy for a lighthouse; **Explore** different ways of producing electricity through activities; **Evaluate** these methods of producing energy for a given application.

Time Frame

5 class periods

Focus Questions

- What is electrical power and how is it related to electrical energy?
- What is a fuse and why is it important?
- What are three different ways to produce electricity?
- What's the difference between AC and DC?
- How are motors and generators similar? How are they different?

Objectives

Students will be able to:
- Explain how power and energy are related
- Calculate electrical power, given voltage and current
- Demonstrate at least three ways to produce electrical energy
- Explain the difference between AC and DC
- Explain how fuses work and why they are important
- Show how motors and generators are similar and different

Materials

For every four students:
1 Snap Circuits™ kit package for ETF curriculum
1 small piece of steel wool from hardware store (no soap pads)

Preparation

Contact your local electricity utility and find out if there is an electric power-generating station in your vicinity. Find out what it uses for fuel, and if it is possible to take your students there on a field trip.

Do all of the activities in Task 4.7 before asking students to do them.

1st Class

1. **Ask your students to read the design challenge on page 59.** Ask your students if any have seen lighthouses at night, and, if so, to describe what the light looks like. (A lighthouse light is very bright. It generally sweeps in a complete circle every few seconds, so from any given position it appears to be a flashing light. Although nearly all lighthouses now run automatically, and most ships have GPS, lighthouses continue to be very important beacons to help prevent accidents at sea.)

2. **Have the students read about electrical power at the bottom of page 59,** and the top of page 60. Have them answer the question at the top of page 60 about the power of a light bulb that draws a current of 0.5 A:

$$P = \Delta V \times I = 120 \text{ V} \times 0.5 \text{ A} = 60 \text{ W}$$

3. **Some teachers find it useful** to have their students draw box diagrams, in which the height of the box equals the voltage difference and the width equals current. Power is then the area of the box. For the example at the bottom of page 60, there is a schematic with a single bulb, a two-cell battery, and an ammeter. In the corresponding box diagram, the left side represents the load, and the right side represents the source. Power produced by the source always equals the power used by the load, so the areas are equal.

Voltage = 3 V
Current = 0.3 A
Power generated by the source (on right) = 3 V × 0.3 A = 0.9 watts
Power used by the load (on left) = 3 V × 0.3 A = 0.9 watts
Power in is equal to the power out.

ERROR: There is an error in the *Engineer's Notebook* on the bottom half of page 60. The box diagram shows a width of 0.6A. Instead there should be two widths indicated, 0.3A for the left side of the box, and 0.3A for the right side of the box. This distinction is important to show that the power that leaves the battery is the same as that used by the load.

4. **Have your students read page 61** and do the activity in which they make and then burn out a fuse. They will use the spring socket module and just one or two strands of steel wool. Ask them to answer the three questions on page 61.

Project 4.0

Answer Key

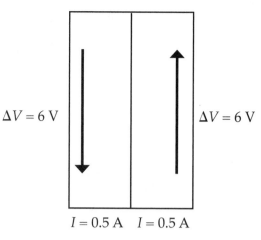

$\Delta V = 6$ V $\Delta V = 6$ V

$I = 0.5$ A $I = 0.5$ A

1) Students will measure a current of about 0.5 A. Voltage in this circuit is 6V, so the wattage of the bulb is

$P = 0.5$ A $\times 6$ V $= 3$ watts.

2) Results of this activity may vary. Students will periodically see a brief increase in current on the ammeter, and/or a brief increase in brightness of the light. When students blow on the fuse, they are causing a decrease in temperature. A decrease in temperature causes a decrease in resistance. A decrease in resistance will cause an increase in current. That is why students will periodically see an increase in current on the ammeter, and/or the increase in brightness of the light. When the current is increased, the fuse may even flare in response.

The converse of this is that, in general, an increase in temperature is associated with an increase in electrical resistance. Electrons move more rapidly and collide more often.

3) The fuse burns out at a current that is lower than what would burn out the lighthouse lamp. Because the fuse burns out first when current increases dangerously, the lighthouse lamp would be protected. The fuse wire must not be too thick.

2nd Class

1. **Ask the students to read page 62,** which presents a relationship between energy and power. This relationship is an especially important concept, so it will be a good idea to discuss it with the entire class. Challenge the students to answer the question at the top of the page: "If the 1,000 watt bulb is left on for a ten-hour night, how much energy will it use?" (It will require 10 kilowatt hours of energy if it burns for ten hours.) Help students as needed.

   The other questions on the page are rhetorical at this point. On the next few pages, students are expected to consider batteries, solar cells, and generators as a source of power.

2. **Will batteries provide a good source?** Hand out a basic Snap Circuits™ kit to each group of two students. Ask them to read page 63 and answer the questions. Students likely will realize that batteries would be a poor source of energy for a lighthouse, but they probably cannot give you a quantitative answer. This page will guide them in making calculations of energy, power, and the total number of batteries they would need to keep the lighthouse going for one night.

Engineering the Future Teacher Guide
©2008 Museum of Science, Boston

Answer Key

1) B. Effects of energy: The bulb lights up and the ammeter needle moves.
2) Students build a simple circuit.
   A. The students should color the top part of the circuit, including the meter red and the bottom part blue.
   B. The current will be about 0.3 A.
   C. The voltage is 3 V.
   D. $P = I \times \Delta V = 0.3\ A \times 3V = 0.9$ watts
   E. Chemicals and two different metals
3) $R = V/I = 3V\ /\ 0.3A = 10\ \Omega$
4) No. You would need too many of them.
5) Enough batteries would be needed for 10,000 Wh. A single battery has 2.25 Wh of energy; $10,000/2.25 \approx 4,444$. You would need 4,445 AA batteries.
   Note: A question for students who want an additional challenge is, "With this simple circuit (one small bulb from the kit), how long do you expect the battery to keep the light on?"
   Power = Energy$/\Delta T$
   ΔT = Energy/Power = 2.25 Wh/0.9 W = 2.5 hours

3rd Class

1. **Hand out one Snap Circuits™ kit package** to each group of four students. Ask them to read pages 64 and 65 and answer the questions on whether solar cells are a good power source.

Answer Key

1) Build a simple circuit in which the solar cell takes the place of the battery and an LED takes the place of a bulb.
   A. Effects of solar energy: You see the light and feel the heat radiated from the sun.
   B. Effects of solar energy transfer: The needle of the ammeter moves and the LED lights up when the switch is closed.
   C. The students should color the top part of the circuit, including the meter red, and the bottom part blue.
2) Voltage range:
   B. Answers will vary, but, in general, voltage will range from about 1V in low room light to 3V or more in sunlight.
   C. Students will observe that gradually covering the solar cell decreases the voltage. In other words, it is the area of the solar cell exposed to light that determines voltage output.
3) What current does it require?
   $P = I \times \Delta V \qquad I = P/\Delta V = 1,000$ watts$/120V \approx 8.33$ A

   What is its the electrical resistance?
   $R = \Delta V/\ I = 120V/8.33A = 14.4\ \Omega$
4) Are solar cells a good energy source for the lighthouse? There are several 1kW solar arrays on the market and available on the Internet. If possible, arrange for all of your students to access the web for at least 15 minutes to view them and note their size and cost. A few lighthouses do use photovoltaic (solar) cells to power the lighthouse beam.

Project 4.0

2. **As homework,** have the students read Chapter 31, "Sunny Side Up," which is about an engineer who uses solar cells in her work.

4th Class

1. **Discuss homework.** Emphasize the pros and cons of solar cells and arrays as sources of power in new buildings.

2. **Hand out one Snap Circuits™ kit package** to groups of four students. (Note: The packages have generators in them.) Have the students read pages 66–68 and answer the questions. You may want to start this lesson by presenting students with the information that nearly all of the electrical energy used in homes and businesses is produced by electric generators, so it's important to know how they work. However, generators may or may not be the best solution for a lighthouse.

Answer Key

1) Build the first circuit with the battery, ammeter, bulb, and motor.
   A. When the circuit is closed the motor will spin, the light will light up, and the meter needle will move (to between 0.1–0.2 A).
   B. When the battery is replaced with a snap wire connector and the motor rotor is spun, the ammeter needle moves! (Although the bulb does not light.)
   C. A source of electrical power will make a motor spin. Physically spinning a motor will also provide a source of electrical power.
   D. Your students will find that a hand-crank generator provides sufficient power to light a bulb and spin a motor.
   Note: Turning the hand-crank generator too fast will burn out certain components, such as the light bulbs in the kit. Urge your students to take care.
   E. The motor and hand-crank generator do the same things, but one produces much more electrical power.
2) What provides the difference in voltage to drive energy flow?
   A. A person's physical effort.
   B. Students will find that when they magnetize the metal rod and move it in and out of the coil, an electric current will be generated in the coil. The direction of current will depend on the direction of motion of the magnetized metal rod. Therefore, there must be a permanent magnet and coil inside a motor and generator.
3) A. The series circuit with all three bulbs requires you to push the fastest.
   B. The parallel circuit requires you to push the hardest.
   C. Parallel circuits are used in homes so that all lights have the same brightness, no matter how many lights are on. (Although, if too many lights are on, the current may get so high that the fuse melts.)
4) Is a generator a good energy source for the lighthouse?
   A. Students will find several alternatives for a 1-kilowatt generator. It will use a moderate amount of fuel.
   B. Wind generators provide a good alternative to a gas generator, although they depend on strong and steady winds.

Engineering the Future Teacher Guide
©2008 Museum of Science, Boston

3. **AC or DC?** Demonstrate AC and DC current using the Hula Hoop. The lighthouse bulb will work with either kind of source.

4. **Assign homework.** Ask the students to read Chapter 32,"Cape Wind," about wind energy, and to answer the questions.

5th Class

1. **Discuss homework.** Emphasize the societal issues surrounding choices of power plants. Note there is never a "perfect" solution. Good decisions mean making the best trade-offs.

2. **Divide the class into teams of four students.** Have the students read page 69, and work on the challenge. A rubric for judging the challenge is at the bottom of the page. Allow about 20–25 minutes for the students to list the pros and cons for each source of electricity, to decide on the two most likely choices, and then to decide which of those would be best. While students should have a chance to discuss this with their teammates, each student should write his or her own report.

Assessment

Have the students complete the benchmarks on page 70. These questions provide a good test of students' abilities to choose the correct formulas, and to use their intuition about electricity.

Answer Key

1) It will draw about 4.17 A.
   $P = I \times \Delta V$ $I = P/\Delta V = 500 \text{ watt} / 120 \text{ V} \approx 4.166666 \text{ A}$

2) Yes.
   $\Delta V = I \times R$ $R = \Delta V / I = 120 \text{ V} / 4.17 \text{ A} = 28.8 \ \Omega$

3) No. The bulbs are wired in parallel, so the resistance is divided by the number of bulbs, not added! $28.8 \ \Omega / 5 = 5.76 \text{ A}$.
   So, $I = \Delta V / R = 120 \text{ V} / 5.76 \text{ A} \approx 20.8 \text{ A}$.

4) Explain that when wiring several resistors in parallel, the electrical resistance is reduced, not added! Students should also wire it with a number of switches so that only two of the bulbs are on at a time. When one goes bad, it should be possible to switch to another bulb. Students then need to calculate resistance based on two bulbs in parallel.

Background and Further Suggestions

Solar cells. Much research has gone into how to make solar cells use more of the energy that strikes them. One factor is the load. The power output of solar cells varies with the load, so one of the design considerations is what load will use the most power from the solar cells. Below is a list of rough measurements on different loads made using a 20W, 12V halogen lamp directed at the solar cell at close range.

R	ΔV	I	P	
0 Ω (short)	0 V	0.017 A	0 W	
50 Ω	0.9 V	0.016 A	0.0144 W	Students can create a graph with resistance (load) on the horizontal axis and power on the vertical axis. Which load produces the greatest power output?
100 Ω	1.7 V	0.017 A	0.0289 W	
200 Ω	2.8 V	0.015 A	0.042 W	
500 Ω	3.4 V	0.0056 A	0.019 W	
1 kΩ	3.7 V	0.0034 A	0.013 W	
Infinite Ω	Voc: 4.2 V	0 A	0 W	

Also consider how to maximize the amount of light shining on the cells for the longest period of time possible. This gets into a discussion of how the sun strikes the earth in different seasons and what the average sunshine is in different parts of the country and world. This also ties into solar heating discussions. Other possibilities include motorized trackers that move the solar cells with the sun throughout the day.

Generators. In rotating the generator, students are transferring energy to the circuit. The same amount of power is needed to light the three bulbs to the same brightness, whether they are in series or parallel. For the series bulbs, the voltage difference must be higher. This means that the generator must be turned faster, though it's easier than for parallel bulbs, which need more current, which makes it harder to push at the same speed. This is because "demanding more current implies more current flowing in each winding of the generator coil, and...the magnetic field caused by these currents oppose (through Lenz's law) the current-originating magnetic field. So it becomes harder to push the generator magnet at the same speed through the coil when more current is demanded by the circuit." (Livelybrooks, 2003.)

Box diagrams were developed by Peter Cheng in the United Kingdom. Cheng developed them into an advanced secondary school class with the help of David Shipstone. They are part of a class of diagrams known as "Law Encoding Diagrams" because they encapsulate Kirchoff's voltage and current laws for a circuit. They also include Ohm's law.

Kirchoff's voltage law is that the voltage differences around a loop sum to zero. It is represented in the equal heights of the source and load boxes. Kirchoff's current law is that the current into a junction is equal to the current out of a junction. It is represented by the equal widths of the source and (overall) load box. This happens because current is conserved. Also, any smaller load boxes due to series and parallel components fit inside the overall load box perfectly; at any junction, the total current is conserved.

The area of the battery box represents the total amount of power provided to the load, and the area of the overall load box is the same size as the battery box because energy is conserved and all energy provided by the source is "used up" (transferred out) by the load.

It might be possible to analyze an electric bill from the point of view of "bars of energy" used by each appliance in the house in a month. The power used by each appliance forms the base of the box ($V \times I$), and the amount of time it is used determines the height ($\times T$). So a kilowatt-hour (kWh) can be seen as a volume, flexible in its dimensions based on its power needs (base) and the amount of time it uses energy (height).

Electrical safety. Batteries carry very little current at low voltages. However, wall current that everyone has in their homes can be very dangerous.

More on AC and DC. Connect a generator to a bulb and move the crank back and forth quickly. This is basically what a bulb plugged into a wall outlet is experiencing. The bulb lights because it does not matter which direction current flows through it—it lights either way if the current is high enough.

How can we use AC to power DC circuits? We can just convert AC to DC with a "rectifier." Diodes are often used. A simple half-wave rectifier is just a diode, so only the current in the direction of the diode makes it to the load. This means that half the power is lost. A full-wave rectifier is an arrangement of four diodes that allows current to constantly pass. If you build a demonstration circuit of the full-wave rectifier using two red LEDs and two green LEDs, it will be easier to trace how it works. Diagrams of this can be found at http://www.allaboutcircuits.com/vol_3/chpt_3/4.html.

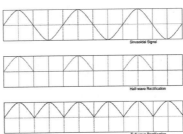

diagram: http://en.wikipedia.org/wiki/Rectification_%28electricity%29

Why are outlets AC? It allows a large amount of power to be transferred via high voltage and low current. Less current means less power loss to the resistance of the transmission wires. The battle between AC and DC is a fascinating one. Both AC and DC date back to the 1800s, when lighting the streets was the primary reason for generating electricity. New technology makes DC a possibility again for long distances.

How long will batteries last? Batteries maintain an approximately constant voltage difference, and they're rated in milliamp-hours. A rechargeable NiMH AA battery, with a voltage difference of 1.2V, might have 2,500 mAh printed on it (fast approaching alkaline AA batteries). Ideally, the NiMH battery could supply 2,500 mA (2.5A) for 1 hour (3,600 seconds).

Larger batteries provide more energy (a NiMH D battery, also at 1.2V, is rated at 10,000 mAh). If the current required from the battery is reduced, the amount of time the battery lasts goes up. That's a large goal in making small electronic devices: use less power, and the battery lasts longer.

For more information, see "Characteristics of Rechargeable Batteries," from http://www.national.com/appinfo/power/files/f19.pdf.

Students can also download datasheets on Energizer batteries to put some of this knowledge into perspective, http://data.energizer.com. Look over the Alkaline, NiMH rechargeable, and NiCD datasheets.

References and Resources
Solar Cells

Chapin, Daryl. *Energy From the Sun*. New York: Bell System Science Experiment No. 2. Available from Comspace Corporation, Amityville N.Y.

Tinker, Robert F., John W. McWane, and J. Edward Neighbor. *Photodectectors*. College Park, MD: American Association of Physics Teachers, 1976.

Pollard, William. "Prospects for Solar Electricity." *The Physics Teacher*. October 1977. Volume 15, Issue 7, 391–395.

Hamakawa, Yoshihiro. "Photovoltaic Power." *Scientific American*. April 1987. Volume 256, 86–92.

Jakovidis, Greg, Michael Morgan, and Ian McLeod. "An Experiment to Measure the I-V Characteristics of a Silicon Solar Cell." *Physics Education*. July 1994. Volume 29, Issue 4, 252–254.

Generators

Livelybrooks, Dean. "'Feel' the Difference Between Series and Parallel Circuits." *The Physics Teacher*. February 2003. Volume 41, Issue 2, 41, 102–103.

Nahrstedt, Gary. *Adventures with the Gencon Hand Operated Generator*. Canada: Nada Scientific Ltd, 1989.

Chiaverina, Christopher, Tom Kobilarcik, and Ed McNeil. "Doing Physics." April 1987. *The Physics Teacher*. Volume 25, Issue 4, 248–251.

Iona, Mario. "Generator Efficiency." *The Physics Teacher*. December 1988. Volume 26, Issue 9, 555.

Lehrman, Robert. "The Back EMF of a Motor." *The Physics Teacher*. May 1983. Volume 21, Issue 5, 315.

Kagan, David T. and Robert Keith. "Building a Cheap Simple Generator." *The Physics Teacher*. April 1999. Volume 37, Issue 4, 248–249.

AC and DC

Higgins, Thomas James. "Evolution of the Three-Phase 60-Cycle Alternating Current System." *American Journal of Physics*. February 1945. Volume 13, Issue 1, 32–36.

Ruby, Lawrence. "Why DC for Long-Range Power Transmission." *The Physics Teacher*, 40, May 2002, 272–274.

Johns, Robert. "Simplifying AC-Current Measurements." *The Physics Teacher*. May 2001. Volume 39, Issue 5, 314–315.

Box Diagrams

Cheng, Peter C-H and David M. Shipstone. "Electric Circuits: A New Approach—Part 1." *School Science Review.* December 2001. Volume 83, Issue 303, 55–63.

Cheng, Peter C-H and David M. Shipstone. "Electric Circuits: A New Approach—Part 2." *School Science Review.* March 2002. Volume 83, Issue 304, 73–81.

Cheng, Peter C-H and David M. Shipstone. "Supporting Learning and Promoting Conceptual Change with Box and AVOW Diagrams. Part 1: Representational Design and Instructional Approaches." *International Journal of Science Education.* February 2003. Volume 25, Issue 2, 193–204.

Cheng, Peter C-H and David M. Shipstone. "Supporting Learning and Promoting Conceptual Change with Box and AVOW Diagrams. Part 2: Their Impact on Student Learning at A-level." *International Journal of Science Education.* March 2003. Volume 25, Issue 3, 291–305.

Cheng, Peter C-H. "Electrifying Diagrams for Learning: Principles for Complex Representational Systems." *Cognitive Science.* November 2002. Volume 26, Issue 6, 685–736.

Cheng, Peter C-H and David M. Shipstone. "Teaching Electric Circuit Theory at A-level with AVOW Diagrams." *ESRC Center for Research in Development, Instruction, and Training.* Technical Report No. 72, June 2001.

Cheng, Peter C.-H. "AVOW Diagrams: A Novel Representational System for Understanding Electricity." In M. Anderson, B. Meyer and P. Olivier (Eds.), *Diagrammatic Representation and Reasoning,* 512–534. Berlin: Springer, 2001.

Task 4.8:   Analyze Consumer Electronics

Overview

Task 4.8 builds on the knowledge that students have gained about electric circuits to investigate the electrical gadgets that they use daily. They build a version of a single pixel on a TV or computer monitor. They compare flashlights to see which have the best designs, and they learn how to use a multimeter—a widely used all-in-one device that measures current, voltage, and resistance with fairly good accuracy.

Five Es

Engage students in looking closely at electronic devices around them; **Explore** these devices and **Explain** how they work; **Evaluate** which devices have the best design elements; **Elaborate** students' understanding of the basic electrical concepts by applying their knowledge to the real world.

Time Frame

5 class periods

Focus Questions

- How do televisions use electronic circuits to create pictures?
- What are the characteristics of good electronic design?
- Why are some electronic components better than others?
- How can a multimeter make electronics work easier?

Objectives

Students will be able to:
- Explain how a TV display works
- Analyze consumer electronics
- Explain why LEDs are better than bulbs for many applications
- Use a multimeter to measure current, voltage, and resistance

Materials

For every four students:
  1 Snap Circuits™ kit package for ETF curriculum
  1 magnifier, at least 10x
  1 small, flat screwdriver to zero adjust multimeters

For the class:
  6 flashlights made by different companies
  Optional: 1 white translucent ping pong ball; 1 of each LED: red,
    blue, and green; 6 wires with alligator clips on both ends
    (from kits)

Preparation

Identify a place where your students can look at a television or computer monitor up close, using magnifiers. It's best if there are at least three or four monitors so that the students can take time, in small groups, observing and discussing what they see.

Collect a half-dozen flashlights that are as different in design as possible. Number each for identification with a permanent marker.

Do all of the activities in Task 4.8 before asking students to do them.

1. **Ask your students to read the introduction on page 71.** Explain that in this last task they will find out how much they've already learned about the electronic devices that are around them all the time. You might also refresh their memory, from Chapter 28, about the use of the terms "electricity" and "electronics":

   Electricity is what you call the charge flowing in wires.

   Electronics is the way you control electricity in various devices.

   Task 4.8 was primarily about different ways of supplying electricity. In this task the focus will be on *consumer electronics*—the things people purchase, which are powered by electricity, to help them in their work or to make their lives easier or more entertaining.

2. **Examine a TV display.** Hand out magnifiers. Three or four students can share one magnifier. Tell the students to read the bottom half of page 71 and to share the magnifiers so that everyone has a chance to see what a TV display looks like close up. They should work as a team to decide how to answer the questions at the bottom of the page. These are open-ended questions, but you can expect answers to look something like the following:

Answer Key

1) It looks like a grid with bright colors.
2) Red, green, and blue—it's not white at all!
3) You actually see just red, green, and blue, but from farther back you see all sorts of colors.
4) Maybe different amounts of red, green, and blue look like different colors to your eyes when you see them mixed together.

3. **Have the students read page 72,** which describes how to create an enlarged pixel. You may want to explain the idea of a pixel to the students. Then hand out a basic Snap Circuits™ kit to every two students. Each group should assemble the circuit at the top of page 72. Encourage students to discuss the questions, but to write the answers in their own notebooks:

Answer Key

1) The switch at the top turns the LEDs on and off. The slider on the variable resistor controls the brightness of the LEDs.
2) Blue and red.
3) Parallel. There is a branch point where the current is split. Also, both LEDs have the same voltage difference across them.

4. **Optional:** If you have the materials, you can make a full-color one-pixel demonstration, as described at the bottom of page 72, with a translucent white ping pong ball and three unmounted LEDs—one blue, one green, and one red. Use alligator clips or other wires to connect the three LEDs to the circuit. Drill a hole in the ping pong

ball and insert the LEDs. If you turn out the classroom lights, you can control the color of the ping pong ball by sliding the sliders on the three variable resistors.

5. **Have the students read page 73** and answer the questions about measuring current. Have students estimate how much current 3 LEDs would draw.

1) Next to either battery.
2) ERROR: There is an error in the *Engineer's Notebook* at the top of page 73. The second bullet should read: "2 LEDs _____ mA." The third bullet, "1 LED + 1 light bulb," should not be there.

1 LED	Est. about 0.03 A (30mA)
2 LEDs	Est. about 0.06 A (60 mA)
3 LEDs	Probably about 0.09A (90 mA)

6. **Why are LEDs replacing bulbs?** Have the students **replace one LED and its 100Ω resistor with TWO light bulbs in series.** Set the slider so the bulb is about as bright as the LED, and measure the current.

*WARNING: Please note that the diagram and text only mention using one light bulb in the circuit. We have found that enthusiastic students have turned the variable resistor attached to the light bulb on low, and the switch attached to the LED off. The light bulb is attached to four AA batteries, so this will cause the light bulb to burn out. If students use two light bulbs in series, this will prevent the burning out of a light bulb. We leave it up to the teacher's judgment whether to alter the activity or to just make the students aware of actions they should avoid.

1 LED	Est. about 0.03 A (30 mA)
1 or 2 light bulbs	Est. about 0.30 A (300mA)
1 LED + 1 or 2 light bulbs	Probably about 0.33A (330mA)

3) Because LEDs draw far less current than light bulbs, even though they are about as bright. That will cost less money, cause less pollution, and so on.

2nd Class

1. **Hand out a basic Snap Circuits™ kit** and a multimeter from the Snap Circuits™ kit package to each team of four students. Have them read page 74 on using a multimeter. Be prepared to help individual teams if they have difficulty identifying the various scales. Some students may want help adjusting the zero adjust with a screwdriver.

2. **Draw a large picture of the range switch** and its various settings on the board. You can then quiz students on the different settings to see whether they have understood the information on page 74 correctly.

3. **Have students read page 75** on the ammeter function. Draw a scale above the range drawing on the board and quiz students about how to read the two ammeter settings. Tell them to read just the black numbers and ignore the others. The 10 mA setting should be read on the 0–10 scale, and the 250 mA setting should be read on the 0–250 scale.

4. **Practice using the ammeter.** Have the students construct the circuits on page 76 and use their multimeter to measure the currents.

Answer Key

1) Build the circuit with a 100 ohm resistor, one LED, and one battery holder.
   A. High
   B. Less than 0.05 A
2) Replace the M2 ammeter with the multimeter.
   A. 10 mA
   B. 6 mA
   C. The multimeter
3) Connect the multimeter in the same place you previously connected the M2 meter, using the black-and-red probes to complete the circuit.

   WARNING: We recommend using two light bulbs in series instead of just one light bulb in this circuit. Students have accidentally burned out the light bulb when a single bulb was used. We leave it up to the teacher's judgment whether to alter the activity or just make students aware of how *not* to burn out the light bulb.

   A. Try each separately to see the current drawn by:
   - The LED—30 mA
   - The light bulb (1 or 2)—more than 250 mA
   - The LED and the light bulb (1 or 2)—more than 250 mA
   B. They are consistent with those results. The multimeter is more accurate, but the ammeter scale doesn't go high enough to measure more than 250 mA.
4) This is a very open-ended question. Results will vary. Look to see if the students have set up and used the ammeter properly (in series with other components).

3rd Class

1. **Have the students read page 77** on the voltmeter function. Refer to the drawing on the board and quiz the students about which scale they should read as the range switch is turned to different ranges.

2. **Use the voltmeter function.** Hand out one Snap Circuits™ kit package to groups of four students. Have them make the measurements using the circuit shown on the bottom of page 77.

Project 4.0

1) Use for 2.5 volts and <u>250</u> volts.
   Use for <u>50</u> volts.
   Use for 10 volts and <u>1,000</u> volts.
2) V1 = 3 V   V2 = 1 V   V3 = 2 V
   The sum of V2 and V3 is V1.
3) Inside a voltmeter is an ammeter (coil and magnet) and a resistor.

3. **Have the students read page 78** on the ohmmeter function. The ohmmeter is a little different from the ammeter and voltmeter, so you might want to draw the scale on the board again and quiz the students after they have read page 78.

   - Notice that the ohmmeter scale is the green scale at the top of the multimeter, and it reads with zero on the right rather than on the left.
   - Do *not* adjust the screw in the center of the multimeter to zero, adjust the ohmmeter. Instead, set the range switch on X1kΩ, touch the probes firmly together, and use the knob on the left side, which is labeled 0ΩADJ.
   - It's a good idea to zero adjust the ohmmeter each time you change scale.
   - Remind the students that they must remove components from the circuit to measure their resistance.

4. **Have the students do the activities on page 79** to practice using their ohmmeters.

3) Both scales are helpful—one for the highest range (x 1,000) and one for the lowest range (x 10).
4) If the reading is too far near the end of the scale, it is not in the right range.
5) The lowest resistance is very close to 0Ω.
6) The highest resistance is about 50,000Ω.
7) Students' predictions should be accurate by now.
   Two 100Ω resistors in series is measured at 200Ω.
   Two 100Ω resistors in parallel is measured at 50Ω.
8) When wired in series, the current is slowed by both resistors, so resistance is greater than one resistor. When wired in parallel, some current gets through each resistor, so resistance is less than one resistor.
9) Results will vary, but, in general, resistance becomes less when salt or vinegar is added to water.

1. **Have students read the challenge on top of page 80,** including the rubric at the bottom of the page. Invite students to ask questions before distributing the flashlights.

2. **Have students work in teams of four,** and give one flashlight to each team. All flashlights should be different! Allow each group to study the flashlight for five minutes, then have teams pass their

flashlight to the next team and take a new one to analyze. Tell the teams to note the number of the flashlight so that they will be able to compare results with other teams later.

Allow time for the teams to discuss the results after all six flashlights have been inspected. Invite teams to borrow one of the flashlights again, if they wish, for further analysis.

Encourage teams to discuss results, then have each student write his or her own report on the results, referring to the rubric at the bottom of page 80.

5th Class

1. **Invite each team to present their results.** Allow other teams to question them. When all teams have presented, lead a discussion to see if there is agreement about which flashlight is better. Ideally, the group will recognize that some flashlights may be better for some purposes or some groups of customers, while other flashlights would be better for other purposes or customers.

2. **Ask teams to read page 81.** Ask students for their reflections on the last page, concerning careers and the value of learning about technology for everyday life.

Assessment

You may want to have students write an end-of-course essay about what engineering and technology means to them, and how what they learned in this course may be helpful to them in the future. You may also want to ask them, "What does it mean to say that You will engineer the future?"

References and Resources
Multimeter
Elenco Dial Scale Reading Kit, DSR-85. Elenco Electronics, 2000.

Iona, Mario. "Ohm's law and Test Meters." *The Physics Teacher.* May 1965. Volume 3, Issue 5, 226.

Lange, Lugwig and Arnold Benton. *The Multimeter (PTM).* College Park, MD: American Association of Physics Teachers, 1975.

Spady, Harold. "A Meter Tester for the High School Laboratory / Another Approach to Ohm's law." *The Physics Teacher,* February 1965, 77–78.

Project 4.0

Teacher Guide to the Textbook

The textbook for *Engineering the Future* (ETF) is written in the first-person, based on interviews with practicing engineers. Men and women, from various ethnic and cultural backgrounds, tell what it is like to practice their professions and how they came to do what they do. The narrators also explore important concepts pertaining to their work.

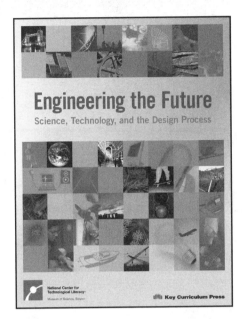

The textbook is divided into four sections, corresponding to the four units of the course. The stories have been edited to communicate important concepts in technology and engineering standards, and to correlate closely with the laboratory activities in the ETF *Engineer's Notebook*.

Although teachers may wish to add assignments, homework for this course is not required every day. Most of the homework assignments are to read chapters in the book, to answer the questions at the end, and to bring the written answers to class the next day. We recommend that students sign out their textbook at the beginning of the school year and keep it at home in a place where they won't lose it, so that they will be able to complete their homework assignments on time.

One problem with most textbooks is that answers to all of the questions at the ends of the chapters can be found easily within the chapters, so that students need only scan for the answers and ignore the meaning of the text. To support more meaningful learning, we created the following kinds of questions:

What's the Story? These questions are about key points in the chapter.

Connecting the Dots. Students are asked to relate information from this chapter to previous chapters.

Designing with Math and Science. These questions ask students to apply a math or science concept, or offer an example of how it might be used in a different context.

What Do You Think? Questions in this category ask students to offer an opinion about the content of the chapter.

Teachers whose students have reading difficulties have found that their students need different kinds of questions to help them make sense of the chapters. ETF developers would like to include these alternative question sets on our web site. If you have some that you'd like to contribute, please send them to editorial@keypress.com.

Table of Contents

Teacher Guide to the Textbook

Unit 1: Creators of the Designed World

Chapter 1: Welcome to the Designed World

In this chapter, Amy Smith, a mechanical engineer instructor at the Massachusetts Institute of Technology, introduces and analyzes some fundamental concepts, such as the relationship between technology, engineering, and science, as she describes her own work designing appropriate technologies for developing countries. Amy is motivated by a deep desire to collaborate with people in developing nations to overcome serious health and environmental problems. She briefly describes her newest effort—designing a new cooking technology that will provide rural Haitians with an alternative to burning wood charcoal. She has chosen this challenge because wood charcoal has contributed to some serious health and environmental problems around the world. Burning wood charcoal produces toxic smoke that is bad to breathe—especially for children. Cutting down trees to make the charcoal has contributed to large-scale deforestation of Haiti. Amy also describes another one of her inventions, the screenless hammermill, a device that allows for more efficient grinding of grain. It is another example of an appropriate technology that people in developing countries can use to create microenterprises. Amy also discusses her atypical approach to patenting. She chooses not to patent her designs so that others are free to replicate, use, and sell them.

Teaching Points

✔ **Technology** refers to everything that people do to change the natural world to suit human needs and wants.

✔ **Engineers** create or improve technologies to suit human needs and wants.

✔ **Scientists** create theories or undertake experiments to learn more about the natural world and how it functions. Engineers and scientists have a reciprocal relationship. Engineers use the laws and theories that scientists develop when creating technologies. Scientists use new technologies (such as a microscope, a laser, or an infrared camera) to observe the natural world.

✔ **Technologies** have so shaped the human experience that major periods in history are named for the prevailing types of technology (i.e., The Stone Age, The Iron Age, The Industrial Revolution, The Information Age).

✔ A **patent** is a document issued by the government that gives an inventor sole right to make, distribute, or sell a particular invention for a certain number of years.

✔ **Appropriate technology** is a technology that can be made, maintained, repaired, and improved with the resources that are available in a particular community.

✔ A **microenterprise** is a small business run by an individual or family.

Engineering the Future Teacher Guide
©2008 Museum of Science, Boston

What's the Story?

1. How has engineering been important in human history? Give at least three examples. *Answer may include all of the ages discussed in chapter sidebar: Stone Age, Iron Age, Industrial Revolution, and so on. Also may include introduction of technologies such as fire, the wheel, the printing press, the light bulb, the telephone, the A-bomb, the Internet, and any number of technologies that have shaped history.*

2. What is the difference between a scientist and an engineer? How are the two related? *A scientist conducts research to learn about the natural world. An engineer develops new technologies in response to human needs and wants. Engineers produce the instruments that scientists need to investigate the natural world. Engineers use science and math to improve or develop new technologies.*

3. According to Amy's definition, the term "technology" refers to anything you do to change the world to suit human wants and needs. List at least ten different technologies you have seen or used in the past hour. List five technologies that may have been involved in the production of this textbook. *Part 1 answers might include computer, television, telephone, pencil, paper, desk, chair, clothing, school building, books, chalkboard and chalk, heating system, cell phone, and so on. Part 2 answers might include printing press, binders, cameras and imaging equipment, computers, paper manufacturing system, ink manufacturing system, and so on.*

4. What does the term "appropriate technology" mean? Give an example of an appropriate technology. Give an example of a technology that is not appropriate. *Appropriate technology refers to technology that can be manufactured, maintained, repaired, or improved with the resources available in a community. Amy's hammermill or the incubator that runs on chemicals are two technologies that are appropriate for where they will be used. An example of a technology that is not appropriate is the electrical incubator used in a place that has no electrical power.*

5. What is a patent, and what motivates engineers to patent new technology they develop? *A patent is a document issued by the government that gives an inventor the sole right to make, distribute, or sell a particular invention for a certain number of years. Most engineers are interested in trying to market and sell the technologies that they develop. Amy Smith is an exception to the rule.*

What Do You Think?

6. How can teamwork lead to better solutions? Why is it valuable to have people with different backgrounds on a team? Give an example from your own experience. *Answers will vary. Should include something about how the different team members might understand the needs of the technology's user differently.*

7. Imagine that you've been hired as a consultant by the International Red Cross to help determine the best ways to foster economic growth in a country where most of the people are very poor. One member of your team is interested in finding American companies to set up branch offices to provide well-paid work for locals. Another team member says it's better to help the people establish their own microenterprise. What course of action do you think is better and why? Be sure to define the term microenterprise in your answer. *A microenterprise is a small business that can be run by an individual or a family. It is better to help people establish their own micro-enterprises; people will open up companies that are specific to their needs, which may help them rise above the poverty line.*

8. Describe a personal experience you've had in solving a design problem. *Answers will vary.*

Chapter 2: Birth of a New Technology

In Chapter 2, Shawn Frayne, an inventor who works in Amy Smith's laboratory, describes how a team of student engineers under Amy's direction used the design process (outlined below) to develop an appropriate technology: a new cooking fuel for rural Haitians. He starts by telling the tale of how the technology was (and is still being) developed. First the team visited Haiti and tried to make pellets out of recycled paper. The pellets did not burn hot enough, and recycled paper was not easy to find in the village. So the team did more research, and prototyped a sawdust pellet that created too much smoke before they landed on a design that met their criteria and constraints: a briquette made of juiced, dried sugar cane stalks and cassava paste, both locally available materials. Even though the team's first two prototypes failed, Shawn is careful to point out that much was learned from those early attempts. This highlights engineers' approach to failure, which can be counterintuitive to students who equate failure with the letter F. For an engineer, failure is an opportunity to learn more about and improve a design.

Teaching Points

✔ The engineering design process is a process engineers use to develop creative solutions to problems. The process involves several steps:

1. *Defining the problem* means describing why the new technology is needed as well as outlining the requirements for a solution. Requirements include criteria—desired elements—and constraints—limitations to the design or design process.
2. *Researching the problem* means learning all that you can about the problem through a variety of means.
3. *Developing possible solutions* often involves brainstorming and creativity.
4. *Selecting the best solution* means choosing a solution that best meets the requirements.
5. *Creating a prototype* means making a working model of the solution.
6. *Testing and evaluating the solution* means making sure that the solution meets all criteria and constraints.
7. *Communicating the solution* means informing the people who will use the technology about it.
8. *Redesigning the solution* means repeating the design process to optimize a solution.

✔ Failure is a necessary part of the design process.

✔ The design process is a guideline, not a rule. Some engineers follow the steps in the order presented here, others do not.

What's the Story?

1. What is the engineering design process? *It is an approach to solving problems involving a series of steps.*

2. Did Shawn's team follow the steps of the design process in order? *No, Shawn used the design process as a guideline, rather than as a rule.*

3. What's the difference between criteria and constraints? *Criteria are desired features, while constraints are limitations in developing or using the technology. Constraints often include costs, time, and materials.*

4. How many prototypes did the team build? How many were successful? *Three. Only one met their criteria for success.*

5. Think about Shawn's response to his first failure. Was he surprised? What do engineers think about failure? How is this different from the way most people think about failure? *No, he was not surprised or discouraged. In the eyes of an engineer, failure provides new and valuable information. It is essential to the process. This way of thinking is contrary to the way most people think about failure; most people get discouraged and sometimes even give up.*

6. Why is communicating the solution an important step? What happens to technologies that are not communicated? *If a new technology is not communicated, no one will know about it. Therefore, no one will use or buy it.*

Connecting the Dots

7. Amy Smith says that engineers use science to develop new technologies. At which point in the design process did the team use science in developing their new technology? *The design team applied science during testing and evaluation. They tested how much heat the burning pellets would produce, and they planned to analyze the chemical composition of the smoke to make sure the smoke was safe.*

8. Why was it critical to use materials that were cheap and easy to find a new cooking technology in Haiti? *It was a part of their criteria. They wanted to develop an appropriate technology for rural Haiti.*

What Do You Think?

9. Your principal just hired you to help solve a problem for your school. Students are sneaking off campus for lunch because they are so unhappy with the food choices at the school cafeteria. The principal has budgeted only $1,000 to solve the problem and she really wants it solved this academic year. How would you use the engineering design process to develop a solution to this problem? Write two or three sentences for each step detailing how you would accomplish it.

Answers will vary. Possible answers may include the following:

Step 1: Define the problem, criteria, and constraints: *Students are sneaking off campus for better food choices. Criteria: The solution must provide incentives for students to remain on campus during lunch. Constraints: The solution cannot cost more that $1,000 and it needs to be implemented this year.*

Step 2: Explain how you would conduct your research: *Interview students to learn about their motivations to leave campus or remain on campus. Ask them about their food preferences. Visit other schools that have solved this problem.*

Step 3: Brainstorm at least three possible solutions: *1. Change food in cafeteria. 2. Ask local restaurants to make their food available in the cafeteria. 3. Enact severe punishments for students who leave campus for lunch.*

Step 4: Describe how you would choose the best solution: *The team would determine which solution best met the criteria and constraints.*

Step 5: Indicate how you would create a prototype: *Try the solution out for one week.*

Step 6: Show how you would test your solution: *See if the "prototype week" has any effect on student behavior.*

Step 7: Explain how you would communicate your solution: *Newsletter, web site, parents' night, posters, and so on.*

Step 8: Describe how you would improve or redesign your solution: *See if the solution truly has solved the problem or if it has introduced any new problems. If not, go back to the research phase and redefine the problem.*

Engineering the Future Teacher Guide
©2008 Museum of Science, Boston

Chapter 3: Designs That Take Flight

In Chapter 3, Jamy Drouillard, another one of Amy's students, describes how he uses the design process to develop a small helicopter that will be used to hold a camera at sporting events. Jamy takes the reader through each step of his process. The "problem" is that sports channels want a better way to capture the action on the basketball court. The helicopter must, therefore, be able to carry a camera and move fast enough to follow a fast break in addition to other criteria. The camera must be designed so that it cannot injure an audience member or team player if it malfunctions. Jamy firmly believes in following the steps of the process in order. Jamy thinks designing technologies is fun, like a game. Still, he cautions that engineers must always make sure that they consider possible negative consequences of a new technology and keep them to a minimum. He hopes that the helicopter design will be purchased and manufactured by a company when it is complete.

Teaching Points

✔   The design process can be used to develop any kind of technology.

✔   Tips for each of the eight steps of the design process:

- Be clear about the problem you're trying to solve.
- There are many ways to research a problem.
- Develop different ideas, even if you think you know the best solution.
- Compare the different solutions using the criteria and constraints.
- You may need to build several prototypes.
- Test the prototype where it will be safe.
- Communicating clearly and persuasively is very important.
- Nearly all new designs will need to be redesigned.

What's the Story?

1.   What problem is Jamy trying to solve? *He's trying to design a helicopter that can carry a small camera, track a player, dispense coupons, make maneuvering decisions on its own, and be controlled by a radio.*

2.   How does Jamy research the problem? *Jamy looks at technologies already on the market that are similar to the technology his team is trying to develop.*

3.   Jamy was a member of the team that went to Haiti. What else did he contribute besides his engineering skills? How did his contributions help the team? *Jamy is fluent in Haitian Creole and understood the people. This helped him communicate with the native people, especially while looking for new materials.*

Connecting the Dots

4.   How is designing a helicopter similar to designing a new cooking fuel for Haiti? *Both involve the design process and both require knowledge of science.*

5. Like Shawn, Jamy talks about the importance of communicating the solution. But the two engineers must communicate their solutions to very different audiences. Who is Shawn's audience? Who is Jamy's? *Shawn's audience is the users. Jamy's audience is a company that may manufacture and sell the helicopter.*

6. Jamy says that engineers should always follow the steps of the design process in order, even though the engineers can go back to the earlier steps and start over if necessary. Would Shawn agree with that? Which engineer is right? *The design process is used as guidance for engineers, not as a rule. Both of them used the design process to guide them to a solution. Neither is wrong.*

What Do You Think?

7. Jamy thinks it's a safe bet that whatever his team develops will eventually need to be redesigned. Why do most technologies need to be redesigned? *No technology is perfect. There is always "debugging" to do. This is true partly because of limitations on time, money, human skill, materials, and so on. It's also true because society is always changing and technologies must be updated continuously.*

8. Every engineer has different motivations. Jamy loves the creative aspects of engineering. To him, developing a new technology is fun, sort of like playing a game. Amy Smith and Shawn Frayne are motivated more by a desire to help improve the quality of people's lives. What might motivate you to learn about and develop new technologies? *Answers will vary.*

Chapter 4: Beyond Words

In Chapter 4, Lam Loc, a CAD technician at an engineering firm, introduces several drawing techniques and discusses the importance of Computer-Aided Design. Lam discusses how engineering drawing is one important way that engineers communicate their design ideas to each other and to clients and users. He describes his firm's approach to the engineering design process, which is slightly different from the approaches described in Chapters 1–3.

Teaching Points

✔ Engineering drawing is one important way that engineers communicate their ideas to each other and to clients and users.

✔ **Oblique** drawings represent objects in three-dimensional space. In an oblique drawing, the front side of an object appears flat; the sides and top of an object are at a 45-degree angle to the horizontal lines of the front. Engineers seldom use oblique drawing.

✔ **Perspective** drawing was developed during the Renaissance. This drawing style uses one or more vanishing points toward which all horizontal lines on the drawing converge. This makes 3-D objects look realistic. Perspective drawing is useful for giving clients or users a sense of how a technology will look, but it is not useful for conveying dimensions of the design.

✔ **Isometric** drawing is a style in which all vertical lines are drawn vertically, but all horizontal lines are drawn at 30° to the horizontal. All of the lines are drawn to scale; therefore, engineers can glean useful information about the dimensions of a design from isometric drawings. Engineers often use this style of drawing.

✔ **Orthographic Projections** are two-dimensional projections of all sides of a design. These drawings are most often drawn to scale. Engineers rely on these drawings for many purposes, including communicating with a construction team.

✔ **Scale drawing** is a method of drawing in which all lines are smaller or larger than the corresponding lines in the real object by a given ratio called the scale factor. A *scale factor* is expressed as a ratio. For example, the sides of an object in a 1/4-scale drawing are 1/4 the length of the sides of the real object.

✔ **Computer-Aided Design** (CAD) systems allow engineers to create precise drawings of their ideas using special computer software.

What's the Story?

1. According to Lam, what's the purpose of engineering drawing? *Engineering drawing helps engineers communicate the details of their design to each other and to a client.*

2. What do oblique and isometric drawings have in common? *Both drawing styles are used to represent three-dimensional objects.*

3. Why was Brunelleschi's contribution to drawing important? (In your answers, describe his contribution.) *Brunelleschi developed a mathematical theory for creating 3-D drawings that looked much more realistic. He developed a scientific explanation for the way humans see in 3-D with a vanishing point.*

Designing with Math and Science

4. On a piece of isometric graph paper, draw an isometric drawing of one of your books using a scale factor of 1:4. Be sure to list the book's measurements, and show all the calculations you did to determine the measurements of the drawing. *Answers will vary.*

5. Using quad-ruled graph paper, create an orthographic drawing of the same book using the same scale factor. *Answers will vary.*

6. Use the conversion chart in the back of this book to determine how many centimeters long a football field is. *A 100-yard football field (not including endzones) is 9,144 centimeters long.*

Connecting the Dots

7. How does the design process at HNTB differ from the one that Shawn and Jamy used? *The major difference is that Shawn and Jamy did not create proposals for clients. They did not have to get client approval before prototyping their designs. Jamy may involve a client once he is satisfied with the design he develops. Shawn may not have a client, per se, but he must design keeping the end user in mind.*

What Do You Think?

8. Lam discusses how drawing helps his firm communicate design ideas to clients and construction teams. We all use drawings to communicate at some time or another. Describe a time when you used a drawing to communicate a message, an idea, or even an emotion. *Answers will vary.*

Engineering the Future Teacher Guide
©2008 Museum of Science, Boston

Chapter 5: The Art of Engineering

In Chapter 5, Robert (Bob) Hartmann, an electrical engineer, describes the design process and various projects at IDEO, an industrial design firm. He discusses the importance of an object's "look and feel" and delves into the role of teamwork at engineering firms. He also discusses the idea that experiences can be designed.

Teaching Points

✔ How a technology looks and feels can be as important to the user as how it functions.

✔ Technologies are designed for a specific market.

✔ **Innovation** involves making improvements to existing technologies. **Invention** involves creating new technologies.

✔ Teamwork is essential for success in engineering. At IDEO, teams are made up of a diverse group of engineers, designers, and specialists.

✔ Even experiences can be designed.

What's the Story?

1. According to Bob, how are artists and engineers similar? How are they different? *Artists create works that bring out an emotional response in people. Engineers develop products that people will buy and use. Both must consider the "audience" or "user" and design for them. There is a degree of "art" in many engineered products.*

2. What does the term "innovation" mean? Give three examples of products that are innovations. *Anything "new and improved." Cell phones with e-mail and digital cameras, hybrid automobiles, laptop computers, and so on.*

3. Give three examples of products developed for niche markets and three examples of products developed for the mass market. *Answers will vary. Here are some possible answers:*

   Niche markets: mountaineering gear, scuba diving tanks, airplanes, and niche magazines such as Golf Digest.
   Mass Markets: Levi jeans, Honda Civics, mainstream magazines such as Time *or* Newsweek.

4. What methods do engineers and designers at IDEO use to ensure their designs will have the right "look and feel"? *They employ industrial designers who make the objects look good and human factors specialists who observe people using an object and determine the best way to redesign it so that it feels good.*

5. Why is it critical to have a diverse group of people on a design team? *The greater the diversity of the design team, the greater the diversity of ideas.*

Teacher Guide to the Textbook

Connecting the Dots

6. How do the engineers who are improving technologies that already exist use the design process differently from engineers who are developing entirely new technologies? What individual steps might be different? *Both inventors and innovators use the design process in very similar ways. However, inventors may need to work harder to define the problem, which is not simply a need to make something function better, but rather a problem that has never been solved before. Each subsequent step may also be more challenging for the inventor because there are no existing solutions to build on.*

7. Engineers apply math and science while developing new solutions. In redesigning a toothbrush handle, how might IDEO engineers have applied math and science? *Answers will vary.*

What Do You Think?

8. Give an example of a technology you use every day that you would like to change. How would you improve it? Would you market it to niche or mass markets? *Answers will vary.*

9. Bob says that working on a team is not always easy. Have you ever had a difficult time working on a team? If so, what did you do, or what could you have done to correct the problem? If not, why do you think your teamwork experiences have been so successful? *Answers will vary. While it is an advantage to have people bring different/fresh perspectives, sometimes their ideas and personalities clash. Clear communication often can solve such problems.*

Chapter 6: Bringing Designed Ideas to the Market

In Chapter 6, Araceli Ortiz discusses her experiences as a manufacturing engineer at Ford Motor Company. Araceli describes her role in redesigning Ford cars to appeal more to women. In doing so, she introduces the concept of market research. She goes on to describe the evolution of manufacturing technologies, the development of the assembly line system and continuous production, and the importance of interchangeable parts and batch production. Finally, Araceli analyzes the mass-production of the automobile and its impacts on society.

Teaching Points

✔ **Manufacturing technologies** are systems of people and machines that transform materials into useful products.

✔ **Market research** is the process of learning more about consumers' attitudes and thoughts about products.

✔ The **assembly line system** allows for continuous production of goods, whereby goods are produced at a steady rate. The assembly line allows for factories to achieve an economy of scale in which costs are spread over a high volume of goods produced.

✔ **Interchangeable parts** are pre-fabricated, standardized parts that are assembled into products.

✔ **Unintended consequences** are effects of a product's use in society that designers failed to foresee. Unintended consequences can be positive or negative.

What's the Story?

1. What are manufacturing technologies? *They are systems of people and machines that transform materials into useful products.*

2. List ten kinds of technologies that are manufactured. *Answers will vary. Many technologies are manufactured, such as paper plates, plastic forks, pencils, erasers, ceramic mugs, futon mattresses, toothbrushes, cell phones, computers, cars, and tons more.*

3. Why had relatively few women purchased Ford cars before Araceli did her research? *Because women of average size or smaller did not fit well into the cars. Ford conducted market research. As a part of that, they interviewed women to learn what women wanted in a car.*

4. How did Ford research the problem? *This may include conducting telephone or Internet polls, looking up information in the public records at the United States Census Bureau (to find out where people live, how much money they make, and how many children they have), as well as organizing focus groups to find out peoples' likes and dislikes.*

5. What is the difference between assembly line production and batch production? *Batch production usually precedes assembly line production in the same or separate factories. During batch production, standardized parts or components are produced in mass quantity. During assembly line production, those standardized parts are assembled into goods at a steady rate.*

6. Why are interchangeable parts critical for the success of an assembly line system? Be sure to define interchangeable parts in your answer. *Interchangeable parts are prefabricated standardized parts that are assembled into products. Before the advent of interchangeable parts, a single craftsman would make all parts and then assemble them into a product. Interchangeable parts allowed for assembly line production.*

7. Why is it more cost effective for companies to produce objects in mass quantities than it is for them to produce only a few? *Because when producing mass quantities, companies can achieve an economy of scale. Materials can be purchased in bulk. Laborers can work in assembly line style. Costs are spread over the larger number of products produced. Total profit is greater.*

Connecting the Dots

8. Considering both the work at IDEO and at Ford, explain why market research is a valuable tool for companies. *Engineers and designers must understand the needs and desires of the end users so that they can design technologies that will meet those needs and desires.*

9. How did Araceli use the engineering design process to change automobile design at Ford? *She first defined the problem, researched, developed possible solutions, created a prototype, tested and evaluated the solution, then redesigned the product.*

What Do You Think?

10. Araceli asks two important questions at the end of the chapter: How can engineers avoid unintended consequences in the future? How much power do consumers have to minimize unintended consequences? Choose one question and answer it in a paragraph. *To avoid unintended consequences, engineers can create a diverse team of experts to explore environmental, health, and other effects of emerging technologies during the design stage. Consumers can reduce the effects of unintended consequences by learning as much as possible about a new technology before purchasing it.*

Engineering the Future Teacher Guide
©2008 Museum of Science, Boston

Chapter 7: A Universe of Systems

In Chapter 7, Dudley Green, a manufacturing engineer at Teradyne Corporation, introduces basic concepts about systems and challenges students to start thinking about technologies as systems with inputs, outputs, processes, feedback, and goals. Dudley then analyzes several of the systems involved with creating printed circuit boards at Teradyne, including the primary processing systems that transform the gold ore into gold sheets and the systems that deal with waste management. Dudley mentions how CAD and CAM (Computer-Aided Manufacturing) systems impact his work. Finally, Dudley explains the idea of life cycle analysis, charting the various inputs and outputs of a system from start to finish, and explains why he believes that more engineers should consider the big picture when designing new technologies.

✔ A **system** is a collection of objects that work together to achieve a goal.

✔ All systems have inputs, outputs, processes, feedback, and goals.

✔ No system functions completely independent of another system. All systems are related in some way.

✔ **Optimization** is the process of making a system as effective as possible given a set of constraints.

✔ **Raw materials** are the natural, unrefined resources of the earth. Raw materials are transformed into useful materials for manufacturing during primary production.

✔ **Waste management systems** deal with the outputs of other designed systems.

✔ **Life cycle analysis** involves charting all of a system's inputs and outputs and gauging the true costs of a product.

What's the Story?

1. How does Dudley define the term "system"? What are the parts of a system? *A system is a collection of objects that work together to achieve a common goal. A system includes inputs, outputs, processes, feedback, and goals.*

2. Draw a diagram of a system for producing potato chips. Be sure to label the different parts of the system. *Diagram might resemble the following process: collect materials (potatoes, cooking oil, etc.), peel skin, wash, cut to desired shape then press, process, package, quality control, then ship out to consumer.*

3. How do the goals of the potato chip production system differ from its outputs? *The goal may be to make a flavorful potato chip. This is different from the outputs listed above. The goal includes the systems interaction with people and society.*

4. What raw materials would be necessary for this potato chip production system? What kinds of waste would the system generate? *Raw materials: potatoes, plants for making oil, steel for the machines, trees for wood for the building, and so on. Wastes: air pollution, paper wastes, used cooking oil, extra bags, and so on.*

5. What kinds of primary processing might be required for the potato chip production system? *Turning plants into oil, farming the potatoes, milling wood for the building, and so on.*

6. List three durable goods and three nondurable goods that you use every day. *Durable: cars, bicycles, desks, chairs, kitchen appliances, and so on. Non-durable: pencils, pens, writing paper, toothbrush, soap, and so on.*

Connecting the Dots

7. What might the inputs, outputs, processes, feedback, and goals of an automobile manufacturing assembly line system be that Araceli described in "Bringing Designed Ideas to the Masses"? ***Inputs:*** *metal, glass, fabricated car parts;* ***Outputs:*** *finished cars, exhaust, waste materials;* ***Processes:*** *forming the body, welding, bolting parts in place, testing;* ***Feedback:*** *number of cars produced per hour would feed back into the system to either increase or decrease production;* ***Goals:*** *Produce high-quality automobiles that everybody wants to buy.*

ERROR: The title of Araceli's chapter is "Bringing Designed Ideas to the Masses," not "Bringing Designed Ideas to the Market" as noted in the textbook for this question.

8. Conduct a life cycle analysis of an automobile. (List all of the inputs and outputs associated with its production and use.) ***Inputs:*** *Production: steel, tires, glass, workers, factories, money, upholstery, energy to run the factory; Use: gasoline, motor oil, knowledge, highways, roads;* ***Outputs:*** *cars, industrial wastes such as leftover material, air pollution, millions of cars on the road, junk cars in wrecking yards, partially recycled and partially in landfills.*

9. What does the life cycle analysis of an automobile lead you to conclude about the unintended consequences of the automobile? How might engineers avoid unintended consequences using life cycle analysis? *Answers will vary but may include that the automobile has had unintended consequences on the environment.*

What Do You Think?

10. Dudley believes that engineers should understand all the processes in a system, no matter what aspect they are specifically involved in. Why do you think he believes this is important? What can this understanding do for the development of new processes and products? *Dudley thinks an interest in systems can lead both to a better product and to fewer unintended consequences.*

Engineering the Future Teacher Guide
©2008 Museum of Science, Boston

Chapter 8: The Making of a New Balance Shoe

In Chapter 8, Christine Epplett, an engineer at New Balance Athletic Shoe, describes the company's approach to research and development. Like at IDEO (Chapter 5), New Balance employees work in diverse teams to develop a new shoe. The team includes marketers, biomechanical engineers such as Christine, CAD technicians, materials engineers, process engineers, manufacturing associates, quality-control personnel, and so on. Christine explains that when designing a shoe, she must always keep in mind the various processes that can be accomplished in the factory. In other words, she must design for manufacturing. Christine then takes the reader on a tour of the factory floor, describing all of the various processes involved in the making of a New Balance Shoe.

Teaching Points

✔ The seven **manufacturing processes** mentioned include the following:

1. **Separating:** removing unwanted materials
2. **Forming:** using pressure or force to shape a material
3. **Assembling (or combining):** putting parts of a product together
4. **Molding and casting:** pouring a liquefied material into a mold, allowing it to solidify in the shape of the mold, then removing the solidified material from the mold
5. **Conditioning:** any process that uses high temperatures, chemicals, or force to change the properties of a material
6. **Finishing:** any final treatment done to the surface of the product to make it more attractive to a consumer
7. **Quality control:** a test or series of tests on samples from the production line to ensure that only high-quality products leave the plant

✔ A **trade-off** is a decision to give up one quality or aspect of something in return for gaining another quality or aspect. Trade-offs are often necessary when optimizing a system.

What's the Story?

1. Christine discussed seven manufacturing processes: separating, forming, assembling, molding and casting, conditioning, finishing, and quality control. What are these processes and how is each used in the New Balance factory?

   - *Separating: Removing unwanted materials. Workers at New Balance use cutting dies to cut fabric for the shoes.*
   - *Forming: Shaping metals or hard materials with force. The cutting dies used in the New Balance factory are formed by a press.*
   - *Assembling: Putting pieces of a product together. Shoes are sewn together during assembly at New Balance.*
   - *Molding and casting: When a fluid material is poured into a mold and allowed to harden. Soles of New Balance shoes are made this way.*
   - *Conditioning: Treating a material to change its chemical properties. The shoes are heated so that the soles will adhere better.*
   - *Finishing: Any final process to improve the look of the product. The New Balance shoes are cleaned, laced, and boxed.*
   - *Quality control: Ensuring that the final product is free of flaws. Shoes at New Balance are spot-checked to make sure they are free of flaws. If flaws are found, the whole batch is checked.*

2. What's a trade-off? What is one trade-off that the New Balance management makes? *A trade-off is a decision to give up one quality or aspect of something in return for gaining another quality or aspect. New Balance never lays off employees when new labor-saving technologies come along. This costs the company money up front, but it keeps the employees happier and possibly boosts their production level.*

Connecting the Dots

3. What processes in the New Balance factory involve batch production, and what processes involve assembly line–style production? *Separating and hand-stitching are done in batches. Conditioning and attaching soles are done in assembly line style.*

4. Robert Hartmann talked a lot about the importance of teamwork. Who are the members of the team involved in R&D (Research and Development) at New Balance? Are they all engineers? *They are not all engineers. The team includes designers, marketers, manufacturing designers, biomechanical engineers, CAD team members, process engineers, manufacturing associates, and quality-control personnel.*

5. How do some engineers at New Balance test prototypes? *By asking people to try them on and by trying them on themselves and wearing them over a period of time.*

What Do You Think?

6. You've just been hired as a consultant to a factory that makes wooden birdhouses. List the manufacturing processes mentioned in the chapter and write how each process might be used in this factory. *Answers may include the following:*

   - *Separating: Wood must be cut to size.*
   - *Molding and casting: Any ceramic or plastic attachments on the birdhouses will be created using molding or casting processes.*
   - *Assembling: Wood will be nailed together.*
   - *Forming: Any metal parts will most likely be created using forming.*
   - *Conditioning: Birdhouses will be sanded and painted with primer.*
   - *Finishing: Birdhouses will be painted.*
   - *Quality control: Birdhouses will be spot-checked to ensure that they are free of flaws.*

7. You've just been hired as a consultant to a second factory. This factory makes ceramic coffee mugs. List the seven manufacturing processes mentioned in the chapter and write how each process might be used in this factory.

   - *Separating: Separate raw materials to get pure clay and quartz sand.*
   - *Forming: Metal or plastic tops for the mugs are produced in various forming machines.*
   - *Molding and casting: The clay is poured into a mold and allowed to harden.*
   - *Conditioning: The soft clay mugs are fired at a high temperature to make them stronger.*
   - *Finishing: A glaze is sprayed on the mugs so that they will hold liquids and to make them shinier and more appealing to the consumer. The mugs are then fired a second time to melt and harden the glaze.*
   - *Assembling: Tops are put on top of the mugs, and they are packaged for shipment.*
   - *Quality control: Sample mugs are inspected for imperfections and tested to be sure they hold hot liquids.*

Chapter 9: Like Nature Intended

In Chapter 9, Saul Griffith, a doctoral student at MIT, describes his process for developing a new manufacturing system for eyeglass lenses. He draws inspiration for his designs from Mother Nature. It's no surprise that Saul is interested in Just-In-Time manufacturing systems that produce goods on demand, eliminating the need for vast inventories of products. In graduate school, Saul learned about how few people in the world have access to eyeglass lenses. After researching the problem, he discovered that eyeglasses are expensive because lens retailers must keep large inventories. He created a desktop lens-making machine that can produce lenses in a matter of minutes. Then he learned of another related problem: Many people in developing countries do not have access to optometrists, so they don't know what prescription they need. To solve this problem, Saul developed an inexpensive machine that can be used by anyone anywhere to diagnose vision problems. He is still in the process of testing this technology. At the same time, he is concerned about having enough funding to complete the design cycle. Saul discusses the importance of funding to engineers.

Teaching Points

✔ **Just-In-Time manufacturing technologies** produce goods on demand, eliminating the need for expensive inventories.

✔ Engineering is an **iterative process**. It's often necessary to go back to the drawing board several times before finding a solution.

✔ Funding is extremely important to engineers. It costs money to develop most new technologies. Funding usually determines what gets made and mass-produced.

What's the Story?

1. You could say that Saul's motives were consistent throughout his career, but his engineering goals changed. What were his motives? How did his engineering goals change as he told his story? *Saul's motives included creating technologies that will be useful and beneficial to people. His engineering goals changed from building bridges to electronic books to lens manufacturing systems to diagnostic goggles.*

2. Saul starts the chapter with the idea that nature is a better manufacturer than humans. Explain what he means. Give an example that's not in the chapter. *Often the products that nature produces are safer for the environment, and are more efficient than human-made products. Examples will vary.*

3. What is "Just-In-Time" manufacturing, and what are its advantages? *JIT Manufacturing means producing goods on demand instead of producing many and keeping a large inventory. JIT manufacturing reduces the need for a large inventory, which cuts costs.*

4. List two kinds of composite materials, two kinds of synthetic materials, and two kinds of natural materials. *Composite: concrete, asphalt, any metal alloy; Synthetic: cellophane, polyurethane, polypropylene; Natural: cotton, wool, wood.*

5. How did Saul research the eyeglass problem and develop possible solutions? *He conducted patent research and then brainstormed possible solutions based on his research.*

Teacher Guide to the Textbook

Connecting the Dots

6. Manufacturing systems don't just involve making a product. They also involve getting the product to the people who will use it. How does the inventory of New Balance Shoes in a sporting goods store compare to the inventory of lenses in an eyeglasses store? *A store has room for only a few hundred shoes, which is enough to fit most people. Eyeglass stores must store thousands of lenses because there are so many possible corrective lenses.*

7. Does Saul follow the steps of the design process in order? Which steps did he repeat? Which steps does Saul have yet to complete? *Yes, to some extent. He started out in the usual order defining the problem, researching, thinking of possible solutions, and creating a prototype. However, he then discovered that another problem needed to be solved before his solution could be implemented. So, Saul went back and repeated the research step. At this point in time, Saul has not completed solving the second problem. He wants to fine-tune the machine to make it more efficient and easier to mass produce.*

What Do You Think?

8. Saul Griffith is clearly motivated by the desire to help people in developing countries, not just to make money. Yet he says that money is very important. What does he mean by this? Why is money so important in engineering? *It costs money to develop most new technologies, and even more to mass produce them. If engineers and manufacturers don't have the funding to develop new technologies, those technologies simply won't get made.*

9. Why might countries restrict companies that want to bring in new technologies such as low-cost eyeglasses or diagnostic goggles? *Because they will take business away from local optometrists or businesses.*

Engineering the Future Teacher Guide
©2008 Museum of Science, Boston

Unit 2: Sustainable Cities

Chapter 10: Redesigning America

In Chapter 10, Peter Park introduces the important idea that urban environments are designed systems. He tells how he's solving urban design problems in cities such as Denver and Milwaukee, while investigating what factors make the most successful and sustainable cities. As he tells his story, he describes New Urbanism, a movement among urban planners, architects, engineers, residents, and city officials to solve some of the design problems of modern American cities. He then explores what qualities the most beloved cities in the world have in common: high population density, public meeting spaces, multi-use structures, and beautiful buildings. Peter also analyzes why so many city designs have led to the deterioration of city centers and air pollution, and traces the evolution of urban sprawl.

Teaching Points

✔ The way a city is designed can affect the health and well-being of its residents.

✔ **Urban sprawl** refers to the rapid expansion of a city toward low-density surrounding areas.

✔ **New urbanism** is a movement among urban planners, architects, engineers, residents, and city officials to solve some of the design problems of modern American cities.

✔ Elements of successful urban design include multi-use structures, public meeting spaces, and attractive buildings.

✔ **Sustainable development** refers to development that meets the needs of current residents without compromising the ability of future generations to meet their needs.

✔ **Zoning laws** dictate how land in a specific location can be used and what kinds of structures can be built on it.

What's the Story?

1. What is New Urbanism? *It is a movement among urban planners, architects, engineers, residents, and city officials to solve some of the design problems of modern American cities.*

2. What does the term "sustainable development" mean? Give three examples of development that might be considered sustainable. *Sustainable development refers to development that meets the needs of the present generation without compromising the ability of future generations to meet their own needs. Examples of sustainable development may vary and may include making cities less car-centered, which can reduce pollution and boost business; constructing multi-use buildings, which leads to denser urban centers; and building more parks with trees, which is good for tourism and air quality.*

3. Why does Peter say that Denver's path of development was not sustainable? What is the solution he is working on? *Denver was growing very quickly, but it was not becoming more densely populated. Instead, natural areas were being destroyed for housing development. In order to bring people from the city to the suburbs, roads were being constructed. These were becoming increasingly congested. If nothing was done to solve the problem, future residents' quality of life may have suffered.*

Teacher Guide to the Textbook

4. How does urban sprawl harm the environment? What are some other problems with sprawl? *Sprawl usually contributes to habitat loss because forests, agricultural land, grasslands, and wetlands are paved over. Sprawl forces people to get around mostly by automobile. Automobile exhaust leads to air pollution, and, consequently, public health problems. Sprawl may contribute to other societal problems as well. Because people are inside of their cars whenever they are traveling through other parts of town, they don't have much interaction with people unlike themselves—at least much less so than if they used public transportation or walked everywhere. This can lead to cultural isolation and breed misunderstanding between people of different demographics (races, classes, ages, etc.). Also, if people travel everywhere by automobile, they get less exercise than if they walk or use public transportation (they have to walk to bus stops, etc.).*

5. What are multiple-use zoning laws? In Peter's opinion, how do multiple-use zoning laws benefit a city? *Zoning laws dictate how land can be used and what kinds of structures can be built on it. Under mixed-use zoning, a single building might contain offices, shops, restaurants, and apartments or condominiums. Multi-use zoning laws allow for greater density and less dependence on the automobile.*

Connecting the Dots

6. What does urban sprawl have to do with the unintended consequences of the automobile that Araceli Ortiz described in Unit 1? *Urban sprawl is in many ways an unintended consequence of the automobile. The automobile is what allowed for cities to spread out in the first place.*

7. After FasTracks is implemented, will Denver's development problems be solved once and for all? Using what you learned about the design process from Shawn Frayne and Jamy Drouillard, explain your answer. *Definitely not! No design is ever really finished because improvements can always be made. Though the designers of FasTracks are doing a lot of research in an effort to determine the future needs of Denver's residents, it's impossible to predict exactly how the city will grow and how those needs will change over time.*

What Do You Think?

8. Every design can be improved upon. Think about your own city or town. What are its major design problems? Write a list of at least three problems and describe what impact these problems have on your community. *Answers will vary.*

9. Prescribe New Urbanist solutions to the problems you identified in your previous answer. *Answers will vary but should include some of the following: increased public transit, pedestrian-friendly streets, multi-use zoning, public meeting spaces, and aesthetically pleasing buildings.*

10. Do you believe that the New Urbanism approach is the best approach to urban planning? Why or why not? *Answers will vary.*

Engineering the Future Teacher Guide
©2008 Museum of Science, Boston

Chapter 11: Bridging the Future

In Chapter 11, field engineer Kirk Elwell describes the creation of the Leonard P. Zakim Bridge, a centerpiece in the historic Central Artery Project (known as the "Big Dig") in Boston. The bridge was designed to serve as a new emblem for the city and to look impressive. The project improved the look of the city and solved some serious problems related to traffic congestion. Kirk describes how the bridge was constructed to support various live and dead loads. He also introduces the concepts of compression, tension, bending, and torsion and how the structural members of the bridge experience these forces. Kirk explores the various materials used to construct the bridge and relates the story of how a piece of metal expanded in the hot sun so much that it halted construction for a whole day. Finally, Kirk explains why it's necessary to keep relationships running smoothly in order to complete a complex task.

Teaching Points

✔ **Engineers** and **architects** work together to design structures. The architect creates the look and form of the structure while the engineer makes sure that the structure can support the necessary loads.

✔ A **dead load** is any load associated with the structure itself. A **live load** is any other force on the structure due to traffic, snow, wind, earthquakes, and so on.

✔ **Compression** occurs when two ends of an object are pushed toward each other.

✔ **Tension** occurs when two ends of an object are moved away from each other.

✔ **Torsion** is a twisting force that occurs when one side of an object twists relative to the other side.

✔ **Thermal expansion** is when a material expands when it gets hotter and shrinks when it gets cooler.

What's the Story?

1. According to Kirk, what are the main problems the Central Artery Project is trying to solve? *The Central Artery had terrible traffic congestion, and the above-ground highway cut off some of the main tourism areas of Boston from the downtown area, which is bad for business.*

2. Three engineers are designing a civic center for a small city: an architect, a structural engineer, and a field engineer. Describe how each team member would contribute to the construction project. Name at least three other individuals who might also work on the project. *Architects would sketch out a design for the civic center; a structural engineer would be responsible to choose the necessary columns, beams, foundations, and other necessary components to make the building stand with a safety factor. A field engineer would supervise the work when the building is being constructed, to make certain that it is built according to the architect's and structural engineer's specifications. Three other individuals who might also work on the project could include electrical, computer, industrial, and geotechnical engineers, as well as plumbers, electricians, carpenters, masons, roofers, and so on.*

Teacher Guide to the Textbook

3. What were the design requirements of the Zakim Bridge? *First, the bridge shouldn't interfere with boat traffic. The bridge also had to allow plenty of sunlight to reach the river beneath it. Finally, the bridge had to look impressive.*

Designing with Math and Science

4. Describe at least three structural components that contribute to the dead load of your school building. Describe at least three components that contribute to the live load. *Dead load: walls, floors, roof, beams, doorways, stairwells, elevator shafts, and so on; Live load: students, teachers, snow on the roof, earthquakes, and so on.*

5. What is the minimum dead load (in tons) of a steel bridge that must carry 100 tons of traffic? What will be the total load of that bridge? *Dead Load: 100 tons (A steel bridge can carry its own weight in live load); Total Load: 200 tons (Total load = live load + dead load)*

6. A scaffold has a dead load that is 60 percent of its total load. If the scaffold weighs 1,200 pounds, how much live load is it supporting? *Dead load/total load = 60/100 = 1,200lb./Xlb.; total load or X = 2,000lb.; live load = total load − dead load = 2,000lb. − 1,200lb. = 800lb.*

7. Define compression and tension. Would the rope in a tug-of-war contest experience compression or tension? *Compression is a force that pushes the ends of an object toward each other. Tension is a force that pulls the ends of an object away from each other. The rope would experience tension.*

8. Describe how bending occurs in a diving board with someone standing on the end. You may want to draw a sketch to help you. *If the beam is supported at one end, when it bends, the top of the board is in tension and the bottom is in compression.*

Connecting the Dots

9. In "The Art of Engineering," Robert Hartmann discussed how an object's "look and feel" is as important as its function. Would Kirk Elwell agree? Copy two or more sentences from this chapter that support your answer. *"But, in general, architects focus more on how the structure will look and how people will interact with it." "The Big Dig will make the roads safer and Boston more beautiful. That's good for tourism and business, and for everyone's quality of life."*

What Do You Think?

10. Kirk talks about the importance of keeping relationships with other organizations running smoothly, even if it means spending more money on the project. What might the consequences be if engineers and managers working on the Central Artery Project ignored the interests of civic organizations? How does this relate to your own life? What relationships are important for you to keep running smoothly every day? *Answers will vary. Students should show that they understand that relationships are critical to accomplishing all tasks, whether or not they involve engineering.*

Chapter 12: Tower in the Sky

In Chapter 12, structural engineer Bill Baker describes how he is designing the tallest building in the world. The Burj Dubai, as the building is called, will be located in downtown Dubai, in the United Arab Emirates. A real estate developer in Dubai commissioned the building to be an emblem of Dubai's prestige and prosperity. Bill talks about the design for the building, as well as how its structure will support a massive dead load and extremely high winds. Bill takes the reader through a brief history of how humans have pushed technology to its limits to build taller and taller buildings, describing the stone minarets and towers of the Middle Ages, the first steel-frame tall buildings, and modern-day skyscrapers. He describes the role of a truss system in counteracting shear and bending. Finally, Bill talks about how the building is designed to "confuse the wind" by changing shape as it gets taller.

Teaching Points

✔ Steel and iron manufacturing techniques allowed for the production of long steel beams in the Industrial Revolution. These could be used to create tall steel-frame buildings.

✔ Most modern skyscrapers are constructed around a strong reinforced core—a long reinforced column that acts like a building's spine. Floors extend from the core with supporting columns around the perimeter. This allows for the outer walls of the structure to be made of glass.

✔ Steel and concrete are common skyscraper building materials. Concrete resists compression very well, but does not perform as well under tension. For this reason, it is often reinforced with steel rebar, which holds up well under tension.

✔ **Shear** is a force that results in the deformation of an object such that the object's parallel planes move past each other.

✔ A **truss** is a triangular arrangement of structural members that reduces the effects of shear and bending.

What's the Story?

1. Why do people in Dubai want to build a super-tall structure in their city? *The structure will be an emblem of growth, technology, and prosperity.*

2. What limited the height of the structures in the Middle Ages? *The structures were supported by thick stone walls. As the structures got taller, the lower walls had to be thicker to support the dead load above them. At a certain point, the walls would get too thick for there to be any dwelling space.*

3. What manufacturing breakthrough led to the development of taller structures in the 1800s? *New manufacturing processes for making long steel and iron beams.*

Designing with Math and Science

4. What is shear? *Shear is a force that acts on the side of an object, causing the object's parallel surfaces to move past each other.*

5. What is a truss and how does it minimize the effects of a shearing force? *A truss is a triangular arrangement of structural members. A truss prevents the joints of a structure from sliding apart.*

6. Why was it necessary for Bill to design the Burj Dubai so that it "confuses" the wind? *The wind can get very strong at high altitudes. It starts creating spinning vortices at the sides of a building. This can cause the building to start rocking back and forth dangerously. If the shape of the building changes, not enough vortices can build up along the structure's side to cause a problem.*

7. Is concrete better at minimizing the effects of compression or tension? What is special about the concrete that Bill is using as a construction material for the Burj Dubai? *Concrete performs very well under compression forces. Modern concrete also uses fly ash from coal-fired power plants, ground up blast furnace slag from steel manufacturing, and silica dust from computer-chip manufacturing as substitutes for some of the cement. These waste products from other industries actually make concrete stronger and contributes to recycling. Concrete is very strong in compression. Unfortunately, it doesn't resist tension forces well. To make it perform better under tension or bending, concrete is reinforced with steel bars (called rebar).*

8. How does the Burj Dubai reflect a New Urbanist's approach to city planning? *The Burj is a multiple-use structure, so it will contribute to a higher-density urban core.*

What Do You Think?

9. Name a structure that is emblematic to your city, town, or region. Find out when it was built and what materials were used in its construction. What do you think would have been different if it had been built more recently? *Answers will vary.*

10. What do you think superstructures of the future will be constructed of? What is special about those materials? *Answers will vary.*

Chapter 13: Home Sweet Home

In Chapter 13, construction manager Prity Rungta describes all the factors that go into building a house. She coordinates everything from the foundation layout to raising the roof. Diagrams are shown to help the reader understand how the foundation and the frame of the house work. In the section "Building It Safe," an editor explains the importance of building codes and how safety factors take into account live loads the house might need to support. At the end of the chapter, Prity stresses the importance of planning and teamwork when troubleshooting problems and reaching her desired goal.

Teaching Points

✔ An **elevation view** is an orthographic 2-D drawing of the above-ground portion of a structure.

✔ A **plan view** shows the top-down view of the structure.

✔ The area contained within the perimeter of the building is called the **footprint**.

✔ A **foundation** transmits loads from the structure to the ground. Foundations usually extend underground.

✔ When determining the live load a building must be able to support, engineers refer to code that is listed as load per unit area, or **stress**.

✔ A **safety factor** is a factor by which a maximum likely stress is multiplied in order to ensure the safety of the structure. Because occupants may use their space in unexpected ways, safety factors are necessary.

What's the Story?

1. Prity does not design structures, but she does use the engineering design process. How? *She explains how she uses the engineering design process to find out how much stress a building should be designed to hold with a specific safety factor.*

2. What is the primary way that the architect communicates his or her building plans to Prity's team? *An architect communicates his or her plans through an elevation drawing and a plan drawing, both of which are orthographic projections.*

3. Prity describes two new construction technologies that help her team deliver a higher-quality product for the money. What are they? *A wood joist system made of composite wood, as well as Insulated Concrete Forms (ICF).*

Designing with Math and Science

4. You are a structural engineer working for a design firm, and you have been given the task of designing a scaffold that can support a load of 300 pounds. The scaffold must have a safety factor of 2. How many pounds must your design be able to support? *600 lb.*

Connecting the Dots

5. Sketch a plan view and elevation view of your school's lunchroom or library. The drawings should not include furnishings, but they should include architectural features such as windows, doors, pillars, or skylights. *Answers will vary.*

What Do You Think?

6. Prity explains that she learned a lot about the construction industry by asking questions of the people she was working with. Describe a time when you've had to ask a lot of questions to learn what you needed to know in order to do a job or an assignment well. *Answers will vary.*

Chapter 14: From the Ground Up

Cathy Bazán-Arias is a geotechnical engineer at a company that designs and builds dams, upgrades electric transmission lines, and improves mass-transit systems. In Chapter 14, she describes her job of analyzing the ground conditions of a structure before it is built to prevent structural failures—like the famous Leaning Tower of Pisa. She is also trained as a structural engineer, so she has to understand the effects of materials, geometry, and load on a structure as well as such factors as the texture of the soil. She takes the reader through the process of choosing the best materials for the foundation and above-ground structure for electrical transmission towers. An editor's note illustrates the math involved in calculating how stress and strain affect the choice of material. Cathy concludes by explaining why soil analysis plays an important role in choosing materials and structural design.

Teaching Points

✔ **Strain** is a measure of how much a material deforms due to stress as compared to its original size.

✔ The **elastic limit** is the point at which a material will no longer return to its original shape due to stress.

✔ At stresses below the elastic limit, a material experiences **elastic deformation**—it returns to its original shape when the stress is removed.

✔ At stresses above the elastic limit, a material experiences **plastic deformation**—when the change is permanent.

✔ As stress increases, a **failure point** is eventually reached when the structure breaks or fractures.

What's the Story?

1. Dr. Bazán-Arias is a geotechnical engineer by training, but she also has some expertise in structural engineering. Why does she believe having both is helpful? *Geotechnical engineers specialize in designing how structures or underground parts of structures interact with the land they are standing on. For this reason, it is also important to understand the structures themselves and how they behave under different conditions.*

2. What are the major factors that engineers consider when selecting materials for a job? *The unique climate and terrain that the structure will be built on as well as the characteristics of the materials themselves, such as their ability to withstand compression, tension, torsion, or shearing, and their resistance to corrosion. Engineers also must consider cost and the length of time the structure is expected to last.*

3. What kinds of information can engineers get by looking at stress-strain curves? *Stress-strain curves are graphs based on laboratory tests that show how a material behaves under increasing stress. These graphs allow engineers to predict the loads a given material can withstand safely, and what will happen to the material if maximum safe loads are exceeded.*

Designing with Math and Science

4. Look at the stress-strain curve below. How much does the material strain under 25 PSI of stress? Will the material return to its original shape after a stress of this magnitude has been applied? *The material will lengthen two inches for every inch of original length. It will not return to its original shape after such a stress.*

5. What is the elastic limit of the material, and how can you tell? How will the material behave under loads higher than the elastic limit? *The elastic limit is about 24 pounds per square inch. That is the point at which the material lengthens rapidly with a slight increase in tensile stress. After about 28 pounds of stress, it will break.*

Connecting the Dots

6. Foundations are important parts of the structural designs described in the three previous chapters. Write a one-sentence description of each of the following structures' foundations:

   1. **The Leonard P Zakim Bridge:** *Each tower has a strong underground foundation that anchors it to solid bedrock, 140 feet below ground level.*
   2. **The Burj Dubai:** *A central core and perimeter columns are supported by deep underground columns called piles that act like the root of a tree.*
   3. **A house:** *Layers of concrete with steel rods running through them offer structural support for each floor.*
   4. **A transmission tower:** *A steel frame anchored in reinforced concrete extends deep underground to offer additional support for the tower. In some cases, the foundation is made entirely of steel.*

What Do You Think?

7. Dr. Bazán-Arias also designs landfills for GAI consulting. Do some research in the library or on the Internet and write two paragraphs about landfill design. In your response, explain some of the decisions that engineers designing a landfill may have to make in terms of location, material selection, and structural geometry. *Answers will vary.*

Engineering the Future Teacher Guide
©2008 Museum of Science, Boston

Chapter 15: Building Green

In Chapter 15, architect Chris Benedict discusses how she designs "green" structures that conserve energy. Before she explains her designs, she introduces some fundamental concepts about energy and energy transfer to be built upon throughout the rest of the course. These include the idea of energy as a substance-like entity that, like matter, is conserved despite the processes involved in a system. Chris explains how a home heating system works using an energy diagram to illustrate how energy is transferred from one object to the next in a system. Next she explains how the heating system in her building has multiple thermostats, which help conserve energy. You must have good insulation on a home, she says, because of the fundamental nature of energy: Like matter, energy always moves from an area of higher concentration to an area of lower concentration. For this reason, hot air and energy escape a heated structure through the walls, windows, and doors.

Teaching Points

✔ Energy acts like a substance in many ways. Like matter, energy in a system is conserved despite the processes involved. Also, like matter, energy can be stored and transferred (moved from place to place). However, energy is not a substance. You can't pick up a handful of energy, and it does not have weight or take up space.

✔ Energy always moves from an area of higher concentration to an area of lower concentration—until something gets in the way or the difference in concentration disappears.

✔ Energy diagrams (as illustrated in the chapter) are useful for tracking how energy moves through a system.

✔ **Heating** occurs when energy is transferred across a system boundary, leading to an increase in the temperature of objects inside the system boundary.

✔ **Temperature** is a measure of the hotness or coldness of an object.

✔ Whenever energy is transferred from one object to another, some energy is "lost" to the environment—that is, it is no longer useful for the intended purpose.

✔ A **conductor** is a material through which energy moves easily. An **insulator** is a material that resists the flow of energy.

✔ **R-value** is a measure of the resistance of an insulator.

✔ A **thermal mass** is a part of a building, such as a thick concrete wall or floor that absorbs and stores energy during the day; it slowly radiates the energy to the interior of the building at night.

What's the Story?

1. What problem do green architects try to solve? *Buildings waste a lot of energy. Much of that energy comes from the combustion of fossil fuels, which contributes to many environmental and public health problems, including habitat destruction, air pollution, and lung disease. These fuels are also expensive.*

2. What makes the heating system in Chris's green building more efficient than the heating system in "conventional" buildings? *The additional thermostats.*

3. Make a list of four materials that Chris will use in her building and briefly explain the function of each material.

   - *Concrete: main structural material, thermal mass*
   - *Steel: main structural material, reinforces concrete planks in floors*
   - *Bricks: outer covering, protects building*
   - *Insulator: prevents thermal energy from leaking to the outside*

Designing with Math and Science

4. Draw an energy diagram of a toaster heating up a slice of bread. *The diagram should use arrows to represent the transfer of energy from the toaster (or the heating element in the toaster) to the bread. Some energy should be shown escaping to the surrounding air.*

5. What's the difference between an insulator and a conductor? Would an engineer choose a good insulator or a good conductor as a material for a coffee mug? What about a saucepan? *An insulator is a material through which energy does not flow well. A conductor is a material through which energy flows well. An engineer would choose an insulator when designing a coffee mug—she would want the mug to keep the thermal energy in the coffee from flowing through the mug to the air surrounding it. This would keep the coffee warmer longer. An engineer would chose a material that is a good conductor for a sauce pan. She would want the thermal energy from the heat source to pass through to the food.*

6. Which is a better insulator, wood or cellulose insulation? (Use the R-value chart earlier in the chapter.) How do you know? *Cellulose insulation is a better insulator. R-value is a measure of a material's ability to resist the flow of energy. Materials with higher R-values have higher resistance to energy flow; therefore, they are better insulators.*

Connecting the Dots

7. Many of the engineers in this book discuss the importance of teamwork. Why is teamwork so critical when it comes to designing green buildings? How is this different from the teamwork in "The Making of a New Balance Shoe" and other earlier chapters? *Teamwork is critical because the parts of the designed system (the entire building) must function well together. They are all interrelated. If each engineer works in isolation, the building's various systems may not work well together. Teamwork is essential at New Balance and IDEO for many of the same reasons. Every team member has a critical role to play in the design and manufacturing process. And each team member must communicate well with the others to ensure that the work is coordinated.*

Engineering the Future Teacher Guide
©2008 Museum of Science, Boston

What Do You Think?

8. Look around your school building and list at least three ways the building could be designed to better conserve energy. *Answers will vary. Students may comment on the heating system, better sealing around windows and doors, and/or better use and placement of the thermal mass.*

9. Chris talks about the role of a building inspector. Why is this an important role? What might result if cities and towns did not employ building inspectors? *Answers will vary. Could include making sure that the building meets health, safety, and energy codes. The building inspector must give the owner or contractor an approval to grant a building permit.*

Chapter 16: A Race for the Sun

In Chapter 16, Lauren Stencel describes how a team of students from her college is building an energy-efficient house on the National Mall in Washington, D.C., to compete in the National Solar Decathlon, an event sponsored by the U.S. Department of Energy. The goal of the contest is to design and build an energy-efficient house that can function independently—not connected to electricity, water, or waste lines—for eleven days. Stencel's team plans to donate their house to a family who needs a home in the Washington, D.C., area after the competition. Lauren describes the systems of the house, with special focus on the heating system, which has both passive and active solar heating elements. When discussing the active solar heating system, Lauren discusses how energy measured in BTUs is stored in the water flowing through the heating system. Lauren also introduces photovoltaic cells and talks about the plumbing system and the importance of the home's look and feel.

Teaching Points

✔ A house in the Northern Hemisphere designed to have a **passive solar heating** system will have large south-facing windows through which sunlight will shine onto a thermal mass. The thermal mass will release stored energy during the night.

✔ An **active solar heating** system uses pumps to move a working fluid from a solar collector to the interior of the structure.

✔ A **British Thermal Unit (BTU)** is the amount of energy it takes to raise the temperature of one pound of water by one degree Fahrenheit. A **Joule** is the metric unit for energy. It takes about 4.186 Joules (or 1 calorie) to raise the temperature of one gram of water by one degree Celsius. Most American engineers use BTUs, so that is the unit used most often in this course.

✔ It's possible to measure the energy that is stored or transferred in a system.

✔ **Energy efficiency** is a ratio of the useful energy outputs to the energy inputs of a system. If all of the inputs of a heating system were used to heat the house, then this ratio would be 1, or 100%.

✔ No heating system is 100% efficient. Some energy is always "lost" to the environment.

What's the Story?

1. What are the two different sets of constraints that Lauren's team must consider when designing the house? *The team must design the house for the competition, during which the house must function independently on the National Mall. The team must also design the house to function in its permanent location.*

2. What's a passive solar heating system? Why is it called "passive"? *A passive solar heating system uses the energy of sunlight to warm a home. Passive solar heating systems involve large south-facing windows, through which the sun can shine onto a thermal mass, warming it up.*

3. How does the team plan to communicate their solution? *Through a web site, newsletter, and through this textbook!*

Designing with Math and Science

4. Draw an energy diagram of the active solar heating system that includes the following: collector, sun, fluid, pipes, floor, and room air. *The diagram may look like the following. It should include arrows going from the sun to the collector, working fluid, pipes, floor, and, finally, the room air. It should also show that some energy is "lost" to the environment at each step by the progressively smaller arrows between objects. The system boundary may be drawn to include the collector, fluid, pipes, and floor. However, different choices for the system elements or boundary are fine if they seem to tell a logical "story" about energy transfer.*

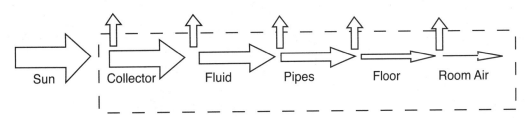

5. What's a BTU? *A British Thermal Unit is defined as the amount of energy it takes to heat one pound of water by one degree Fahrenheit.*

Connecting the Dots

6. Where should a thermal mass of a structure be located in order for passive solar heating to work well? *Inside the structure. Chris Benedict explains why in "Building Green." The sunlight heats up the thermal mass and the thermal mass slowly releases thermal energy to the interior of the building. If the thermal mass is on the exterior of the building, it would release the thermal energy outside, which doesn't help with heating the building.*

What Do You Think?

7. You've been hired by an architecture firm as an energy efficiency specialist. As a first assignment, the firm has asked you to make a presentation in which you describe the attributes of an energy-efficient building. List attributes having to do with the location, the architectural design, the construction material, and the heating system of the building.

   - *Location: The building should be sited so that one wall faces south. This will allow for passive solar heating, solar day lighting, and will provide good surfaces for attaching solar panels.*
   - *Architectural design: The building should be designed with large, south-facing windows and a thermal mass on the interior of the building. Windows and doors should be designed to leak as little thermal energy to the environment as possible. Window coverings should be designed so that sunlight coming in to the building can be reduced in the summer months. This will keep the building cooler.*
   - *Construction materials: A good insulator should be chosen to prevent the flow of thermal energy through the walls and roof. Again, a material that is a good thermal mass should be placed on the interior of the building strategically so that it is warmed by the sun and/or the building's heating system.*
   - *The heating system: The heating system should include a thermostat in every room, and could use radiators or embedded floor pipes. Pipes in the heating system should be insulated as well. (This last point is not covered in the chapter.)*

Teacher Guide to the Textbook

8. Look at the table of common fuel sources shown in Lauren's story. Do you think these are equivalent quantities? How does this affect how someone might support using one type of fuel versus another? Work with a partner to calculate how many pounds of wood would need to be burned to equal the energy content in a ton of coal or a gallon of heating oil. *Answers regarding the equivalency of the fuel sources may vary because different types of fuels are needed for different jobs. Thus, 3,000 lb. of wood would be necessary to equal the energy content in a ton of coal, and 17.5 lb. of wood equals the energy in one gallon of oil.*

Unit 3: Going with the Flow

Chapter 17: In Deep

In Chapter 17, Bob Brown, a design engineer at Woods Hole Oceanographic Institution, explains the redesign process for a deep-water submarine named Alvin. He first explains how Alvin will explore deeper waters in remote regions to get a glimpse into places that humans have never seen before. In order to do so, he explains how Alvin will cope with extreme pressure environments. Bob discusses the concept of buoyant force and how it affects the submarine's movement. He ends the chapter by discussing how a strong arm attached to Alvin will function, as well as how it will benefit the team's effort to research deeper waters.

Teaching Points

✔ **Pressure** is defined as force per unit area.

✔ A **fluid** is a substance that flows easily, such as a liquid or a gas.

✔ When there is a fluid pressure difference, fluid will flow from the area of higher fluid pressure to the area of lower fluid pressure until there is no difference, unless something gets in the way.

✔ **Compressible** fluids occupy a smaller and smaller volume when under increasing pressure.

✔ **Incompressible** fluids do not change volume under increasing pressure.

✔ Liquids are nearly **incompressible** fluids.

✔ For an object that is submerged in a liquid, the upward push on the object—the **buoyant force**—equals the weight of the volume of water displaced.

✔ **Hydraulic systems** use liquid to transmit power by taking advantage of fluid characteristics and pressure changes.

✔ *W=Fd*—The work done on an object equals the force on the object times the distance traveled, where "work" is defined as mechanical energy.

What's the Story?

1. List three systems on the Alvin that Bob's team is planning to redesign for the Alvin's replacement. *The replacement of the structural system will be made with titanium alloy to withstand the demanding pressure at its depth limit. The buoyancy system replacement will not use steel weights to submerge; rather, a system called Variable Ballast System (VBS) will be used to ascend and descend. Lastly, the new Alvin will be equipped with a robotic arm that can pick up rock, sediment, or marine life.*

2. How is the Alvin an example of the relationship between engineers and scientists? *Engineers design the technologies that allow scientists to descend far deeper than any human could go, and to gather specimens of rock, sediment, or marine life for study. The scientists and engineers apply their different expertise to the goal of learning more about life in the extremely high-pressure environment of the deep ocean.*

Designing with Math and Science

3. Imagine that you've just inflated a kick ball and are holding the air in the ball with your finger over the opening. What happens when you remove your finger and the air can pass freely through the opening? Explain why this happens in terms of pressure differences and fluid movement. *There is a pressure difference between the high pressure inside the ball (due to the air you put in and the elasticity of the ball's material) and the lower-pressure atmospheric air. This difference will cause air to move rapidly from inside the ball to the outside until there is an equal amount of pressure inside and outside the ball.*

4. How is the compressibility of gases used in a designed system described in this chapter? How is the incompressibility of liquids used in a different designed system described in this chapter?

   - *Compressibility of gases: The compressibility of gasses is used in the variable ballast system. Pushing water into the ballast tank compresses the air. The additional water reduces the sub's buoyancy so it can dive. When the water is pumped back out, the air expands, increasing the buoyancy of the sub so it can resurface.*
   - *Incompressibility of liquids: The incompressibility of liquids is used in the robotic arm. Increasing the pressure on one side of a working fluid in a hydraulic cylinder pushes on a piston, causing it to move. The piston is connected to one part of the robotic arm, causing it to move.*

5. A hydraulic system in the elbow joint of the Alvin is pressurized so that there is a pressure difference of 20 PSI between the working fluid on one side of a piston and the working fluid on the other side. What is the surface area of the piston if it is pushed with a force large enough to lift a five-pound rock? (Remember: $P=F/A$)

$$A = F/P = 5\text{lb.} / (20\text{lb.} / \text{in.}^2) = 0.25 \text{in.}^2$$

What Do You Think?

6. Pneumatic systems are similar to hydraulic systems, but they use a gas, such as air, as a working fluid. Conduct library or Internet research, and write a description of a technology that uses a pneumatic system. How is the pneumatic system designed to work using pressure differences? How is the fact that gases are compressible incorporated into the design? *Answers will vary.*

7. Develop and sketch a design for a robotic arm that can pick up a paper cup. Will your robotic arm be moved by a hydraulic or pneumatic system? Why? *Answers will vary.*

Engineering the Future Teacher Guide
©2008 Museum of Science, Boston

Chapter 18: Shooting for the Moon

Chapter 18 reveals a team's effort to fly from Earth to Mars and back again. Aprille Joy Ericsson, an astronautical engineer at NASA's Goddard Space Flight Center in Maryland, discusses some of the cutting-edge technologies involved in this ambitious goal. Aprille reveals the design challenge for this space mission in terms of its goal, cost, and date. She explains concepts like resistance-free travel and a low pass maneuver the spacecraft will perform when landing on Mars. Finally, she stresses the importance of minimizing the potential for failure by testing and evaluating system components before finalizing the design. An editor's note on "Rocket Science" describes how Newton's third law applies to rocket propulsion.

ERROR: The last paragraph at the bottom of page 168 was inadvertently partially covered with the photo of Aprille Ericsson. The text should read: The SCIM proposal I'm working on is very exciting, and I truly hope it will be selected for funding. The process for selection is very competitive. NASA starts by issuing an "Announcement of Opportunity" (AO). This document invites teams of researchers, scientists, and engineers from universities, industries, government, and nongovernment organizations all over the world to submit proposals for a solution to an engineering design challenge.

Teaching Points

✔ An **engine** is a system that uses temperature differences to create differences in pressure.

✔ On launch, fuel and liquid oxygen are pumped into the **combustion chamber** of the rocket where they combine and burn explosively. The expanding gases from the intense, continuous burning of fuel increase the pressure in the combustion chamber enormously. The hot gases from the burning fuel escape through a small opening, called a **nozzle**.

✔ Newton's Third Law of Motion states that every action has an equal and opposite reaction.

✔ **Thrust** is determined by the rate the mass is ejected from the nozzle, the velocity of the escaping gas, and the pressure at the nozzle exit.

✔ **Resistance** opposes movement. Every object is subject to resistance of some sort.

✔ The atmosphere of our earth protects us from high-energy particles from space called **cosmic rays**.

What's the Story?

1. Why is it important that the Mars SCIM may bring dust from the Martian atmosphere back to Earth? *The tiny pieces of dust could reveal secrets about the red planet's past and future—including its potential to sustain life.*

2. How will the engineers on Dr. Ericsson's team test the spacecraft before it is launched? *It will be tested in a vacuum chamber where pressure changes the aircraft will experience on the journey can be simulated.*

Designing with Math and Science

3. What is Newton's third law? Use it to explain how a rocket engine propels a spacecraft into outer space. *Every action has an equal and opposite reaction. Thrusters will propel the spacecraft into outer space by pushing hot gases out at a very high velocity. According to Newton's third law, the spacecraft will experience an equal and opposite force, propelling it upward into space. Students may add that the acceleration of the gases times their mass equals the acceleration of the rocket times its mass.*

4. Why must engineers like Dr. Ericsson consider pressure differences when designing components such as the fuel tank? Explain your answer in terms of fluid movement and pressure differences. *Changes in pressure pose a serious problem because, in space, air pressure can be so low that it's negligible. This causes problems for the fuel tank, which would expand as the spacecraft gained altitude, and possibly rupture in space. The fuel tank must be able to adjust its internal pressure during launch, and the flow of liquid fuel into the combustion chamber must also be kept constant during launch.*

5. What is meant by the term "resistance"? Explain a scenario in which you have experienced fluid resistance. *Resistance opposes forward movement. Answers will vary.*

What Do You Think?

6. Describe at least three other technologies that use Newton's third law. *Answers will vary and may include such ideas as jet airplanes, fireworks, and the recoil of guns.*

Engineering the Future Teacher Guide
©2008 Museum of Science, Boston

Chapter 19: Fuel from the Fields

In Chapter 19, Joshua Tickell describes how he retrofitted his van to burn biodiesel, a fuel made from plant oil. Josh is an ardent environmentalist who loves driving. He wanted to find a way to keep driving without contributing so much to air pollution—the environmental degradation that results from drilling and transporting fossil fuels. Josh describes how a diesel engine works and explains how he traveled the country communicating the solution he found.

✔ Obtaining, transporting, and burning fossil fuels contributes to a number of environmental and health problems.

✔ Many scientists believe that increased use of fossil fuels has resulted in global warming trends that may contribute to severe climate change.

✔ A diesel engine uses the relationship between pressure, volume, and temperature to spin the wheels of a car.

✔ A **renewable** resource is a resource that can regenerate or replenish itself in a relatively short amount of time. A **nonrenewable** resource cannot regenerate or replenish itself in a practical amount of time.

What's the Story?

1. What's the difference between a gas engine and diesel engine? *The main difference between the two types of engines is in the way that they ignite the gas-air mixture. Gasoline engines take in a mixture of gas and air, compress it, and then ignite it with a spark from a spark plug. Diesel engines take in just air, compress it, and then inject fuel into the compressed air. The air is compressed enough to raise its temperature sufficiently so that the injected fuel will ignite it.*

2. Give both an advantage and a disadvantage of a diesel engine over a gasoline engine. *Diesel engines are more powerful, and therefore are used to power trains, cargo ships, and other heavy vehicles. Diesel engine exhaust contains more soot and other particulate pollutants than gasoline engines.*

Designing with Math and Science

ERROR: Question 3. Is a typo. It should read:

3. What is the relationship between volume, temperature, and pressure that is useful for designing engines? *Volume, temperature, and pressure are related by the equation "Pressure (P) is proportional to the temperature (T) of the gas, divided by the volume (V) of the chamber," which is written as:*

$$P \propto \frac{T}{V}$$

4. What information would you need to know to determine the force with which the piston pushes the air during the second step of the diesel cycle? (Remember: the formula for pressure in Chapter 17.) *P=F/A, therefore F = A × P. You would need to determine the pressure in the chamber and the surface area of the piston.*

Teacher Guide to the Textbook

5. What will happen to the pressure of the gas in the chamber as the volume of the chamber expands in the third step? *Pressure will drop, as stated in the equation above, which relates pressure, temperature, and volume.*

Connecting the Dots

6. Whenever energy is transferred, some energy is always transferred to the environment. Where might a diesel engine transfer some energy to the environment? *Some energy released in combustion will heat up the engine. Also, the air expelled through the exhaust system is warmer than the surrounding air.*

What Do You Think?

7. Other engineers have tackled the problem of making more efficient cars. What are some new car technologies in development today that are designed to reduce the use of fossil fuels? *Hybrid vehicles have both gas engines, and electric motors and batteries, so they can use both energy sources, either one at a time or together. Hybrid vehicles capture energy from braking to generate electricity and charge the batteries. Solar-powered vehicles use photovoltaic (solar) cells; hydrogen-powered vehicles are reenergized with hydrogen gas, or are powered by fuel cells.*

Engineering the Future Teacher Guide
©2008 Museum of Science, Boston

Chapter 20: An Ingenious Engine

In Chapter 20, Chris Langenfeld, an engineer at Deka Research, tells the story of how his team of engineers redesigned an external combustion engine, called a Stirling engine, so that it could power a wheelchair quietly. The Stirling engine illustrates how a different engine design harnesses energy to do work. Chris describes the Stirling cycle, then explains how advances in battery technology eventually led his team to choose a battery over the Stirling engine for the wheelchair. But the team plans to use the Stirling engine to power a water purification system for developing countries, and they are considering using it to provide electrical power for truckers who spend the night in their cabs.

Teaching Points

✔ The **Stirling** engine is a closed system, which means that the working fluid remains inside the system. It is also an **external combustion engine**, which means that fuel is burned outside the engine.

✔ The hot side of the Stirling engine is the energy or heat source. The cool side of the engine is an energy or heat sink. It does not make sense to say that the cool side is a cool source, because energy moves from a higher to a lower concentration.

What's the Story?

1. Why is the Stirling engine considered a closed system? *Because the working fluid remains inside the engine. Only energy crosses the system boundary.*

2. What were the design requirements for the wheelchair engine? Why did the Stirling engine seem like it might meet the criteria? *The engine had to be quiet and had to deliver a lot of power. Because the Stirling engine is an external combustion engine, there are no explosions inside of the combustion chamber. Therefore, the engine is very quiet.*

3. Why wasn't the engine that Chris's team redesigned used in the wheelchair? How might it be used? *The engine was not used in the wheelchair because battery technology improved, and batteries met the requirements even better than the Stirling engine did. The engine could be used to power water purification systems in developing countries or to provide electrical power to diesel truck cabs.*

Designing with Math and Science

4. Chris describes the cooling source as an "energy sink." Why is the term "energy sink" more appropriate? *Energy does not move from cold to hot objects, only from hot to cold. Nothing is flowing from the cooling source, so "source" is not really an accurate description. "Sink" is a more appropriate term.*

5. Chris says that the greater the temperature difference between the top and bottom of the Stirling engine, the greater the amount of energy transferred to move the pistons and spin the flywheel. Explain. *Differences in temperature and pressure drive energy transfer, so the greater the difference, the more rapidly energy will transfer.*

Connecting the Dots

6. In a Stirling engine, the working gas never leaves the engine. Describe how this is different than a combustion engine. *A combustion engine is an open pneumatic system—air and fuel vapor enter the chamber on every cycle, are burnt, then are forced out into the open air.*

7. Given what you know about renewable energy sources, explain how the Stirling engine may be used in a way that is beneficial to the environment. *A renewable energy source—such as solar energy, geothermal, biomass, beeswax candles, and so on, may provide the hot side for the engine. This may reduce fossil fuel consumption and consequent air pollution.*

What Do You Think?

8. If you were to manually turn the crankshaft of a Stirling engine, the engine would work in reverse. It would pump energy from one side of the engine to the other. Over time, one side of the engine would become cool, and the other side hot. What might be some practical applications of this? *Refrigeration and climate control.*

9. Be creative and think of a way that a closed system engine like the Stirling engine might be applied. *Answers will vary.*

Engineering the Future Teacher Guide
©2008 Museum of Science, Boston

Chapter 21: Energy from the Earth

In Chapter 21, geothermal energy consultant Ron Dippipo describes the benefits of using renewable energy sources to generate electric power. He explains how conventional fossil fuel–burning power plants work, focusing on how convection currents cause the turbine blades to spin. He also compares the efficiency of geothermal power plants and fossil fuel–burning power plants.

Teaching Points

✔ Most power plants generate electricity by burning a fossil fuel—natural gas, coal, or oil—to heat water. The water boils and turns into steam. This steam is then used to turn a steam turbine. The spinning of the turbine drives a generator. (How a generator produces electricity is described in Unit 4.)

✔ **Convection** is energy transfer due to fluid motion.

✔ Geothermal power plants eliminate the need for burning fossil fuels altogether. A geothermal power plant uses steam and hot water from geothermal wells.

✔ A **renewable** energy source is an energy source that can regenerate or replenish itself in a relatively short amount of time. A **nonrenewable** energy source cannot regenerate or replenish itself in a practical amount of time.

What's the Story?

1. Why are there so few geothermal power plants in the United States? *Geothermal plants require geothermal wells. There are not very many areas in the U.S. where there are active geothermal wells.*

2. According to Ron, what are some of the benefits of geothermal power plants? *They are more efficient and provide electric power relatively cheap and with little or no pollution.*

3. What's the basic difference between fossil fuel–burning power plants and geothermal power plants? *Fossil fuel plants burn fuel to make steam, which is used to turn a turbine. Geothermal plants don't have to burn anything. The steam used to turn a turbine is taken right out of the ground.*

Designing with Math and Science

4. What is convection? *Convection refers to energy traveling in a fluid current.*

5. Why is convection critical to the function of a steam turbine? *Convection currents cause the blades of a turbine to spin. The spinning fan blades drive the electrical generator.*

6. Why are geothermal power plants usually more efficient than fossil fuel–burning power plants? *Because there is no energy lost to combustion. Another way to think of it is that energy is lost every time it is transferred. Geothermal plants require fewer transfers.*

Teacher Guide to the Textbook

Connecting the Dots

7. Ron mentions that geothermal energy is a renewable energy source. What other renewable energy sources have you learned about in this book? *Biodiesel and solar energy.*

What Do You Think?

8. Imagine you have been asked to design your own power plant with an unlimited budget. Use your imagination to brainstorm some other ways you could make a turbine spin to generate electricity without burning a fossil fuel. *Answers will vary. Here are some possibilities: Could burn wood, trash, or use biodiesel to heat water and make steam. Could turn the turbine by hooking it up to bicycle wheels and having humans ride the bicycles. (Maybe even charge for the workout.) Could put the turbine blades in a strong wind. Could use water flowing in a stream to turn a turbine.*

Chapter 22: Good Chemistry

As a nuclear engineer, Dr. Rebecca Steinman helps nuclear power plants meet federal regulations by making them safer, more reliable, and well maintained. In Chapter 22, she discusses the basics of nuclear power plants in terms of how they work and what resources allow the plant to function. Rebecca assures the reader that today's nuclear power plants are safe. She also states some reasons why nuclear power is a cleaner alternative to fossil fuels. One section discusses the importance of her line of work—a nuclear plant must meet all of the federal safety regulations to make sure that it's safe for workers, as well as the environment. Lastly, Rebecca touches on the controversy about spent nuclear fuel, and how the country plans to deal with it.

Teaching Points

✔ A **molecule** is the smallest particle of a compound that still has all the chemical properties of that compound. Usually a molecule has two or more atoms.

✔ An **atom** is the smallest particle of an element that retains its chemical properties.

✔ **Elements** are substances that have only one kind of atom.

✔ When molecules break apart and atoms are rearranged into new molecules, a **chemical reaction** occurs.

✔ A **nuclear reaction** is when the atoms themselves—not the molecules—break up.

✔ The **nucleus** is at the center of an atom where there is a tiny, dense ball of matter. The nucleus consists of two types of particles: **protons** and **neutrons**.

✔ The element **uranium** is important to nuclear engineers because it can be used as a very efficient fuel.

What's the Story?

1. What are the benefits of nuclear power plants? *Nuclear power plants do not require combustion, so they do not release soot or carbon dioxide or other pollutants into the atmosphere. Also, they do not use oil, which is a diminishing natural resource.*

2. List three ways that engineers ensure the safety of nuclear power plants. *Electrical engineers ensure the plant's electrical wiring is updated and functioning well; mechanical engineers ensure that the plant's environments are suitable for equipment and personnel; and structural engineers make sure the plant is structurally sound and that the equipment is protected from accidental damage.*

Designing with Math and Science

3. What is the difference between a chemical reaction and a nuclear reaction? When coal is burned, is it a chemical reaction or a nuclear reaction? *A chemical reaction is when molecules break apart and the atoms are rearranged into new molecules. A nuclear reaction is when the actual atoms break up. The burning of coal is a chemical reaction because its molecules, not its atoms, break apart.*

4. How do the control rods in a nuclear power plant control the rate of the nuclear reaction? *Control rods are used to absorb some of the neutrons to avoid a chain reaction, leading to a nuclear explosion.*

Connecting the Dots

5. How is nuclear power generation similar to power generation at a geothermal power plant? How is it different? *Nuclear power plants are similar to geothermal power plants because they both use steam to turn a turbine, which spins an electric generator. They are different because nuclear power plants use energy released by nuclear reactions, whereas a geothermal plant uses steam from deep in the earth.*

What Do You Think?

6. Conduct library and Internet research and write a paragraph about how and where spent nuclear fuel is stored. Write at least one more paragraph describing the controversy surrounding the storage of spent fuel. *Answers may vary.*

7. Dr. Steinman mentions some other applications, aside from generating electrical power, that use nuclear reactions. What are they? Conduct library and Internet research, and write a list of at least five specific technologies. *Nuclear technologies can be used for medical diagnosis and treatment, smoke detectors, irradiation to kill harmful organisms in foods and sterilize medical equipment, power for ships and spacecraft, or weapons of mass destruction. Expect other answers too.*

Engineering the Future Teacher Guide
©2008 Museum of Science, Boston

Chapter 23: Down the Pipes

In Chapter 23, environmental engineer Lisa Bina describes her work creating computer models of sewage systems in the Greater Boston Area. Boston's antiquated sewage system has a big problem: During heavy rainfall the system overflows, sending untreated wastewater into rivers and other bodies of water. Lisa describes how the gravity-driven water system brings fresh water to homes and residences. She then explains how wastewater is removed and treated. Finally, she clarifies how the system is being updated to solve the problem of overflows.

Teaching Points

✔ In a gravity-driven water system, the weight of water in the pipes creates pressure differences that drive water flow. **Pascal's equation**, $\Delta P = 0.43\,(h_2 - h_1)$, can be used to calculate the pressure in the pipes at different points in the water column. It also explains why tall buildings need pumps.

✔ When a fluid moves through a pipe, it encounters resistance to forward movement at the inner surface of the pipe. The smaller the pipe diameter, the greater the resistance.

✔ When the fluid moving through a pipe moves through a constriction, the fluid velocity increases in the constriction. This is because the volume of fluid moving before and after the constriction remains the same. Therefore, fluid must move faster through the section of pipe that has the smaller diameter.

✔ Management systems for clean water and wastewater are essential to the environmental health of a region and the public health of a community.

What's the Story?

1. In what ways was Lisa's work in Thailand and the United States similar? *In both countries she worked on waste-treatment systems that screen out solids and chemically treat both screened solids and the remaining liquids for safe disposal.*

2. What problem does Lisa describe in Boston's sewage system? *The system handles rainwater and wastewater together, so when rainfall is heavy the wastewater backs up, resulting in untreated water overflowing into neighboring bodies of water.*

3. How is a reservoir different from a lake? *A lake is a natural body of water. A reservoir, which is often human-made, collects and stores water for a region. In some cases, lakes do serve as reservoirs, but in most locations the lake level is not high enough to serve as a reservoir.*

Designing with Math and Science

4. Why is the location of a reservoir significant? *Reservoirs are situated in areas higher in altitude than the areas they service, so water can flow downhill toward its intended destination.*

5. What is the maximum height water will flow up into a skyscraper in Boston without the need to use pumps? *Boston is served by the Quabbin Reservoir, which has a height above the city of 525 feet. So, one answer is 525 feet. However, at that level the water would just trickle out of the faucet. Pressure should be at least 50 PSI. The height of a skyscraper that would allow for 50 PSI of pressure without pumps can be found from Pascal's equation, as shown here:*

$$50 \ PSI = 0.43 \ (525 \ ft. - h_1), \text{ so } h_1 \approx 408.7 \ ft.$$

6. What happens to the velocity of water as the diameter of the pipe in which it flows is decreased? *The velocity of water increases as the pipe diameter decreases.*

7. Why can't engineers handle excess wastewater problems by designing a system with larger pipes? *Given that water flows more slowly through pipes with larger diameters, pipes large enough to handle overflow conditions would carry water too slowly for normal conditions. Slow flow would lead to odor and rot. Also, larger pipes are more costly to install.*

What Do You Think?

8. Lisa is an environmental engineer. Use the library or the Internet to do some research on the field of environmental engineering. What other kinds of jobs do environmental engineers hold? *Answers will vary. Environmental engineers work on a wide variety of problems in which they apply science to meet human needs while protecting the environment. They find ways to avoid air or water pollution, reduce the impact of new roads on ecosystems and wildlife, and develop systems to protect the environment around manufacturing plants.*

9. Do reservoirs ever get too full? What happens in a drought? Find out how much water your local drinking water reservoir can hold, and find out when backup reservoirs would be activated in a drought situation. *Answers will vary.*

Engineering the Future Teacher Guide
©2008 Museum of Science, Boston

Unit 4: Power to Communicate

Chapter 24: A Highway for Ideas

In Chapter 24, computer scientist David Clark describes his role in designing the Internet. Clark begins by defining the problem: At the height of the Cold War, the United States felt that it was lagging behind the Soviet Union in terms of technological advancement. The Soviets had been the first to launch a satellite. The U.S. government formed an agency to keep the U.S. ahead in using technology. This agency soon started improving computer technologies, and eventually developed a computer network that would enable researchers and engineers to communicate more effectively. This early network, using the telephone system, was the origin of the modern-day Internet. Clark talks about how the Internet was purposefully designed to encourage innovation—it places few constraints on its users. Clark describes these constraints and charts how the Internet grew from a small network of researchers to a colossal information web that has transformed the daily lives of millions of people the world over.

Teaching Points

✔ The Internet was originally developed to provide a way for researchers and engineers to communicate more effectively. It was seen as a way to help us compete with the Soviet Union during the Cold War.

✔ **Digital signals** are a discrete, limited set of numerical values. **Analog signals** are continuous over all values within some range. Signals can be converted from analog to digital.

✔ The designers of the Internet imposed four main constraints on its users:

1. Information must be encoded in a digital signal.
2. Every computer on the network must have an address.
3. The packets can only be so large.
4. The packets must be sequenced.

✔ The Internet was purposefully designed to inspire innovation. Some innovations have included streaming video, voiceover IP, and the World Wide Web.

✔ The Internet and advances in computing technologies have had such an impact on society that the modern era is often referred to as the Information Age.

What's the Story?

1. What major historical events led to the formation of the Internet? *The Cold War, Sputnik, the development of the Interstate Highway System.*

2. What problems were the developers of the Internet trying to solve? *They felt like researchers should be able to communicate better in order to advance science and engineering.*

3. What are the design constraints placed on Internet users? *Information must be digital, in small packets, addressed, and sequenced.*

4. Why must data packets be small and sequenced? *The data packets must be small so that they don't hold up the line and sequenced so that the receiving computer can put the packets in the correct order again.*

Designing with Math and Science

5. What's the difference between an analog signal and a digital signal? Give examples of each. *An analog signal is continuous over a range of numbers, such as varying current. A digital signal is made of discrete pieces of data. Telephone signals and record players are analog. Computers, CDs, and DVDs use digital signals.*

What Do You Think?

6. In your opinion, what are some of the key ways the Internet has affected our society? *Answers may include that people have unprecedented access to information so they can learn about health issues, financial issues, world news, and so on. Whereas people used to get information from experts (doctors, analysts), they can now look up information online. Many people shop for goods and services online. The Internet has been detrimental to some industries. The music industry has suffered due to software that allows people to exchange music files online—in some cases, illegally.*

7. Do you think that it's good thing that anyone can put anything (or find anything) online? What are some of the unintended consequences of that freedom? *Answers will vary. Possible unintended consequences may include: detrimental effects of music shareware on the music industry, minors have access to information and images their parents would not like them to see, individuals can conduct illegal activities online, and so on.*

Engineering the Future Teacher Guide
©2008 Museum of Science, Boston

Chapter 25: Teaching a Machine to Listen

In Chapter 25, computer programmer Sol Lerner explains the complexities of creating voice recognition systems—computerized systems that respond to spoken prompts much like a human would. Sol's company develops these systems for businesses that use them for customer service and for people who are not able to use keyboards. Sol introduces some fundamental concepts about communications systems and describes how a designed system can encode a message into a signal, transmit the signal, and then receive and decode it. Sol describes how a telephone works, illustrating the importance of electricity in communications systems. Then he describes how a computer can "hear" spoken words based on the same premises. Getting the computer to "listen," however, is a much more complex task. The human brain is well-designed to tease apart the nuances of spoken language, while machines must be taught thousands of rules governing human speech patterns in order to interpret the meaning of spoken language.

Teaching Points

✔ People communicate face-to-face and through designed systems.

✔ A designed system encodes, or translates, a message into a signal that can be transmitted by the system. The system then receives the signal and decodes it so that the receiver can understand the message.

✔ A signal is an encoded message transmitted by a communications system. In a telephone system, the signal is a varying electric current.

✔ Transmission of telephone signals over long distances may be encoded in the form of light or radio waves, then changed back into an electrical signal before it is decoded as a sound wave.

✔ Language is based on rules.

What's the Story?

1. What reasons does Sol offer for wanting to develop speech recognition systems? *It might be a good business prospect. It may give people with injuries or disabilities access to the world of computers.*

2. Why is it challenging to design a computer system that can recognize and interpret human speech? *It is difficult because human speech follows incredibly intricate rules for pronunciation and grammar. We use context a lot when we speak. (Example: "I know you ate the cake" versus "Eye no ewe 8 the cake.")*

Designing with Math and Science

3. What's the difference between a signal and a message? *A signal is the part of a communication system that carries information. A message is the information being sent over the network. In other words, a signal carries the message, but it is not the message itself.*

4. What parts of the telephone communications system are the encoder and the decoder? What is being encoded? Why is encoding necessary? *The diaphragm in the mouthpiece of the telephone is the encoder. It encodes spoken words into electrical signals. Encoding is necessary to put a message into a form that can be transmitted through the system. There is also another diaphragm in the receiver of the phone that decodes the message.*

Connecting the Dots

5. How is electricity used in the two communications systems described in this chapter? *1) In a telephone system, the sound the person makes will produce a signal, which is carried over a wire and then received and decoded by another telephone, back into the same sound vibrations that created the signal at the first phone. 2) A computer system changes the analog electrical signal from a person's voice into a digital signal for the computer to understand. The computer receives and decodes the information, and interprets it according to a large number of rules, and then displays the information on a screen or transmits an appropriate signal, which can then be encoded as an analog signal for translation back into sound.*

What Do You Think?

6. What are some other ways that humans communicate with or through machines? *Fax, phone, e-mail, and so on.*

7. Sol says that technologies have brought people closer together, but some people disagree. Do you agree? Explain why or why not. *Answers will vary. Students may point out that technologies like the computer, the Internet, phone, or fax keep people connected across distances. But sometimes it's hard to get in contact with a "real human being" because of complex voice response systems or businesses that only provide customer support through their web sites or via e-mail.*

Engineering the Future Teacher Guide
©2008 Museum of Science, Boston

Chapter 26: Shedding Light on Communications

In Chapter 26, test engineer Nanette Halliburton explains how information can travel encoded as in a light signal through a communication system. Nanette explains the role of reflection and refraction in the transmission of light through a fiber-optic cable as well as the importance of the fiber-optic cable to the country's communications infrastructure. She then traces an e-mail message from sender to receiver. All the while, Nanette explains the importance of testing.

Teaching Points

✔ **Noise** is anything that interferes with the clarity of a signal. Current traveling through electrical wires creates a magnetic field, which interferes with electrical signals traveling in other wires. Light signals in fiber-optic cables do not have this problem.

✔ A message can be encoded as a light signal. First, the signal must be converted from an analog to a digital signal. Then, a laser is turned on and off in sequence with the digital signal. The pattern of on-off light pulses travels through a fiber-optic cable at the speed of light.

✔ Light can travel long distances through fiber-optic cables due to the materials used in the cable. Light is reflected as it passes from the core of the optical fiber onto the cladding, which surrounds the core. (**Refraction** is the bending of light that occurs when light moves through one medium to another.) The materials of the cladding and core are such that the light is reflected back into the core. It's as if the light bounces right off of the core wall. This is referred to as Total Internal Reflection.

✔ An e-mail message spends part of its journey encoded as an electrical signal and part of its journey encoded as a light signal.

What's the Story?

1. What does noise refer to in this chapter? *Noise is anything that disrupts the signal in a communications system.*

2. Why are fiber-optic cables better than telephone wires for transmitting information over long distances? *Because the electric signal creates a magnetic field around the wire it travels through. The magnetic field disrupts the current and creates noise in nearby wires. Due to this noise, the electrical signal must be regenerated every mile or so along the wire. With fiber-optic cables the message only has to be regenerated every 50 to 60 miles.*

Designing with Math and Science

3. Explain how light travels through a fiber-optic cable, using the terms "reflection" and "total internal reflection." *When light enters the fiber, eventually it hits the interior walls of the fiber. The light is reflected back into the core when it hits the cladding, which acts like a mirror. As long as the angle with which the light hits the fiber wall is greater than the critical angle, all of it will be reflected. This is called "total internal reflection."*

4. Why does the light signal have to be regenerated? *The signal must be regenerated because impurities in the glass absorb some of the light and degrade the signal.*

5. How can ones and zeros be encoded in a light signal? *By flashing the laser light on and off (on for "one"; off for "zero").*

Connecting the Dots

6. Nanette talks about how every technological system is like a puzzle, and that all of its pieces must fit—and work—together properly. Describe how this applies to at least two other technological systems you've studied in this course. *This applies to all designed systems—coal power, electrical generating plants, sewage systems, eye glasses manufacturing system, and so on.*

7. Nanette is a test engineer. Why is testing a critical part of the development process? Describe how at least two other engineers you've learned about test the technologies they've designed. *Testing is a critical part of the development process because it ensures the product is reliable and well-suited for the real-world market. Examples of other engineers who have tested their designs are Aprille Joy Ericsson (an astronautical engineer) and Bob Brown (a design engineer).*

What Do You Think?

8. Do some library and Internet research to find the disadvantages of optical cables. Consider the cable materials and the installation processes in your response. *Answers will vary. Some disadvantages include: Fiber-optic cables break easily; they are very expensive to install and manufacture. Unlike telephone systems, the country is not already wired with fiber-optic cable. It may be years before every community has access. There is some environmental impact when fiber-optic cables are laid in the ground, sometimes creating controversy (especially with trans-Atlantic cables).*

Engineering the Future Teacher Guide
©2008 Museum of Science, Boston

Chapter 27: Riding the Waves

In Chapter 27, communications engineer Alex Hills explains how the satellite communications systems he designed for rural Alaskans helped him develop Wi-Fi (wireless network) systems. Hill starts out by describing his experience in the Alaskan bush in the 1970s. Because of tough terrain, laying telephone wire was not feasible, and shortwave radio signals often met interference from the Northern Lights. Alex helped devise a communications system using satellite technologies that allowed rural Alaskans to communicate across the tundra. Eventually, Hills was instrumental in linking the state's university campuses together via satellite. The wireless network inspired Hills to develop the first wireless computer networking technologies (Wi-Fi) at Carnegie Mellon University in the 1990s.

✔ There are many types of electromagnetic radiation, including visible light, radio waves, microwaves, and gamma rays. **Electromagnetic radiation** is often described as a wave.

✔ Electromagnetic waves have associated wavelengths and frequencies. The **wavelength** is a measure of the distance from one crest to the next of a wave. **Frequency** refers to the number of complete wave cycles that occur in a unit of time. Wavelength and frequency are inversely related. The unit for frequency is the Hertz (Hz).

✔ Information can be encoded in radio wave signals.

✔ Wireless communications systems can be established in locations where laying telephone lines is not practical.

What's the Story?

1. When Alex arrived in Alaska in 1970, why didn't people in the Alaskan bush have telecommunications services? How did rural Alaskans communicate over long distances? *The terrain was too rough and the distances between villages too great for laying telephone lines to be cost effective. Rural Alaskans could write letters or make radio broadcasts.*

2. How did Alex draw on his earlier work in Alaska when developing Wi-Fi technology? *He used radio waves to develop a communication system without wires.*

Designing with Math and Science

3. Why wouldn't shortwave radio solve the communications problem in rural Alaska? How did satellites solve the problem? Be sure to define the term "wavelength" in your response. *Shortwave radio did not work because its signals were often distorted by the Aurora Borealis (the Northern Lights). A wavelength is one complete wave, from one peak to another. The short wavelengths in Alaska bounce off a layer in the atmosphere called the ionosphere, and come back to the earth. The Northern Lights interfere with this bounce. Satellites solve this problem because the satellites have a much higher frequency. This means that the wavelengths are extremely small—small enough to pass freely through the ionosphere to satellites and back to the people in Alaska without interference.*

4. What is the frequency of the broadcast by your favorite radio station? *Answers will vary. A station at 93.9 broadcasts at 93.9 megahertz, or 93,900,000 Hertz. One Hertz is one cycle (or wave) per second.*

Connecting the Dots

5. Draw a communications diagram of a typical Wi-Fi network call. Label the parts with the following terms: sender, receiver, signal, encoder, and decoder. Label where the signal is an electrical signal and where the signal is a radio wave.

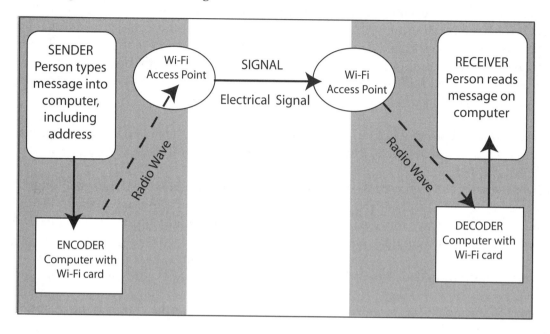

Note: The above diagram is consistent with the textbook, but there are some differences between the textbook and *Engineer's Notebook*. In the EN the originator of the message is the SOURCE, and the person receiving it is the DESTINATION. The term "receiver" is used to designate the equipment that receives and decodes the signal, like a radio receiver.

6. Some rural Alaskan villages are not on the Alaskan power distribution grid. List a few ways that the towns might power the communications technologies they now use. *They could use solar cells, or have a generator that runs on fuel piped or shipped in from other locations in Alaska. The generator could also be turned by wind power.*

What Do You Think?

7. Using the Internet and the library, find other common communications technologies that use radio waves. List at least three in addition to those mentioned in this chapter. *Answers will vary. Possible answers include cell phones, radio-controlled model airplanes, personal digital assistants (PDAs), garage-door openers, GPS units, Bluetooth computer keyboards, and some computer mice.*

Chapter 28: Designed Learning

In Chapter 28, Joel Rosenberg, a curriculum developer who helped create this course, describes his struggles to understand electrical circuits. Joel discusses some of the models he has used to understand circuits, including models that use water and air as an analogy for flowing charge. Joel defines current, resistance, and "electric pressure difference," or voltage. He also introduces Ohm's law, which is a statement about the relationship between voltage, current, and resistance. Finally, Joel discusses the relationship between voltage, current, and power.

Teaching Points

✔ **Electricity** is what we call the charge flowing in wires. **Electronics** is the way we control that electricity to accomplish tasks.

✔ An **"electric pressure difference"** causes charge to flow from a region of higher electric pressure (charge concentration) to a region of lower electric pressure, the same way an air-pressure difference causes air to flow. "Electric pressure difference" is often referred to as **voltage**. The unit for voltage is the **volt**.

✔ **Current** is the flow rate of charge moving through a circuit. The unit for current is the ampere, or **amp**.

✔ **Resistance** is the opposition to flow experienced by the current. The components of a circuit—the conductors and the load—offer resistance. The unit for resistance in electrical systems is the **ohm**.

✔ **Ohm's law** is the mathematical relationship between voltage (V), current (I), and resistance (R): $\Delta V = I \times R$. Only linear resistors obey Ohm's law.

✔ Power is related to voltage and current by the equation $P = I \times \Delta V$.

What's the Story?

1. Joel's early model of electricity used water as an analogy for charge. His current model uses air as an analogy. Why does he think air is a better analogy? *Air is a compressible fluid. It can be compressed into regions of higher pressure, and will flow from regions of higher pressure to regions of lower pressure. This is similar to the way a battery supplies a voltage difference that causes charge to move from the area of higher "electric pressure" to the area of lower "electric pressure." Water is not compressible, so it is not analogous to charge in this way.*

2. What's the difference between electricity and electronics? *Electricity is what we call the charge flowing in wires. Electronics is the way we control that electricity to accomplish tasks.*

Teacher Guide to the Textbook

Designing with Math and Science

3. Using words and drawings, describe voltage, current, and resistance. *Voltage is the electric pressure difference that pushes charge through a wire. The wire resists the flow of charge. Current is the rate at which charge flows. There are many ways that these ideas could be expressed in drawings. Here is one possibility using a water analogy.*

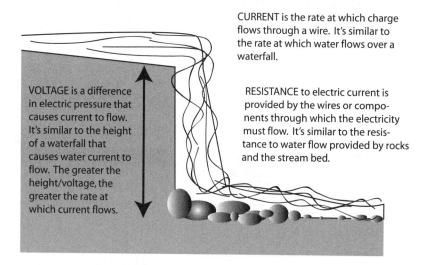

CURRENT is the rate at which charge flows through a wire. It's similar to the rate at which water flows over a waterfall.

VOLTAGE is a difference in electric pressure that causes current to flow. It's similar to the height of a waterfall that causes water current to flow. The greater the height/voltage, the greater the rate at which current flows.

RESISTANCE to electric current is provided by the wires or components through which the electricity must flow. It's similar to the resistance to water flow provided by rocks and the stream bed.

4. Using Ohm's law, calculate the voltage required for a current of 3 amps to flow through a wire with a resistance of 2 ohms. Draw a diagram of this circuit. *ΔV = 6 volts*

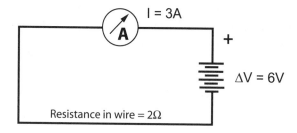

I = 3A

+

ΔV = 6V

Resistance in wire = 2Ω

5. Two 9-volt batteries provide power to a cordless iron. If the resistance of the iron is 36 ohms, how much current is flowing through the iron? Draw a diagram of this circuit. *I = 0.5 amps*

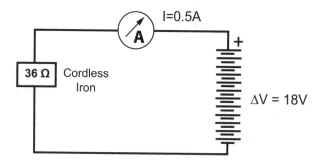

I=0.5A

36 Ω Cordless Iron

+

ΔV = 18V

Engineering the Future Teacher Guide
©2008 Museum of Science, Boston

Connecting the Dots

6. There are extensive electrical grids that distribute electricity from power plants to our homes. The long distances the electrical charge must move creates extremely high resistances, so very high voltages are used. Use what you've learned about the relationship between voltage, current, and resistance to explain why high voltages might be used to move an electrical charge through the distribution grid. *Given Ohm's law, a very high resistance would mean a very low current. So, to keep a measurable current flowing, the voltage also must be very high.*

What Do You Think?

7. Why are models important for teaching and learning about subjects such as electricity? Can you think of other models you've used to describe or learn about other concepts in this class? *Models are necessary because you cannot see electricity—thus, models help you picture what's going on. We used scale models to see how an object or a building will look when it is built at full scale. We also drew diagrams of energy flowing through walls and through fluid systems. These energy diagrams are a kind of model because we cannot actually see the energy flow. The frame of a building can be modeled as the "bones" of the building.*

Chapter 29: On the Grid

In Chapter 29, chemical engineer Soung Sik-Kim describes her work optimizing the efficiency of coal-fired power plants. According to Soung, coal has many benefits as an energy source: It is plentiful, easy to store and transport, and the majority of power plants in the U.S. are already designed to burn it. However, coal has some downsides. Pollution from coal-fired power plants formed acid rain that became a serious problem in the 1980s, leading to public outrage. The government has since invested in clean coal research like the kind Soung is doing. Soung described how a power plant generates electricity and how that electricity is distributed through the power distribution grid. She also describes the grid as a large interconnected set of circuits, and explains some of the basic elements of a circuit. She then discusses how some coal plants have been modified to increase efficiency.

Teaching Points

✔ **Electricity** is charge moving through a wire. **Energy** is required to make charge move. A power plant is designed to use the chemical energy in fossil fuels to move charges through wires.

✔ A **circuit** is a closed continuous conducting path along which charge can flow. A circuit has an energy **source** (a battery or a power plant), a **conductor** (often a wire), and a **load** (an electrical device that uses the energy carried by the charge to do work).

✔ The electrical distribution **grid**, or just "the grid," is a vast system connecting millions of end users to electric power. Power plants are connected to the grid and supply the voltage difference to move charge through the grid. The power plants provide energy on demand. When more loads are connected to the grid, electrical generation at power plants increases. Energy is not stored anywhere in the grid.

✔ The circuits on the grid use the earth as the return path for moving charge.

✔ **Power** is a rate at which energy is produced or consumed. The unit for power is the **watt (W)**. One watt equals one joule/second. Engineers often describe power in terms of kilowatts (1,000x) or megawatts (1,000,000x).

✔ In reference to energy consumption, we often use the unit **kilowatt-hour (kWh)**.

✔ When the efficiency of a power plant is increased, less fuel must be burned to produce the same amount of energy. So improved efficiency means lowered costs for the consumer and less pollution for the environment.

What's the Story?

1. What is Soung referring to when she talks about "the grid," and how does "the grid" supply our electrical power? *"The grid" is a massive system of interconnecting circuits that provides electric power to end-users: homes, businesses, industries, and schools. There are ten grids in North America. The electricity that power plants generate enters the grid directly. Power companies provide grid access to end-users and charge for energy consumed. Power companies also make sure that power plants provide enough electrical power to the grid to meet their end-users' needs.*

Engineering the Future Teacher Guide
©2008 Museum of Science, Boston

2. What caused the U.S. government to start funding clean coal research like the kind that Soung does? *In the 1980s, there was public outrage over acid rain, which was created when sulfur dioxide and nitrogen oxide in the air combined with rainwater, making the rainwater acidic. The acid rain hurt plants and animals in entire ecosystems and damaged buildings and statues made of marble and limestone. In response to public concern, the U.S. Environmental Protection Agency (EPA) placed limits on the amount of toxic gases power plants may release. The government started funding clean coal research in an effort to help power plants meet those limits.*

3. Describe two ways that Soung is making coal-fired power plants more efficient and cleaner for the environment. *1) Installing sensors to monitor the temperature of gases in the combustion chamber makes it possible to adjust the flame size or oxygen level so that as much energy as possible is transferred to the water in the boiler. 2) Removing soot from the boiler tubes so as to remove unwanted insulation in order to transfer as much heat as possible to the water in the boiler. 3) Reducing waste by using fly ash from coal burning as an ingredient in concrete, and using molten ash, called slag, in roof shingles. 4) Reducing atmospheric pollution by using a "scrubber" to remove sulfur from the exhaust and combining it with limestone to make Gypsum, which is used as a building material.*

Designing with Science and Math

4. What is necessary for charge to flow through a circuit? *The circuit must be a continuous, closed conducting path. Also, energy is required to make charge move, so there must be a power source.*

5. What is the relationship between energy and power? What are the units for each? *Power is the rate at which energy is consumed or produced. The units used most frequently for energy are the joule, the BTU, and the kilowatt-hour. The units used most often for power are the watt (j/s), the kilowatt, and the megawatt.*

6. If two power plants each output the same amount of electricity every hour, but one requires 2 million tons of coal per year and the other requires 1.75 million tons of coal per year, which is more efficient? Explain how you know. *The second plant is more efficient because it requires fewer inputs for the same amount of outputs.*

Connecting the Dots

7. Is any process 100 percent efficient? Why or why not? Give some examples from previous chapters to explain your response. *No. Energy is always transferred to the environment along the way, so it is no longer useful. This is illustrated in geothermal power plants, diesel engines, heating systems, Stirling engines, and every system that involves the transfer of energy.*

What Do You Think?

8. In the last paragraph of the story, Soung says, "Good engineering is not just about designing something new." What does she mean by that? Do you agree? Use an example that you've learned about in this class or outside of class to explain why or why not. *Soung means that it often makes more sense to redesign something that already exists than to invent a new technology. Students may describe their experiences redesigning the putt-putt boat, or another example.*

9. Go home and find out what your power company charges for each kWh of electricity. What is your average electric bill per month? How much energy does your household use per year?
The energy costs for a region will be the same, so your energy bill will have the same information as your students' energy bills. If your students live in an apartment or group living situation, ask them to find out who pays the bills for the building and to ask that person about the electrical energy costs.

Engineering the Future Teacher Guide
©2008 Museum of Science, Boston

Chapter 30: Electrifying!

In Chapter 30, Ken McAuliffe explains the complexities of wiring a large building for electricity. He describes how electrical blackouts happen and explains how the Museum of Science is equipped with a battery and a back-up generator to provide uninterrupted power to the server room and the exhibit hall lights in the event of power loss. Ken explains the difference between AC and DC, and that current from the uninterrupted power source battery must be converted from DC to AC. Ken then explains why many of the lights in the museum are wired in parallel instead of in series. Finally, Ken explores some important safety precautions that anyone working with electricity must take, involving circuit breakers, ground wires, and short circuits.

Teaching Points

✔ **Alternating current**, or AC, is the type of current produced by power plants. It moves in one direction and then the opposite direction repeatedly. Many electrical appliances that plug into a wall socket use AC. Direct current, or DC, only flows in one direction. Batteries provide DC. Most electronic devices use DC. AC often needs to be converted to DC, and vice versa.

✔ A **series circuit** is a circuit in which resistors or loads are arranged one right after the other in a chain. Total resistance (R_T) for resistors R_1, R_2, and R_3 in series is given by the following formula:

$$R_T = R_1 + R_2 + R_3$$

✔ A **parallel circuit** is a circuit in which the current branches on the way to each resistor, then comes back together after it has passed through the resistors. Total resistance for resistors R_1, R_2, and R_3 in parallel can be found using the following equation:

$$1/R_T = 1/R_1 + 1/R_2 + 1/R_3$$

✔ When working with electricity, you must take safety precautions. You should never work with circuits when water is present—water can create a short circuit. Whenever possible, disconnect the circuit from the power source when working on it. Use ground wires whenever possible.

✔ A **short circuit** is an accidental lower-resistance connection between two points on a circuit. A short circuit connects the hot wire to the ground wire, excluding the load from the circuit. In a short circuit, resistance drops and current can become dangerously high.

What's the Story?

1. In your own words, write a paragraph explaining how the museum's electrical system would work if an electrical blackout happened. *Answers will vary. The answer could explain that when a blackout occurs, an Uninterrupted Power Source (UPS) system keeps the power up long enough for a generator to start functioning and provide power to essential systems.*

2. What is a short circuit? Why can short circuits be dangerous? *A short circuit is an accidental lower-resistance connection that bypasses the load or the resistance in a circuit. This is dangerous because in a short circuit the current follows the path of least resistance, such as a metal bar, another conductor, or a person's body. This causes resistance to drop and the voltage to remain constant, which makes the current very strong. In wall current, a short circuit will occur when the hot wire*

is connected to the ground wire. Current and voltage are already high, so a short circuit can be very dangerous. Although the electrical energy in a battery is much less, accidentally connecting the positive and negative sides of a battery with a wire will drain the battery very quickly, and heat up the wire.

3. What is alternating current (AC)? What is direct current (DC)? What kinds of devices require AC? What kinds of devices require DC? *Electrical generators produce AC (alternating current) power. The spinning magnets of a generator in a power plant generate a voltage difference that continuously switches directions. DC (direct current) flows in one direction, like in a battery. Most electrical devices, such as dishwashers, lamps, or electric heaters, require AC power, while others require DC. The products that require DC usually have an adapter that converts the AC power from a wall socket.*

Designing with Math and Science

4. Draw a diagram of a circuit with three resistors connected in parallel. Calculate the total resistance in the parallel circuit you drew if each resistor has a resistance of 3 Ohms.

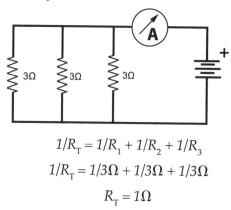

$$1/R_T = 1/R_1 + 1/R_2 + 1/R_3$$
$$1/R_T = 1/3\Omega + 1/3\Omega + 1/3\Omega$$
$$R_T = 1\Omega$$

5. Draw a diagram of a circuit with three loads connected in series. Calculate the total resistance in the series circuit you drew if each load has a resistance of 3 Ohms.

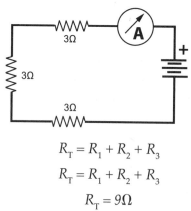

$$R_T = R_1 + R_2 + R_3$$
$$R_T = R_1 + R_2 + R_3$$
$$R_T = 9\Omega$$

Engineering the Future Teacher Guide
©2008 Museum of Science, Boston

Connecting the Dots

6. Use Ohm's law to calculate the current in the series circuit above if the voltage difference is 15 volts.

$$\Delta V = I \times R \quad and \quad I = \Delta V / R$$

$$I = 15V/9\Omega \approx 1.67\ A$$

What Do You Think?

7. Name an electrical device you use often that plugs into a wall. Do some research to determine the following about the device (you may be able to determine some of the answers simply by looking at the device or its box). *Answers will vary. All devices that plug into the wall outlet have a ground wire. Devices that use an AC adaptor may appear to have one wire going to them, but if you look closely at the end, you can see two connectors. If you take apart the wire, you can see two wires — one in the core, surrounded by an insulator, and one outside the inner insulator, all surrounded by an additional insulating layer. DC devices that use batteries have two wires — one for the positive and one for the negative side of the battery. Usually, these devices (such as flashlights) are not grounded. But all electrical devices must have complete circuits, with a wire running to and from each load.*

	Bulb	*Printer*
a. Does the device require AC or DC? Does it have an adapter?	*Either – No*	*AC – No*
b. Does the device use a ground wire? Why?	*Yes*	*Yes*
c. What is the voltage difference required by the device?	*120V*	*120V*
d. How many watts of power does the device consume?	*60 watts*	*84 watts*
e. How much energy does the device use every hour?	*60 watt-hrs*	*84 watt-hrs*

Chapter 31: Sunny Side Up

In Chapter 31, materials engineer Christine Bordonaro explains how the energy in sunlight—solar energy—can be used to generate electricity. She talks about the pros and cons of using photovoltaic (PV) cells to provide electrical power and discusses why more people use them in other countries. Christine discusses what her company, Evergreen Solar, is doing to make solar panels cheaper and more efficient.

Teaching Points

✔ In **centralized electrical generation systems**, large volumes of fossil fuels are mined, stored, and transported to power stations that generate and distribute electricity through an extensive network of wires. Much of the energy in the fuels is "lost" on the way to end users.

✔ Solar electrical generation does not require storing, transporting, and burning fossil fuels for electrical power. And it does not require connection to a grid. Solar electrical generation is a **decentralized electrical generation system**. In such a system, very little energy is "lost" before it gets to end users, and there is much less pollution.

✔ **Radiation** is the energy transported by light—any kind of light, not just sunlight.

✔ Sunlight provides energy to make charge flow in photovoltaic panels.

✔ While photovoltaics offer many advantages, there are some problems associated with them. They are quite expensive and they are not very efficient. Engineers are working to optimize PV cells and manufacturing processes to solve these problems.

What's the Story?

1. Why is it beneficial to use renewable energy sources? *The supply of fossil fuels on our planet is limited. They will become more expensive as the supplies that are easier to extract are used up. Renewable sources of energy like the sun will not be used up. Solar energy also has less impact on the environment because it does not need to be extracted from the ground or transported.*

2. Why does Christine say that solar technologies represent decentralized power generation? What are the advantages of this type of power generation? *Solar technologies do not need to be connected to the grid. They can be set up anywhere. Also, there is no need to extract, transport, and store fuels, so such decentralized electrical generation systems are much more efficient than large centralized systems.*

3. How do homes powered by PV panels get power at night? *Homes get power at night from the grid or with a battery that stores excess electricity the solar cells produced during the day.*

Designing with Math and Science

4. Christine says that solar panels are only about 15 percent efficient. What are the inputs and outputs of the solar panel system that Christine is using to determine efficiency? *The input is solar energy from sunlight; the output is the energy in electricity.*

5. What is radiation? *Radiation is the energy transported from a source in the form of waves and rays, like light.*

Connecting the Dots

6. What are some differences between how solar panels generate electricity and how a generator in a coal-fired power plant generates electricity? *In a coal-fired power plant, coal is burned to heat water and turn a turbine, which spins an electrical generator. A solar panel is made up of solar cells. Each cell produces an electric current when exposed to sunlight—no moving parts are needed. Another difference is cost. At this writing, energy from solar cells costs a lot more than energy from a coal-fired power plant due to the high production and installation costs of solar panels.*

What Do You Think?

7. Imagine that you've just been hired by the marketing department of Evergreen Solar. Your job is to create an advertisement for a national magazine that will get more people interested in solar panels, despite the costs of installing them. Your ad must describe how the benefits of solar outweigh the installation costs. Use drawings and text to describe what your ad would be like. *Responses will vary. Ad copy should include the idea that the savings over time offset start-up costs. Also, in many locations people are paid to add electricity to the national electricity grid.*

Teacher Guide to the Textbook

Chapter 32: Cape Wind

In Chapter 32, entrepreneur Jim Gordon describes the controversy over an offshore wind farm his company is building near Cape Cod, off the coast of Massachusetts. Jim makes the case for the wind farm, explaining how his company has a history of building high-efficiency power plants all over New England. Jim believes that wind-energy technology promises to reduce fossil fuel consumption, air pollution, and our nation's reliance on foreign sources of fossil fuels. He describes the technology and concedes that there are some disadvantages to wind power.

Teaching Points

✔ Energy technologies are often surrounded by controversy.

✔ Wind energy is a renewable energy source.

✔ There are many ways to spin an electrical generator.

✔ There are pros and cons associated with any technology.

What's the Story?

1. Why does Jim want to build a wind power plant off of the coast of Nantucket? *Many reasons. There is a lot of wind in that area, and the electricity demand is rapidly increasing. Cape Cod also has a problem with air pollution and has been the site of oil spills, so he hopes this will help reduce emissions and focus the community on ways to improve the environment.*

2. Describe two features that increase plant efficiency in the combined cycle power plants that Jim developed. *These power plants are combined cycle natural gas plants, so energy is extracted twice from burning natural gas. As the natural gas is burned, it expands rapidly and turns a generator. The hot exhaust gas, which would otherwise be discarded, is used to boil water into steam, which turns a second generator. So, energy that would otherwise be "lost" is used to produce more electricity.*

Designing with Math and Science

3. Using what you know about turbines, explain with words and drawings how a wind turbine generates electricity.

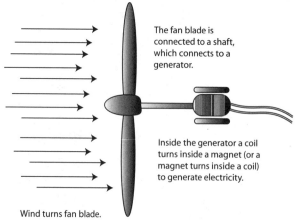

The fan blade is connected to a shaft, which connects to a generator.

Inside the generator a coil turns inside a magnet (or a magnet turns inside a coil) to generate electricity.

Wind turns fan blade.

A wind turbine is a device that produces electrical energy from wind. It consists of a fan blade called a rotor, a shaft, and an electrical generator.

Engineering the Future Teacher Guide
©2008 Museum of Science, Boston

Connecting the Dots

4. What advantages does wind power generation have over coal-fired power plants? What are the disadvantages? ***Advantages:*** *Wind is renewable and does not create pollution. It does not need to be mined, transported, or stored.* ***Disadvantages:*** *Wind speed varies from day to day, so it's hard to predict what the daily output will be. Turbines must be located where the wind is because wind cannot be stored.*

What Do You Think?

5. Use the library and the Internet to research other types of renewable energy sources. *Possible answers:*

    - *Hydroelectric power*
    - *Geothermal power*
    - *Power from ocean tides*
    - *Ethanol, biodiesel, and other biofuels*

6. Based on what you know about electricity generation, how might falling water, found in a water fall or a stream flowing downhill, be used to generate electricity? *The use of flowing water to produce electricity is called hydroelectric power, or just hydropower. The force of the flowing water turns a kind of water wheel, which is connected by a shaft to an electric generator. There are good descriptions on the Internet for how different types of hydropower turbines work.*

Assessment Tools

Engineering the Future uses three types of tools that are aimed at helping students and teachers continually assess understanding:

1) Benchmark questions at the end of several tasks in the *Engineer's Notebook* invite students to apply the key ideas from that task.

2) Project rubrics for assessing individual and team performance on creative engineering design tasks are included in the *Engineer's Notebook,* so that students can participate in their own evaluation.

3) A section called "Assessment" at the end of the task guidelines offers additional questions and suggestions.

This final section of the *Teacher Guide* offers three additional assessment tools:

4) Self-evaluation forms to enable students to build their teamwork skills

5) Concept maps, which provide an alternative way of measuring student learning

6) Four end-of-project tests, which can be administered after each quarter of the course to measure the students' abilities to apply the knowledge and skills that they gained during the course

These three additional assessment tools are described below.

Teamwork assessment forms. Two one-page forms are provided for students to evaluate their team's effectiveness and their own contributions to their team. You may wish to use either or both of these pages whenever you want to strengthen your students' abilities to function as effectively as a team. Teamwork and Individual Assessment rubrics were drawn previously from the Lemelson-MIT InvenTEAMS web site. Resources can also be found at The Lemelson Center for the Study on Invention & Innovation website at http://invention.smithsonian.org/resources/.

Concept maps. Concept maps provide an alternative way for your students to show what they have learned through the project activities and the corresponding textbook readings. This section of the Teacher Guide includes six pages on concept mapping. The first two sheets provide an orientation to concept mapping with reference information. The additional sheets are complete concept maps for the four projects of the ETF course.

Final assessments. These tests are designed to measure students' understanding of the concepts presented in both the *Engineer's Notebook* and textbook. They may be used as a final assessment, when concluding each of the four main projects of the course. They also may be used prior to the start of the course as a diagnostic instrument, to see what your students already know about engineering and technology, and what misconceptions they may hold. The answer key at the end of each final assessment is only a guide, as teachers and students may have different interpretations of these questions. So that these tests measure students' abilities to apply what they learned to solve problems, rather than memorize formulas, we recommend that teachers give students a summary of important formulas to use while taking the test. We provide such a list on the next page, which can be copied and provided to students at any time during the course.

Teamwork Assessment Form

Your name: Names of group members:

Name of project:

Check the box with the appropriate rating for each aspect of your team's work.

1 is excellent; 2 is good; 3 is adequate; 4 is poor; 5 is absent.	Rating				
Aspect	1	2	3	4	5
1. The group cooperated. Everyone played a role and carried it out.					
2. Everyone contributed to the discussion.					
3. Everyone's opinion was valued.					
4. The group was organized.					
5. Materials and resources were gathered, distributed, and shared.					
6. Problems were addressed as a group.					
7. All parts of the assignment were completed within the time assigned.					

Comments: What do you think your team could do to be more effective?

Individual Assessment Form

Check the box with the appropriate rating for your individual work.

1 is excellent; 2 is good; 3 is adequate; 4 is poor; 5 is absent.	Rating				
Aspect	1	2	3	4	5
1. I followed directions and listened carefully to instructions.					
2. I actively participated in group discussions and group work.					
3. I stayed on task during all activities and did my part of group work to my best ability.					
4. I interacted well and respected others at all times.					

Comments: What do you think you could do to be a more effective team member?

Teamwork Rubric

Name:	Title of work:			Date:	
	4	**3**	**2**	**1**	**Points**
Helping Students on your team frequently offer assistance to each other.	Always	Most of the time	Some of the time	Never	____
Listening Students listen to each other's ideas respectfully.	Always	Most of the time	Some of the time	Never	____
Participating Each student contributes to the project.	Always	Most of the time	Some of the time	Never	____
Persuading The students exchange, defend, and rethink their ideas.	Always	Most of the time	Some of the time	Never	____
Questioning The students discuss each others' ideas, and pose questions to each other.	Always	Most of the time	Some of the time	Never	____
Respecting Students encourage and support each other's ideas and efforts.	Always	Most of the time	Some of the time	Never	____
Sharing The students offer ideas and report their findings to each other.	Always	Most of the time	Some of the time	Never	____
Overall Comments:				Total Points	____

Concept Mapping

Concept maps are composed of concepts connected by lines that explain how the concepts are related. Two concepts linked by a phrase form a proposition or statement. An example is shown at right. The structure of a concept map—not only the number of concepts, but also the variety of ways they are connected— indicates how deeply the creator of the map understands the topic.

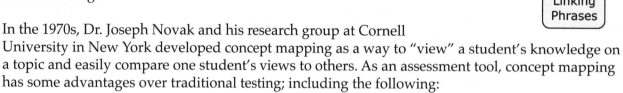

A concept map for each *Engineering the Future* (ETF) project has been included in this Teacher Guide. These can be used in various ways: handed out as an advanced organizer at the start of a unit, as a review guide at the end of a unit, or as a means of assessing student understanding.

In the 1970s, Dr. Joseph Novak and his research group at Cornell University in New York developed concept mapping as a way to "view" a student's knowledge on a topic and easily compare one student's views to others. As an assessment tool, concept mapping has some advantages over traditional testing; including the following:

- It is constructed by the student in response to his or her ideas—not guided by a list of questions. Consequently, students are free to show what they've learned, not just whether or not they know the answers.
- Concept mapping is nonlinear. Students can lead the teacher along their own pathways, offering insight into how they think about the subject, revealing correct ideas, possible misconceptions, and possibly new and unexpected ways of thinking and reasoning.
- Concept maps are a creative process and therefore more likely than tests to engage students' enthusiasm and draw on their best thinking.

Naturally, students need to be introduced to concept mapping before it can be used as an assessment tool. A number of helpful sources, cited in the list of References and Resources, can be found on the Internet. Novak and Gowin provide a detailed how-to on introducing concept mapping to various grade levels in *Learning How to Learn* (1984). Especially relevant to *Engineering the Future* are the suggestions by Weerasinghe and Salustri for using concept mapping to facilitate innovation and communication of ideas within the engineering design process (2006).

References and Resources

Bransfield, J. D., A. L. Brown, and R. R. Cocking, editors. *How People Learn: Brain, Mind, Experience, and School*. Washington, D.C.: National Academies Press, 1999.

Committee on the Support for Thinking Spatially. *Learning to Think Spatially: GIS as a Support System in the K–12 Curriculum*, D.C.: National Academies Press, (2006): 112.

Ericsson, K. A., and N. Charness. "Expert performance: Its structure and acquisition." *American Psychologist*, 49(8), (1994): 725–747.

Halpern, D. F. "Teaching critical thinking for transfer across domains: Disposition, skills, structure training, and metacognitive monitoring." *American Psychologist*, 53, (1998): 449–455.

Horton, P. B., McConney, A. A., Gallo, M., Woods, A. L., Senn, G. J. and D. Hamelin. "An investigation of the effectiveness of concept mapping as an instructional tool." *Science Education*, 77, (1993): 95–111.

Kinchin, I. M., Hay, D.B., and A. Adams. "How a qualitative approach to concept map analysis can be used to aid learning by illustrating patterns of conceptual development." *Educational Research*, 42, (2000): 43–57.

Lawless, C., Smee, P. and T. O'Shea. "Using concept sorting and concept mapping in business and public administration, and in education: an overview." *Educational Research*, 40, (1998): 219–35.

Martinson, Barbara, and the Regents of the University of Minnesota, "Concept Map [Assessment Rubric]." University of Minnesota, (2004). http://dmc.umn.edu/activities/mindmap/assessment.pdf.

Novak, J. D. and D.B. Gowin. *Learning How to Learn*. Cambridge: Cambridge University Press, 1984: 36–37.

Novak, J. D. "Concept mapping: a useful tool for science education." *Journal of Research in Science Teaching*, 27, (1990): 937–949.

Novak, J. D. "Concept mapping: a tool for improving science teaching and learning." In *Improving Teaching and Learning in Science and Mathematics*, edited by Treagust, D. F., Duit, R. and Fraser, B. J., 32–43, New York and London: Teachers College Press, 1996.

Novak, J. D. *Learning, Creating and Using Knowledge: Concept Maps as Facilitative Tools in Schools and Corporations*. Hillsdale, NJ: Lawrence Erlbaum, 1998.

Santhanam, E., Leach, C. and C. Dawson. "Concept mapping: how should it be introduced, and is there evidence for long term benefit?" *Higher Education*, 35, (1998): 317–328.

Trifone, J. "To What Extent can Concept Mapping Motivate Students to Take a More Meaningful Approach to Learning Biology?" *The Science Education Review*, 5, (2006): 122.

Weerasinghe, J. S., and F. A. Salustri. *"Use of Concept Maps to Aid Early Engineering Design."* In *The Third CDEN/RCCI International Design Conference*, University of Toronto, (2006). http://www.cden2006.utoronto.ca/data/10041.pdf.

Yin, Yue, and Richard J. Shavelson. *"Application of Generalizability Theory to Concept-Map Assessment Research."* Center for the Study of Evaluation (CSE), National Center for Research on Evaluation, Standards, and Student Testing (CRESST), (2007). https://www.cu.edu/academicaffairs/assessment/assessment_toolbox/documents/CncptMpAssessSTANFORD_001.pdf.

Assessment Tools

Project 1.0: Design the Best Organizer in the World

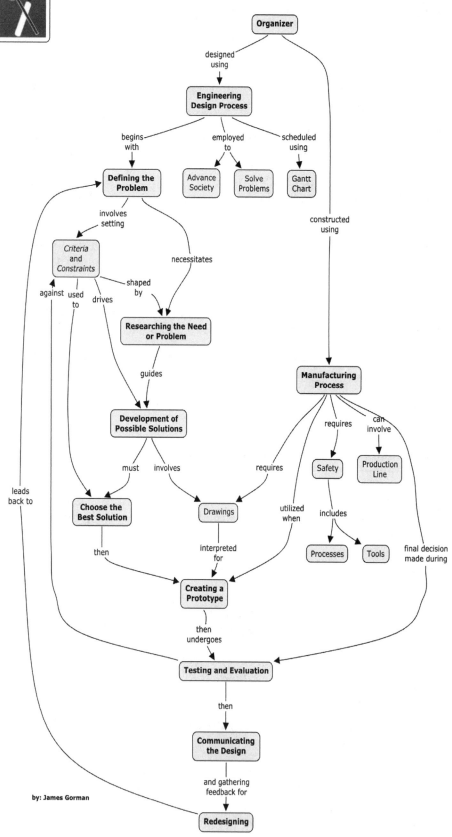

by: James Gorman

Engineering the Future Teacher Guide
©2008 Museum of Science, Boston

Project 2.0: Design a Building of the Future

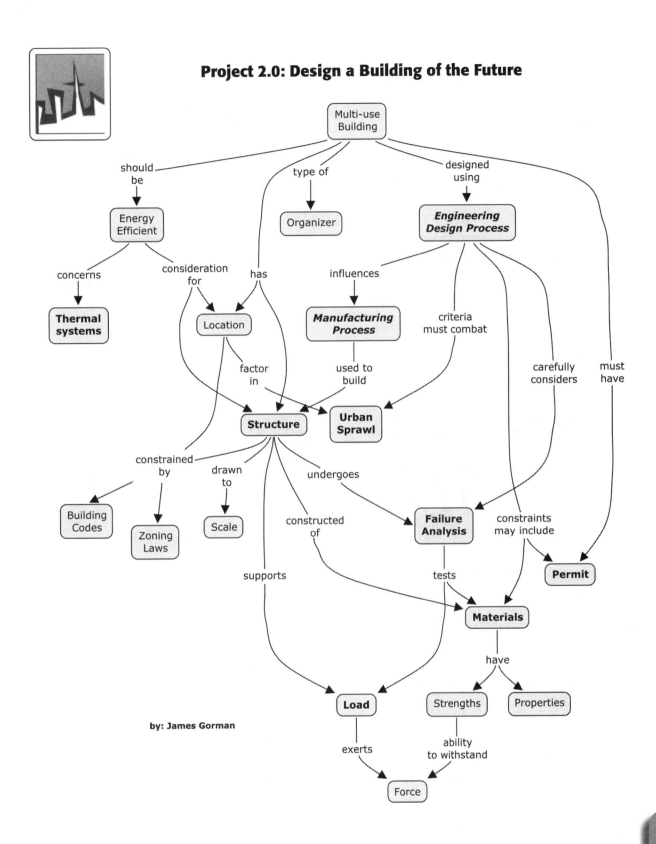

by: James Gorman

Project 3.0: Improve a Patented Boat Design

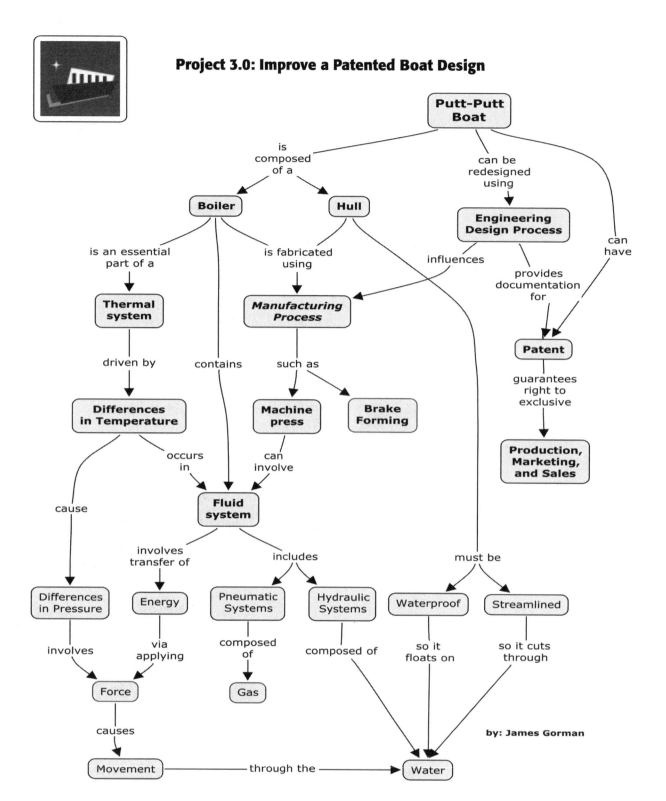

Engineering the Future Teacher Guide
©2008 Museum of Science, Boston

Project 4.0: Electricity and Communication Systems

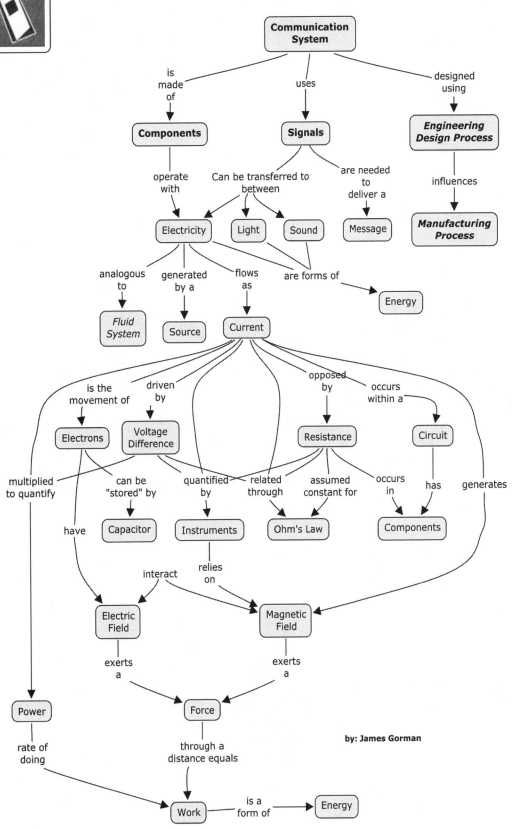

by: James Gorman

Assessment Tools

Name_____   Date_____

Project 1.0 Final Assessment

1. **Read through the following list of definitions. Choose the one that provides the broadest definition of the term** *technology.*

    A. Any human-made device that helps machines run more efficiently.

    B. A process that involves using computers in the work that people do.

    C. Any device that has a computer or an engine that allows it to do work.

    D. Changes made to the world to satisfy human needs or wants.

    E. A machine that is used to solve a problem.

2. **Look at the list below. Please <u>circle all</u> that are <u>clear</u> examples of** *technology.*

shoes	subway	dandelions	cell phone
oak tree	bridge	television	cup
parrot	factories	bandage	house
power lines	bicycle	lightning	books

Assessment Tools

3. **What kinds of work do engineers do? Please <u>circle all</u> kinds of work you think an engineer might do.**

4. **Circle the phrase that is the most accurate ending for the sentence: "The main work of engineers is to…**

    A. …use various kinds of machines."

    B. …find out what's wrong and fix things."

    C. …improve technologies or invent new ones."

    D. …build bridges, buildings, and other structures."

5. Below are the eight steps of the engineering design process, and they are not in the correct order. Please fill in the blanks with the letter of each of the steps to show the correct order.

A. Communicate the solution   **E.** Research the problem

B. Create a prototype   **F.** Choose the best solution

C. Redesign   **G.** Define the problem

D. Develop possible solutions   **H.** Test and evaluate

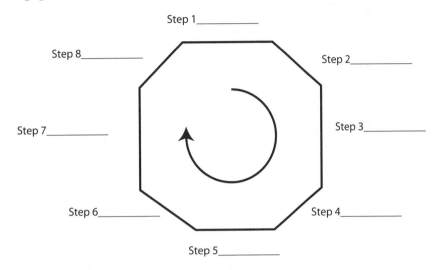

Step 1_____

Step 8_____

Step 2_____

Step 7_____

Step 3_____

Step 6_____

Step 4_____

Step 5_____

6. Is it always necessary to follow these steps in order? Why or why not?

7. Give examples of how three different kinds of engineers use the engineering design process:

A. Kind of engineer_____   Example:

B. Kind of engineer_____   Example:

C. Kind of engineer_____   Example:

Assessment Tools

A friend is preparing for college and asked for your help in selecting a computer. You asked her questions about what she wanted in a computer and created the following Pugh chart for her.

	Maximum points	Joy Book Plus	Digital Notebook	Handy Dandy
Low cost	15	$699.99 Points: 14	$1,149.99 Points: 7	$999.99 Points: 9
Small size	20	2" thick Points: 8	1.3" thick Points: 18	1.8" thick Points: 13
Lots of RAM	15	512 MB Points: 12	512 MB Points: 12	256 MB Points: 6
Lots of memory	20	120 GB Points: 18	80 GB Points: 13	160 GB Points: 19
Attractive	5	OK Points: 3	Wow Points: 5	Good Points: 4
Lightweight	10	Heavy Points: 2	Light Points: 9	Heavy Points: 2
Large monitor	5	17" Points: 5	14" Points: 3	15" Points: 4
Total Points				

8. What are the <u>two</u> most important criteria on this chart?

A. Low cost
B. Small size
C. Lots of RAM
D. Lots of memory
E. Attractive
F. Lightweight
G. Large monitor

9. Complete the analysis of the Pugh Chart by summing to find the Total Points.

10. Based on this analysis, the best computer your friend would buy is:

A. Joy Book Plus
B. Digital Notebook
C. Handy Dandy
D. None of the above

Engineering the Future Teacher Guide
©2008 Museum of Science, Boston

The following are four drawings of a chalkboard eraser. In each case, circle the letter that best describes the kind of drawing you see.

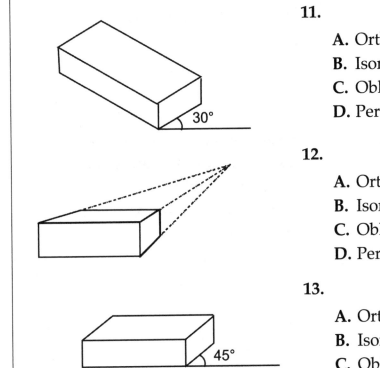

11.

A. Orthographic

B. Isometric

C. Oblique

D. Perspective

12.

A. Orthographic

B. Isometric

C. Oblique

D. Perspective

13.

A. Orthographic

B. Isometric

C. Oblique

D. Perspective

14.

A. Orthographic

B. Isometric

C. Oblique

D. Perspective

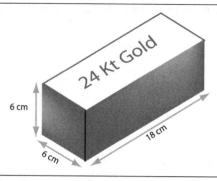

6 cm

24 Kt Gold

18 cm

6 cm

15. **What is the area of the top surface of the gold bar in cm²?**

Please show your work.

16. **What is the volume of the gold bar in cm³? Please show your work.**

17. **What is the mass of the gold bar in kilograms? Round up to the closest whole number.**

(Density of gold is about 19.3 g/ cm³)

(1,000 g = 1 kg)

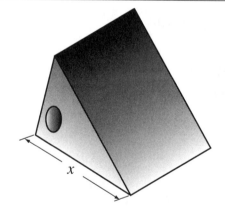

x

Scale: 1 in. = 5 in.

18. **At left is a scale drawing of a metal pen holder given to a manufacturer. If *x* measures 0.5 inches in the drawing, what value should length *x* be in the completed product?**

A. 0.5 inches

B. 2.0 inches

C. 2.5 inches

D. 5.0 inches

Engineering the Future Teacher Guide
©2008 Museum of Science, Boston

Engineers often create scale models. The scale of the house model below is 1:48, or 1 inch = 4 feet.

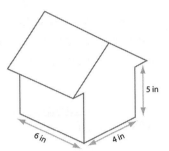

5 in

6 in   4 in

Scale: 1 inch = 4 feet

19. What is the <u>actual length</u> of the house in feet?

Please show your work below.

20. What is the actual area of the floor of the house in ft.²?

Please show your work below.

21. Why do engineers use scale models and drawings?

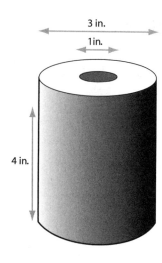

3 in.

1 in.

4 in.

Just about everything that spins or turns depends on ball bearings or roller bearings. As shown at left, a roller bearing is a cylinder with a perfectly centered round hole from one end to the other. An engineer who works for a company that repairs roller coasters has been asked to order 1,000 new roller bearings from a manufacturer, but the plans for how to make them have been lost.

22. What is the minimum number of <u>orthographic</u> views needed to show all of the dimensions of the bearing? _____
Explain why you chose that number.

23. In the space below, make all of the necessary <u>orthographic drawings</u> so that the manufacturer can make new roller bearings. (Scale: 1 inch = 2 squares)

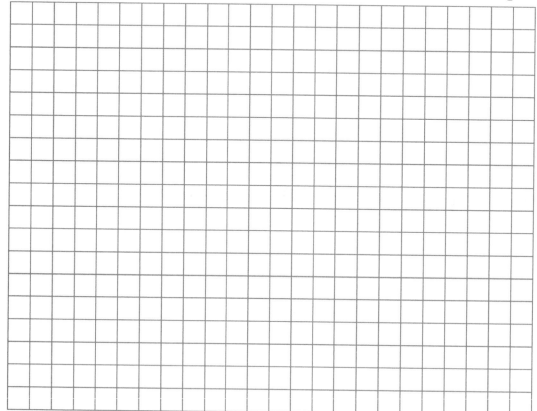

Engineering the Future Teacher Guide
©2008 Museum of Science, Boston

24. **Fill in the blanks below with the letter of the appropriate manufacturing process. Some manufacturing processes may be used more than once.**

A. Forming   C. Casting & molding   E. Conditioning
B. Separating   D. Assembling   F. Finishing

_____ Pouring liquid plastic into a mold, and allowing it to solidify

_____ Putting a final glaze on a ceramic bowl

_____ Sanding a piece of wood before painting it

_____ Cutting out pieces of cloth to make suits

_____ Installing car doors and windows

_____ Using a hydraulic press and die to make cups from sheet metal

_____ Applying safety labels to completed ladders

_____ Using a sewing machine to make wallets

25. The manager of a school cafeteria has been under fire for going over budget and for failing to have students' lunches prepared on time. How could the manager use <u>systems analysis</u> to improve the operation of the cafeteria? (Use the back of the page if you need more space.)

Answer Key for Project 1.0 Final Assessment (Max = 100)

	Points		Points
1. D	2	15. $A = L \times W =$ 18 cm $\times$ 6 cm = 108 cm^2	2
2. All are clear examples of technology except dandelions, oak tree, parrot, and lightning. Award 1 point for each of 12 correct answers.	12	16. $V = L \times W \times H =$ 18 cm $\times$ 6 cm $\times$ 6 cm = 648 cm^3	4
3. All are the kinds of work that engineers do for their jobs except construct buildings, drive machines, arrange flowers, install wiring, sell food, repair cars, and clean teeth. Award 1 point for each of 9 correct answers.	9	17. Density = Mass / Volume Mass = Density $\times$ Volume Mass = 19.3 g / cm^3 $\times$ 648 cm^3 Mass = 12,506.4 g Mass $\approx$ 13 kg	6
4. C	2	18. C	2
5. Order of the steps is G, E, D, F, B, H, A, and C. Award 2 points if 4 or more are correct, 4 points if 7 or more are correct.	4	19. Scale 1 in. = 4 feet or 1:48 Length = 6 in. $\times$ (4 ft. per in.) = 24 feet	4
6. No. The engineering design process is a guide for how to solve problems systematically, but it does not need to be followed exactly. You can always return to an earlier step. Award 2 for "No," 4 more for a clear explanation.	6	20. Scale 1 in. = 4 feet or 1:48 Length = 6 in. $\times$ (4 ft. per in.) = 24 ft. Width = 4 in. $\times$ (4 ft. per in.) = 16 ft. Area = $L \times W$ Area = 24 ft. $\times$ 16 ft. = 384 ft.^{2}	6
7. Student names three different kinds of engineers (1 point each) and appropriate examples (1 point each).	6	21. Engineers use scale drawings and models to test ideas and find weaknesses.	2
8. B and D	2	22. Either 2 or 3 are acceptable, with an appropriate explanation.	2
9. 62, 67, 57	2	23.	4
10. B	2	24. C, F, E, B, D, A, F, D. Award 2 points if 4 or more are correct, 4 points if 7 or more are correct.	4
11. B	2	25. Award 4 points if student applies the engineering design process and 4–9 points if answer indicates thinking about the cafeteria as a system, with inputs, processes, feedback, outputs, and goals.	9
12. D	2		
13. C	2		
14. A	2		

Maximum Score = 100

Summary of Class Results for Project 1.0 Final Assessment

Please help the authors of ETF validate these assessments and use the results to improve the course by completing the chart with the results of the final assessment for Project 1.0, and sending a copy to *Engineering the Future*, NCTL, Museum of Science, 1 Science Park, Boston, MA 02114-1099. Questions are in vertical columns; students are in horizontal rows.

	1	2	3	4	5	6	7	8	9	10	11	12	13	14	15	16	17	18	19	20	21	22	23	24	25	T
1																										
2																										
3																										
4																										
5																										
6																										
7																										
8																										
9																										
10																										
11																										
12																										
13																										
14																										
15																										
16																										
17																										
18																										
19																										
20																										
21																										
22																										
23																										
24																										
25																										
26																										
27																										
28																										
29																										
30																										
31																										
32																										
T																										

Assessment Tools

Project 2.0 Final Assessment

1. The drawing below is a plan view of a two-car garage. Assuming each car is 6 ft. wide by 15 ft. long, what is the best estimate for the area of the floor in this garage?

   A. 180 sq. ft.
   B. 400 sq. ft.
   C. 900 sq. ft.
   D. 1,600 sq. ft.

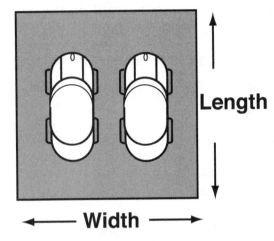

Length

⟵ Width ⟶

2. The snow on a supermarket roof has a density of 100 kg/m^3 and is 0.2 m deep. The roof is 20 m wide and 40 m long. What is the load of the snow on the roof?

   A. 160 kg
   B. 1,600 kg
   C. 16,000 kg
   D. 160,000 kg

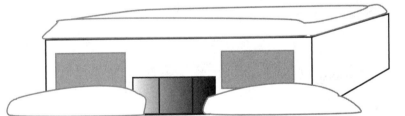

3. **Which would you use to answer to each question: Building Codes or Zoning Laws? Label each question as either BC (Building Codes) or ZL (Zoning Laws).**

BC or ZL	Questions
	How tall can I design a building in a given part of the city?
	Can I open a restaurant on the first floor of my apartment building?
	How can I reinforce my home to prevent earthquake damage?
	What is the allowable load for the porch I am adding to my house?
	Where can we plan a new city center to reduce urban sprawl?
	What are the concrete mixture requirements for a house foundation?

4. **Look at the school building shown below. In order to indicate whether the elements contribute to live load or dead load of the building, please label each element as either LIVE LOAD or DEAD LOAD.**

Live Load or Dead Load?	Item
	Milk Man
	Outside Wall
	Roof
	Second Floor
	Globe

Engineering the Future Teacher Guide
©2008 Museum of Science, Boston

Given the following information, answer the questions below.

LADDER	
Length:	20 ft. long
Step:	3 in. × 10 in. × 1 in.
Overall weight:	10 lb.
Weight of step:	0.25 lb.

KIMBERLY	
Height:	5 ft. 8 in.
Weight:	135 lb.

CHRISTIAN	
Height:	3 ft. 2 in.
Weight:	60 lb.

PAINT CAN	
Weight:	5 lb.

RADIO	
Weight:	2 lb.

5. Kimberly climbs up the ladder carrying the paint can and her radio. What is the live load on the ladder?

   A. 7 lb.

   B. 128 lb.

   C. 135 lb.

   D. 142 lb.

6. Kimberly gets halfway up the ladder with the can of paint and her radio. If Christian starts to climb up the ladder behind Kimberly, what is the total load?

   A. 212 lb.

   B. 202 lb.

   C. 152 lb.

   D. 79 lb.

7. The largest expected load of the ladder is about 200 lb. If the ladder is designed with a safety factor of 4, what is the maximum live load the ladder could support before failing?

   A. 50 lb.

   B. 204 lb.

   C. 800 lb.

   D. 1,000 lb.

Assessment Tools

8. The diagram below shows a joint comprised of a bolt holding together two parts of a deck. Failure at the joint is most likely caused by:

A. Compression

B. Tension

C. Shearing

D. Torsion

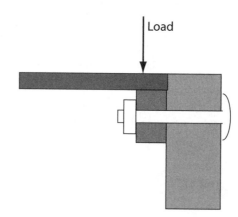

9. The figure below shows the handle of a spoon that bent while being used to scoop frozen ice cream.

What does the bend indicate about the property of the material in the spoon's handle that made it inappropriate for this use?

A. It was too brittle.

B. It was too malleable.

C. It was too elastic.

D. It was too dense.

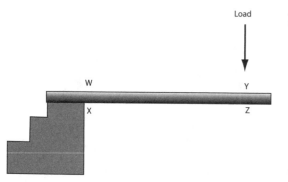

10. The diagram to the left shows a diving board. At what point is the maximum tensile stress when a load is applied to the end of the board?

A. Point W

B. Point X

C. Point Y

D. Point Z

Engineering the Future Teacher Guide
©2008 Museum of Science, Boston

The picture below shows a tower, secured by two cables. Please answer the questions below:

11. **What is the main type of force tower M must withstand?**

    A. Compression
    B. Torsion
    C. Shear
    D. Tension

12. **What is the main type of force cables L and N must withstand?**

    A. Compression
    B. Torsion
    C. Shear
    D. Tension

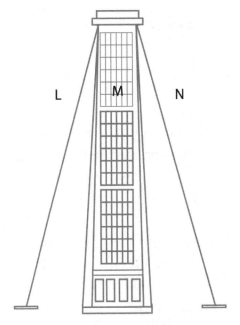

13. **If someone is changing the tire on a car, what kind of force is being exerted if he or she is using a lug wrench to remove the wheel nuts?**

    A. Compression
    B. Torsion
    C. Shear
    D. Tension

14. **Match each of the following terms associated with materials with the appropriate definition. (Not all definitions will be used.)**

A. Point at which a material will not go back to its original shape when stress is removed

B. Ratio of an applied force divided by the area over which the force acts

C. Difference between the tension capacity and the compression capacity of a material

D. Measure of how much a material deforms due to applied stress

E. Ability of a material to be stretched or deformed and return to its original shape

F. Describes materials that do not deform plastically but fracture shortly after reaching their elastic limit

G. Ability of a material to be hammered or rolled to change its shape or thickness

____ Strain

____ Malleability

____ Elasticity

____ Stress

____ Elastic limit

____ Brittle

15. **Which of the following properties is most important for steel used to make springs?**

A. Conductivity

B. Malleability

C. Elasticity

D. Plasticity

Engineering the Future Teacher Guide
©2008 Museum of Science, Boston

16. A person walking across a simple plank bridge exerts a downward force in the middle. The plank is supported by an upward force at each end.

At which point are cracks in the board due to <u>tension</u> most likely to appear first?

A. Point W
B. Point X
C. Point Y
D. Point Z

17. The following table provides information about the R-values for different wall insulation layers.

Insulation Layers	R-Value
Plywood sheet (1" thick)	0.77
Rock wool (1" thick)	3.14
Brick (4" thick)	0.44
Concrete block (4" thick)	0.80

Four houses are constructed, similar to the one pictured, with different combinations of insulation. Based on the R-value table, which house is the most economical to heat?

A. House A	The walls of this house are made of one layer of brick, one layer of concrete block, and one plywood sheet.
B. House B	The walls of this house are made of one layer of brick, one layer of rock wool, and one plywood sheet.
C. House C	The walls of this house are made of two layers of brick, two layers of concrete block, and two plywood sheets.
D. House D	The walls of this house are made of two plywood sheets and one thickness of rock wool.

18. **A manufacturer has hired a chemical engineer to develop a new-and-improved home insulating material. Which of the following properties will be most important for the new insulator to have?**

   A. Low thermal conductivity
   B. Low thermal expansion
   C. Low density
   D. Low R-value

19. **Consider the three types of buildings shown below.**

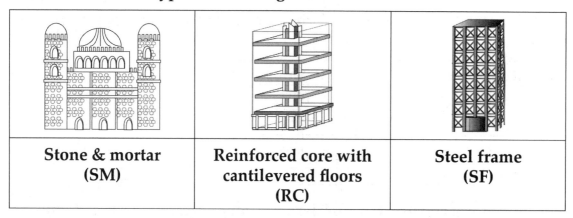

| Stone & mortar (SM) | Reinforced core with cantilevered floors (RC) | Steel frame (SF) |

The following relate to the three types of buildings. Label each of the following as either SM (stone & mortar), RC (reinforced core with cantilevered floors), or SF (steel frame).

SM/RC/SF	Description
	This type of building allows for the greatest usable area on each floor.
	The first skyscrapers were supported with this design.
	This type of building would allow offices with the most window space.
	Walls in this type of building are very thick in order to support the weight of the structure.

Engineering the Future Teacher Guide
©2008 Museum of Science, Boston

20. **Please choose one of the three ways by which each of the following four objects <u>primarily</u> transfers its energy:**

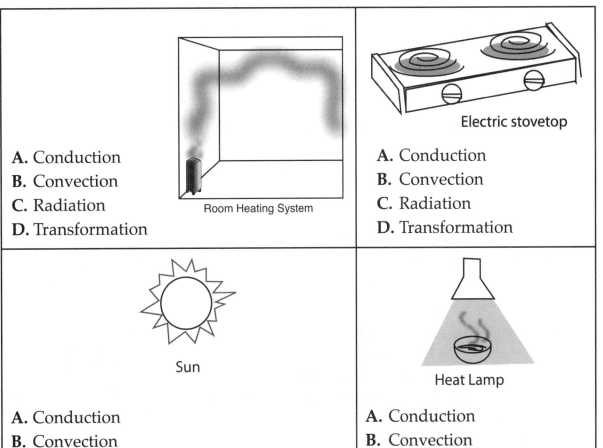

Room Heating System

A. Conduction
B. Convection
C. Radiation
D. Transformation

Electric stovetop

A. Conduction
B. Convection
C. Radiation
D. Transformation

Sun

A. Conduction
B. Convection
C. Radiation
D. Transformation

Heat Lamp

A. Conduction
B. Convection
C. Radiation
D. Transformation

21. **If you want to use <u>passive solar heating</u> for a home in northern Maine, what structural features would you include? (Put an "X" beside all answers that apply.)**

___ Thin glass windows

___ Concrete or stone floors

___ Large south-facing windows

___ Hot water radiators

___ Solar collector and pump

___ Ceiling fans

___ Gas furnace

___ Insulation with high R-value

22. **It is summer and the temperature outside is 95°F. The air conditioning is turned on and doors and windows are closed, so the temperature inside is 65°F. If you turn off the air conditioning and keep the doors and windows shut tight, the house will warm up because**

   A. hot air from outside will draw out the cool air through tiny cracks and holes.
   B. cool air from inside will push out through tiny cracks and holes.
   C. heat energy from outside will move through walls and windows to the inside.
   D. cold energy from inside will move through walls and windows to the outside.

23. **Many home heating systems have fans that hang from the ceiling. Which of the following best explains why these fans are used in the winter time, in cold climates?**

   A. They cool the room so it doesn't get too hot.
   B. They stir the air so that the warm air doesn't stay only near the ceiling.
   C. They keep the pipes from freezing.
   D. The fans are connected to the heater, so they cannot be turned off.

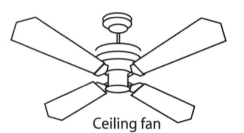
Ceiling fan

24. **Why do pipes carrying hot water run along the floors and not the ceilings?**

   A. If people's feet are kept warm, their entire bodies will feel warm too.
   B. It makes walking barefoot more pleasant.
   C. The pipes heat the floor, which in turn warms the air, which rises.
   D. If there is a leak, it will do less damage if the water runs beneath the wooden floor.

Engineering the Future Teacher Guide
©2008 Museum of Science, Boston

Mr. K., who lives in Arizona, had an idea for reducing energy costs during summer, when it gets very hot during the day but is cool at night. His idea was to open all the windows at night so the house will cool off, then close the windows in the morning before the sun rises. That way it will stay cool all day, and he won't have to turn on his air conditioner.

25. Below, write a short letter to Mr. K., telling him whether or not you think his idea is a good one, and explain your answer in terms of what you know about energy transfer. Also, give him any other tips you can think of that may help him save on energy bills during summer, and explain your suggestions in terms of energy transfer.

Answer Key for Project 2.0 Final Assessment (Max = 100)

	Points		Points
1. C	4	15. C	3
2. C	6	16. C	3
3. ZL, ZL, BC, BC, ZL, BC	6	17. D	4
4. A. Live, B. Dead, C. Dead, D. Dead E. Live	5	18. A	3
5. D	3	19. RC, SF, RC, SM	4
6. A	3	20. Room Heating System: B, Electric Stovetop: A, Sun: C, Heat Lamp: C	4
7. C	3	21. ___thin glass windows (poor insulator) ___solar collector and pump (active solar) ___concrete or stone floors (thermal mass) _x_ ceiling fans (active heating system) ___large south-facing windows (faces sun) _x_ gas furnace (active heating) ___hot water radiators (active heating) _x_ insulation with high R-value (+2 for each correct, −1 for each incorrect)	6
8. C	3	22. C	3
9. B	3	23. B	3
10. A	3	24. C	3
11. A	3	25. Award up to 3 points if the student offers reasonable suggestions. Award up to an additional 7 points if the student can justify his or her suggestions with key ideas about energy transfer: that thermal energy flows from regions of high temperature to regions of low temperature (difference drives change), and the flow of energy out of the house can be slowed with good insulation (energy flow is inversely proportional to resistance). Students may also add that "it takes a difference to make a difference," meaning that energy must be added continuously to keep the house at an even temperature that is different from the temperature outside.	10
12. D	3		
13. B	3		

14. A. Elastic limit   B. Stress
    D. Strain   E. Elasticity
    F. Brittle   G. Malleability
 	
 Note that definition C does not match any of the terms. Award 2 points for each correct answer.
	6		

Maximum Score = 100

Summary of Class Results for Project 2.0 Final Assessment

Please help the authors of ETF validate these assessments and use the results to improve the course by completing the chart with the results of the final assessment for Project 2.0, and sending a copy to *Engineering the Future*, NCTL, Museum of Science, 1 Science Park, Boston, MA 02114-1099. Questions are in vertical columns; students are in horizontal rows.

	1	2	3	4	5	6	7	8	9	10	11	12	13	14	15	16	17	18	19	20	21	22	23	24	25	T
1																										
2																										
3																										
4																										
5																										
6																										
7																										
8																										
9																										
10																										
11																										
12																										
13																										
14																										
15																										
16																										
17																										
18																										
19																										
20																										
21																										
22																										
23																										
24																										
25																										
26																										
27																										
28																										
29																										
30																										
31																										
32																										
T																										

Assessment Tools

Name_____   Date_____

Project 3.0 Final Assessment

1. **Why is a city water system considered an <u>open</u> system?**

   A. Because anyone has access to the water.
   B. Because the water systems has valves that can be opened.
   C. Because the working fluid in the system is water.
   D. Because the working fluid only passes through once.

2. **What happens to the <u>velocity</u> of gas flowing through the pipe as it moves from the portion of the pipe labeled X to that labeled Y?**

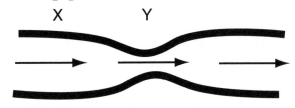

   A. It increases.
   B. It decreases.
   C. It stays the same.
   D. There is not enough information.

3. **In a fluid system, a difference in pressure drives what kind of energy flow?**

   A. Chemical energy
   B. Electrical energy
   C. Thermal energy
   D. Mechanical energy

4. **When water boils in the putt-putt boat boiler and becomes steam, its volume**

   A. decreases.
   B. disappears.
   C. increases.
   D. stays the same.

5. The following table relates to Hydraulic Systems and Pneumatic Systems. Label each of the following as either H (Hydraulic System), P (Pneumatic System), or B (Both).

H/ P/ B	Description
	This type of system uses pressure difference in gas to do work.
	This system can transfer energy to move an object.
	Jackhammers tend to involve this type of system.
	The working fluid used in this system cannot be compressed.
	This system can take a small input force and transmit a larger output force.
	This type of system tends to have smoother movements for precise energy transfers.
	The working fluid used in this system can store energy.
	This system has some "springiness."
	This system can be analyzed for the relationship among pressure, force, and area.
	The working fluid of this system transmits a force right away.

Engineering the Future Teacher Guide
©2008 Museum of Science, Boston

6. **The following diagram shows a working model for a heat engine.**

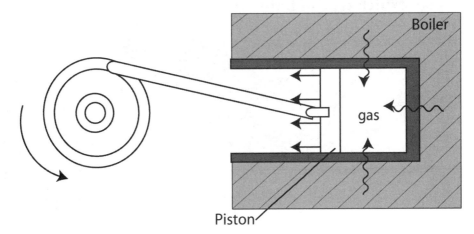

Please choose the <u>best</u> answer to complete the statement below:

The wheel in this engine will turn because _____

A. energy is added to steam, which rotates the wheel.

B. gas is cooled, which increases the pressure and pushes the piston out.

C. heat energy is added to gas, which increases the pressure and pushes the piston out.

D. gravity pulls the wheel, which then pulls out the piston.

7. **What is the purpose of the water flowing around the engine shown below?**

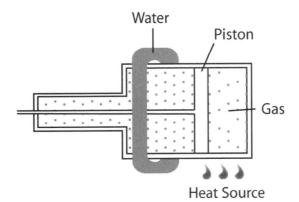

A. Water adds energy to the engine to make it work faster.

B. Water is boiled in order to push the piston.

C. Water helps filter pollutants out of the engine.

D. Water is used to cool the engine so the piston can return and the cycle can start again.

8. The machine shown below increases the force from a foot pedal to stamp sheets of metal. Which type of fluid system is illustrated here?

A. Hydraulic lift
B. Hydraulic press
C. Pneumatic lift
D. Pneumatic press

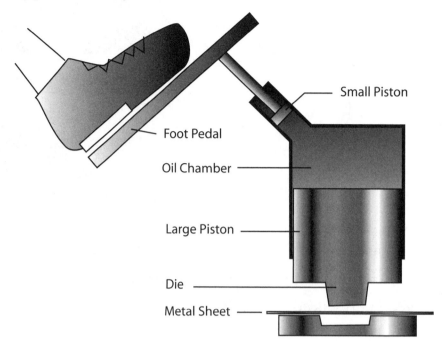

Small Piston

Foot Pedal

Oil Chamber

Large Piston

Die

Metal Sheet

9. What is the name of this manufacturing process?

A. Assembly
B. Casting & molding
C. Forming
D. Separating

Engineering the Future Teacher Guide
©2008 Museum of Science, Boston

The tank in this diagram is filled with oil. The area of plunger X is 5 in.² and the area of plunger Y is 10 in.²

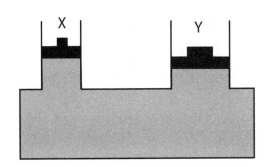

10. Complete the following statement: If you pushed down piston X, then the upward force on Y should be _____ the downward force on X.

   A. the same as
   B. greater than
   C. less than
   D. There is not enough information.

11. If you pushed down piston X with a force of 10 lb., what would be the force on piston Y?

   A. 5 lb.   B. 10 lb.   C. 20 lb.   D. 50 lb.   E. 100 lb.

12. If you pushed down piston X a distance of 4 in., what would be the distance moved by piston Y?

   A. 1 in.   B. 2 in.   C. 4 in.   D. 8 in.   E. 12 in.

13. According to Pascal's law about the pressure of fluid in a container, which of these statements is true?

   A. When piston X is pushed down, the pressure of the fluid under X is greater than under Y.
   B. When piston X is pushed down, the pressure of the fluid under X is less than under Y.
   C. When piston X is pushed down, the pressure of the fluid under X and Y increases the same amount.
   D. When piston X is pushed down, the pressure of the fluid in the tank does not change.

14. **Order the pipes below from the most resistance to fluid flow to the least resistance to fluid flow.**

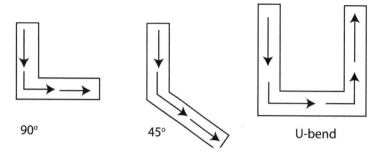

90°   45°   U-bend

A. U-bend pipe, 90° angle pipe, 45° angle pipe

B. 45° angle pipe, 90° angle pipe, U-bend pipe

C. 90° angle pipe, U-bend pipe, 45° angle pipe

D. 90° angle pipe, 45° angle pipe, U-bend pipe

15. **As shown in the diagram below, the tallest building in Golden City and Silver City rises 40 ft. above ground level, and both cities have a 100-ft.-tall water tower. However, Silver City placed its water tower on a hill 50 ft. above the city, while Golden City placed its water tower at ground level. Which city will have greater water pressure on the top floor of their tallest building?**

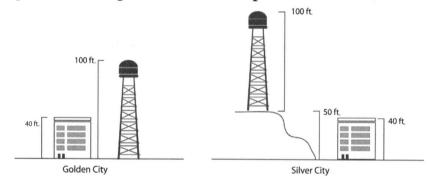

Golden City   Silver City

A. Golden City, because there is a smaller difference in the height between its water tower and the 40-ft. building.

B. Silver City, because there is a larger difference in the height between its water tower and the 40-ft. building.

C. The same, because the height of their water towers is equal and the buildings are both 40 ft. tall.

D. It is not possible to answer the question with the information given.

Engineering the Future Teacher Guide
©2008 Museum of Science, Boston

16. Give three different examples of problems that require engineers to use mathematics.

    1. _____

    2. _____

    3. _____

Choose <u>one</u> of the following vehicles and answer the questions about it below. Circle the vehicle you have chosen.

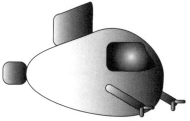

    A. A research submarine such as the Alvin   **B.** A spacecraft to visit Mars

17. Describe, as fully as you can, how <u>the work of engineers supports scientists</u> in learning about the natural world, using the vehicle you have chosen as an example. Your description should include at least two examples of scientific discoveries that would not have been possible without the work of engineers.

18. Describe, as fully as you can, how <u>the work of scientists supports engineers</u> in improving or developing new technologies, using the vehicle you have chosen as an example. Your description should include at least two scientific principles used in designing the vehicle.

Assessment Tools

19. Below, list six different changes in technology that make the lives of today's teens different from the teens of 100 years ago.

	100 Years Ago	Today
Ex.	Students who live more than a mile away walked to school.	Today, most students who live more than a mile away ride the bus to school.
1.		
2.		
3.		
4.		
5.		
6.		

20. Choose one technology from the above list, and explain how the actions of thousands (and perhaps millions) of people contributed to that technology being widely available.

21. Choose a different technology from the above list, and give at least two unintended effects (outcomes that were not expected by the people who invented the technology). Explain why each of these outcomes were positive, negative, or both.

Engineering the Future Teacher Guide
©2008 Museum of Science, Boston

22. Most of the energy that is used in the U.S. for transportation, manufacturing, and home heating and lighting comes from fossil fuels. Name three different types of fossil fuels and explain why they are called "fossil" fuels.

a._____ b._____ c._____

Why are these called "fossil" fuels?

23. List at least two ways that fossil fuels negatively impact the environment.

24. List at least two ways that new or improved technologies are reducing the negative environmental impact of fossil fuels.

25. Below, write two paragraphs. Use the back side of this page if necessary.

In the first paragraph, describe a future world in which there is no careful planning for technological change. There are no restrictions on products that are offered for sale.

In the second paragraph, describe a future world in which technological change is carefully planned, and the possible future impact of a new technology is taken into account before the product is manufactured.

Answer Key for Project 3.0 Final Assessment (Max = 100)

	Points		Points
1. D	3	15. B	3
2. A	3	16. Award two points for each different kind of problem, such as calculating speed of liquid in pipes, or finding the mechanical advantage of a machine.	6
3. D	3	17. Description should illustrate how scientists depend on instruments and vehicles designed by engineers, and give at least two examples of scientific discoveries enabled by engineering.	6
4. C	3	18. Description should illustrate how the engineers who designed the vehicle used scientific principles. Students do not have to name the principles, but they should describe them clearly and how they enable the engineering.	6
5. P, B, P, H, B, H, P, P, B, H (one half-point for each correct answer)	5	19. One point for each different technology developed in last 100 years.	6
6. C	3	20. Answer should reflect the importance of market forces in determining which technologies are chosen.	4
7. D	3	21. Award one point for each different unintended outcome, and one point for indicating whether it's +, –, or both.	4
8. B	3	22. Coal, oil, and natural gas are called "fossil fuels" because they are made from the bodies of long-dead organisms. Award 1 point for each type of fuel, and 2 points for explanation of "fossil."	5
9. C	3	23. Students may list air or water pollution, global warming, and so on.	4
10. B	3	24. Students might list alternative energy sources, ways to conserve energy, or clean the environment after it's polluted.	4
11. C	3	25. First paragraph (4 points) should show awareness of how new technologies could be harmful. Second paragraph (4 points) should identify the role of society in considering possible side effects before a technology is released.	8
12. B	3		
13. C	3		
14. A	3		

Maximum Score = 100

Summary of Class Results for Project 3.0 Final Assessment

Please help the authors of ETF validate these assessments and use the results to improve the course by completing the chart with the results of the final assessment for Project 3.0, and sending a copy to *Engineering the Future*, NCTL, Museum of Science, 1 Science Park, Boston, MA 02114-1099. Questions are in vertical columns; students are in horizontal rows.

	1	2	3	4	5	6	7	8	9	10	11	12	13	14	15	16	17	18	19	20	21	22	23	24	25	T
1																										
2																										
3																										
4																										
5																										
6																										
7																										
8																										
9																										
10																										
11																										
12																										
13																										
14																										
15																										
16																										
17																										
18																										
19																										
20																										
21																										
22																										
23																										
24																										
25																										
26																										
27																										
28																										
29																										
30																										
31																										
32																										
T																										

Project 4.0 Final Assessment

1. On the left are the components of a communication system. Fill in the blanks on the right with the most appropriate letters to complete the sentences.

   A. A decoder   __ sends the signal.

   B. An encoder   __ produces the message to be sent.

   C. A receiver   __ is the person or thing for whom the message is

   D. A transmitter   intended.

   E. The source   __ receives the signal.

   F. The destination   __ changes a message into a signal.

                             __ changes the signal back into a message.

2. Following are three technologies that depend on the flow of energy from one place to another. In each case, what is the source of <u>resistance</u> to energy flow? How can resistance be <u>increased</u>? How can it be <u>decreased</u>?

System	Source of RESISTANCE	How Can Resistance Be INCREASED?	How Can Resistance Be DECREASED?
Thermal energy flows out of a house with a heater inside and cold winter snows outside.			
Mechanical energy flows from the brake pedal on a car to the brakes on all four wheels.			
Electrical energy flows through a circuit with five light bulbs in series and five in parallel.			

3. Two people are having a telephone conversation over a fiber-optics network. Explain how energy is transferred in this system. Use an additional sheet of paper if you need more room.

4. **Will adding a 1.5 V cell to a 3.0 V battery increase the current in a circuit? Why or why not?**

    A. Yes. There is more energy in three cells than in one.

    B. Yes. More power means more current.

    C. Yes. A greater difference in voltage drives an increase in energy flow.

    D. No. Only voltage will increase, not current.

5. **The diagram below shows a simple circuit. The arrow next to Wire #1 in the circuit shows the direction the electrical current in that wire is flowing. What do you think is happening in Wire #2?**

    (a) In Wire #2, there is

    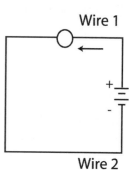

    A. an electric current flowing toward the bulb.

    B. an electric current flowing away from the bulb.

    C. no electric current flowing at all.

    D. no way to determine which way it is flowing.

    (b) Compared to Wire #1, Wire #2 carries

    A. more electric current.

    B. less electric current.

    C. no electric current at all.

    D. the same amount of electric current.

6. **An ammeter has been connected to a circuit as shown in the diagram below. Which of the following is the best answer?**

    A. The ammeter will accurately measure the current through Bulb B.

    B. The ammeter should be connected in parallel to Bulb B in order to measure the current through Bulb B.

    C. An ammeter measures the electric potential difference across a circuit component.

    D. The ammeter will accurately measure the voltage through Bulb A.

    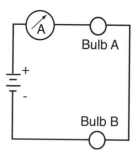

Engineering the Future Teacher Guide
©2008 Museum of Science, Boston

7. Which of the following circuit diagrams shows a voltmeter correctly attached to measure the voltage change across <u>R</u>$_3$?

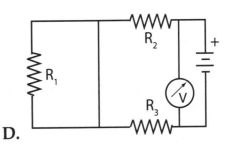

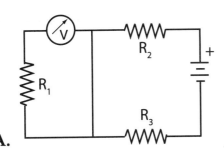

A.

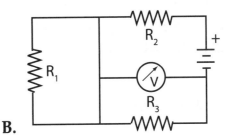

B.

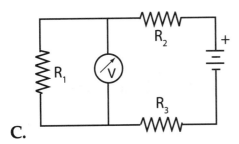

C.

D.

8. A toaster with a resistance of 15 ohms is connected to a 120 volt outlet. What is the approximate current in the circuit?

A. 8 A

B. 15 A

C. 105 A

D. 180 A

9. If a 60-watt incandescent lamp and a 15-watt fluorescent lamp produce the same amount of light, which one is more efficient?

A. 60-watt incandescent lamp

B. 15-watt fluorescent lamp

C. They are equally efficient.

D. None of the above.

Answer the following questions based on the simple circuit and series circuit diagrammed below. **Please explain your reasoning for each question.**

10. **How does the brightness of Bulb A compare with the brightness of Bulb B?**

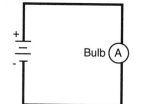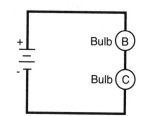

    A. Bulb A is brighter than Bulb B.

    B. Bulb B is brighter than Bulb A.

    C. Bulbs A and B are equally bright.

    D. Bulb C is the brightest.

    <u>Explain your reasoning:</u>

11. **In the diagram above, how does the brightness of Bulb B compare with the brightness of Bulb C?**

    A. Bulb B is brighter.

    B. Bulb C is brighter.

    C. Bulbs B and C are equally bright.

    D. There is less current flowing through Bulb C.

    <u>Explain your reasoning:</u>

Engineering the Future Teacher Guide
©2008 Museum of Science, Boston

The following questions concern the same simple circuit and series circuit shown on the previous page, except they ask about the strength of the electrical current. Please explain your reasoning for each question.

12. **How does the current at Point 1 compare with the current at Point 2?**

    A. There is more current at Point 1 than at Point 2.

    B. There is more current at Point 2 than at Point 1.

    C. The currents at Points 1 and 2 are equal.

    D. The most current flow through Point 4.

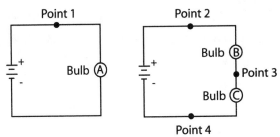

    Explain your reasoning:

13. **How does the current at Point 2 compare with the current at Point 3 and Point 4?**

    A. The current at Point 2 is greater than at Point 3, which is greater than at Point 4.

    B. The current at Point 4 is greater than at Point 3, which is greater than at Point 2.

    C. The current at Points 2 and 4 are equal, but greater than at Point 3.

    D. The current is the same at Points 2, 3, and 4.

    Explain your reasoning:

Answer the following questions based on the simple circuit and parallel circuit diagrammed below. **Please explain your reasoning for each question.**

14. **How does the brightness of Bulb A compare with the brightness of Bulb B?**

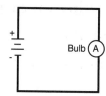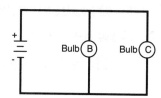

   A. Bulb A is brighter than Bulb B.
   B. Bulb B is brighter than Bulb A.
   C. Bulbs A and B are equally bright.
   D. Bulb C is the brightest.

   <u>Explain your reasoning:</u>

15. **In the diagram above, how does the brightness of Bulb B compare with the brightness of Bulb C?**

   A. Bulb B is brighter.
   B. Bulb C is brighter.
   C. Bulbs B and C are equally bright.
   D. Bulb A is the brightest.

   <u>Explain your reasoning:</u>

16. **How do charge, resistance, and energy differ in the two circuits above?**

   A. There is twice as much electric charge in the circuit with Bulbs B and C.
   B. There is twice as much resistance in the circuit with Bulbs B and C.
   C. Charge leaves the circuit twice as fast in the circuit with Bulbs B and C.
   D. Energy leaves the circuit twice as fast in the circuit with Bulbs B and C.

Engineering the Future Teacher Guide
©2008 Museum of Science, Boston

The questions below concern the same simple circuit and parallel circuit shown on the previous page, except they ask about the strength of the electrical current. <u>Please explain your reasoning for each question.</u>

17. **How does the current at Point 1 compare with the current at Point 2?**

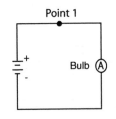
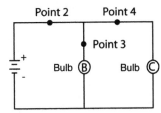

   A. There is more current at Point 1 than Point 2.

   B. There is more current at Point 2 than Point 1.

   C. The currents at Points 1 and 2 are equal.

   D. The most current flows through Point 4.

   <u>Explain your reasoning:</u>

18. **How does the current at Point 2 compare with the current at Points 3 and Point 4?**

   A. The current at Point 2 is greater than at Point 3, which is greater than at Point 4.

   B. The current at Point 2 is greater than at Point 3, which is the same as at Point 4.

   C. The current at Point 4 is greater than at Point 3, which is greater than at Point 2.

   D. The current is the same at Points 2, 3, and 4.

   <u>Explain your reasoning:</u>

19. In the diagram below, which of the following options will double the current through the ammeter?

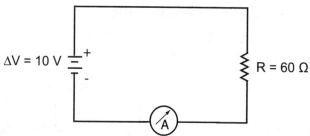

A. Replacing the battery with a 5V battery
B. Adding a 30Ω resistor in parallel with R
C. Replacing the resistor with a 30Ω resistor
D. Adding a second 60Ω resistor in series with R

20. In the schematic diagram below, a potentiometer (variable resistor) is used to control the light output of a bulb. Which of the following is the source in this circuit?

A. Switch
B. Potentiometer
C. Bulb
D. Battery

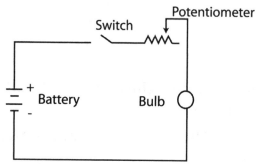

21. In the diagram above, which of the following are both controllers in the circuit?

A. Bulb and potentiometer
B. Switch and potentiometer
C. Battery and bulb
D. Switch and battery

Engineering the Future Teacher Guide
©2008 Museum of Science, Boston

22. The current in the circuit below is 2 A. The resistances of R_1, R_2, and R_3 are shown in the diagram. What is the voltage for this current?

A. 2 V

B. 120 V

C. 240 V

D. 420 V

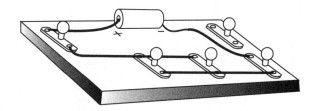

Show your work below.

23. A battery is connected to some bulbs to make a circuit, as shown at right. Circle the letter of the schematic diagram that shows how this circuit is connected.

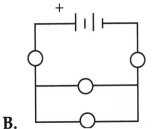

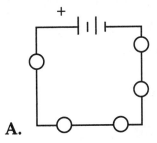

A.

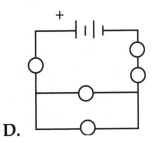

B.

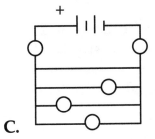

C.

D.

24. **Below are pairs of circuits. The circuit to the left stays the same in each box, while the circuit to the right varies in terms of the number of batteries and the number of bulbs. Predict which battery set will last longer, and explain your reasoning.**

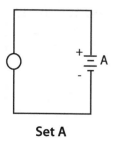
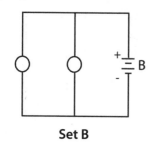

Set A   Set B

A. Battery Set A will last longer.
B. Battery Set B will last longer.
C. The duration of Battery Set A and B is equal.
D. More information is needed.

Please explain your answer:

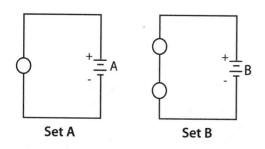

Set A   Set B

A. Battery Set A will last longer.
B. Battery Set B will last longer.
C. Battery Set A and B will last the same amount of time.
D. More information is needed.

Please explain your answer:

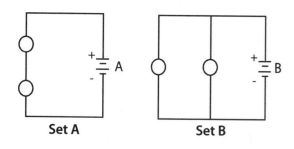

Set A   Set B

A. Battery Set A will last longer.
B. Battery Set B will last longer.
C. The duration of Battery Set A and B is equal.
D. More information is needed.

Please explain your answer:

25. **Currently, energy for heating and cooling, transportation, and manufacturing primarily comes from coal, oil, or gas. Do you think that will still be the case 25 years from now? Explain your answer. If you think our sources of energy will be different, predict what they will be and explain why. Use the back of the page if you need more room.**

Engineering the Future Teacher Guide
©2008 Museum of Science, Boston

Answer Key for Project 4.0 Final Assessment (Max = 100)

	Points		Points
1. D, E, F, C, B, A	7	15. C. Circuit is parallel; both branches have the same voltage difference.	4
2. Thermal energy—source: insulation in walls; add more insulation to increase resistance; remove insulation or open window to decrease resistance. Mechanical energy—source: friction in tubes; make tubes smaller or add bends to increase resistance; make tubes larger or straighten to decrease resistance. Electrical energy—source: very thin wires inside light bulbs; put more bulbs in series to increase resistance or put bulbs in parallel to decrease resistance.	9	16. D	4
3. Person (source) produces sound energy (vibrations in air). Microphone converts sound to electrical signal. Amplifier increases signal strength. Laser or LED converts electrical signal to light signal, receiver converts light to electrical signal, and speaker converts electrical signal to sound again for the destination.	5	17. B	4
4. C	2	18. B	4
5. B, D	4	19. C	2
6. A	2	20. D	2
7. B	2	21. B	2
8. A	3	22. C	4
9. B	2	23. B	3
10. A. Bulbs in series increase resistance so B and C will be dimmer than A.	4	24. A, B, A	6
11. C. The same current runs through all parts of a series circuit.	4	25. Provide up to 4 points for a logical explanation rather than the prediction itself. Award up to 3 more points if student points out pros and cons of different energy sources, and up to 2 additional points for any mention of energy saved by using decentralized sources rather than transporting energy over long distances, or other thoughtful considerations.	9
12. A. Resistance is higher with two bulbs in series. Since $I=V/R$, current is greater at Point 1 than at Point 2.	4		
13. D. Current is the same everywhere in a series circuit.	4		
14. C. Second circuit is parallel, so all loads have the same voltage difference as the first circuit.	4		

Maximum Score = 100

Summary of Class Results for Project 4.0 Final Assessment

Please help the authors of ETF validate these assessments and use the results to improve the course by completing the chart with the results of the final assessment for Project 4.0, and sending a copy to *Engineering the Future*, NCTL, Museum of Science, 1 Science Park, Boston, MA 02114-1099. Questions are in vertical columns; students are in horizontal rows.

	1	2	3	4	5	6	7	8	9	10	11	12	13	14	15	16	17	18	19	20	21	22	23	24	25	T
1																										
2																										
3																										
4																										
5																										
6																										
7																										
8																										
9																										
10																										
11																										
12																										
13																										
14																										
15																										
16																										
17																										
18																										
19																										
20																										
21																										
22																										
23																										
24																										
25																										
26																										
27																										
28																										
29																										
30																										
31																										
32																										
T																										

Important Formulas

-- Project 1.0 --

Area Formulas

Square: $A = s^2$

Rectangle: $A = lw$

Volume Formulas

Cube: $V = s^3$

Box or Right Rectangular Prism: $V = lwh$

Sphere: $V = \dfrac{4}{3}\pi r^3$, $\pi \approx 3.14$

Circle Formulas

$C = 2\pi r$, $\pi \approx 3.14$

$A = \pi r^2$, $\pi \approx 3.14$

General Formulas

$Density = \dfrac{Mass}{Volume}$

-- Project 2.0 --

Safety Analysis

$S_F = \dfrac{Max.\ Load\ Structure\ Will\ Support}{Max.\ Expected\ Load}$

Thermal(Heat) Energy

$Q = \dfrac{A\ \Delta T}{R}$,   ($R$ = R-Value)

Stress and Strain

$Stress(\sigma) = \dfrac{Force}{Area}$, $Strain(\varepsilon) = \dfrac{\Delta L}{L_0}$

General Formulas

$Average = \dfrac{Sum\ of\ Items}{Number\ of\ Items}$

-- Project 3.0 --

Gas Laws

Boyle's Law (Constant T): $P_1 V_1 = P_2 V_2$

Charles' Law (Constant P): $\dfrac{V_1}{T_1} = \dfrac{V_2}{T_2}$

Gay Lussac's Law (Constant V): $\dfrac{P_1}{T_1} = \dfrac{P_2}{T_2}$

Combined Gas Law (Closed System):

$\dfrac{P_1 V_1}{T_1} = \dfrac{P_2 V_2}{T_2}$, ($V$= volume, P= pressure, T= temperature)

Mechanical Energy

$W = Fd$

Pressure

$Pressure = \dfrac{Force}{Area}$, $P = \dfrac{F_1}{A_1} = \dfrac{F_2}{A_2}$

Fluid in Pipes

$Resistance \propto Length \propto \dfrac{1}{Area}$

$velocity \propto \dfrac{1}{Area}$, $v_1 A_1 = v_2 A_2$

General Formulas

$Efficiency = \dfrac{Useful\ Outputs}{Total\ Inputs}$

-- Project 4.0 --

Ohm's Law

$\Delta V = IR$

ΔV= Voltage Difference in volts (V)
I= Current in amps (A)
R= Resistance in ohms (Ω)

Electrical Power(P) and Energy(E)

$P = \Delta V \times I$, P(watts)=(volts)(amps)

$E = P \times t$, E=(watt-hours)

Resistance(R) in a Circuit

Resistances in Series: $R_T = R_1 + R_2 + R_3 ...$

Resistances in Parallel:

$\dfrac{1}{R_T} = \dfrac{1}{R_1} + \dfrac{1}{R_2} + \dfrac{1}{R_3} ...$